AM

AN

REPTILES

IN

WEST VIRGINIA

Amphibians and Reptiles in West Virginia

N. BAYARD GREEN and THOMAS K. PAULEY

University of Pittsburgh Press
in cooperation with the
West Virginia Department of Natural Resources
Nongame Wildlife Program

Published by the University of Pittsburgh Press,
Pittsburgh, Pa., 15260

Feffer and Simons, Inc., London

Manufactured in the United States of America

Library of Congress Cataloging-in-Publication Data

Green, N. Bayard, 1905–
Amphibians and reptiles in West Virginia.

Bibliography: p. 197
Includes index.
1. Amphibians—West Virginia—Identification.
2. Reptiles—West Virginia—Identification. I. Pauley,
Thomas K., 1940– II. Title.
QL653.W5G74 1987 597.6′09754 86-19291
ISBN 0-8229-3819-7
ISBN 0-8229-5802-3 (pbk.)

Photo credits (by species or subspecies number): Robert Birch, 21, 41, 66; Joseph T. Collins, 49, 63; W. Gene Frum, 30; N. Bayard Green, 18, 24, 39, 45, 47, 65, 67, 68; E.L. Jarroll, Jr., 51; Fred Kirchner, 50, 72; John MacGregor, 1, 2, 3, 4, 5, 6, 7, 8, 9, 10, 11, 12, 13, 14, 15, 16, 19, 20, 22, 25, 26, 27, 28, 29, 31, 32, 34, 35, 36, 37, 38, 40, 42, 43, 46, 56, 57, 58, 59, 60, 61, 62, 64, 69, 70, 73, 74, 75, 76, 77, 78, 79, 80, 81, 82, 83, 84, 85; Michael Seidel, 44, 48, 52, 53, 55.

Contents

Snakes

Preface

THIS GUIDE is the first comprehensive account of the amphibians and reptiles in West Virginia. Its purpose is twofold: first, to place on record a summary of available information concerning distribution, habitat, and seasonal activities of various species, and second, to provide a manual for naturalists and students who have had no previous experience with amphibians and reptiles.

Within recent years there has been increased interest in the flora and fauna of our state. Many government agencies, youth organizations, senior citizens' groups, and sportsmen's clubs are encouraging participation in outdoor activities. These programs bring people in contact with the natural environment and encourage study and identification of plants and animals. Along with the emphasis on outdoor recreation has come growing interest in finding ways to preserve our wildlife. One way to accomplish this is to have an informed public. It is hoped that this guide will kindle a stronger curiosity about living things in our environment, especially the amphibians and reptiles.

Each of the amphibians and reptiles described in this guide has been collected within our state. Eighty-three species and subspecies are documented by specimens in the West Virginia biological Survey Collection at Marshall University; the corn snake, the northern pine snake, and the Cumberland Plateau salamander are in other collections. Many of our species are so common that a short walk along a forest stream or a woodland path would disclose them, while others are so uncommon that they may never be observed within one's lifetime. Yet there are undoubtedly other species that still lurk within the wilder regions of our state waiting for the eager collector to discover them.

The study of amphibians and reptiles can be a fascinating hobby and one in which there is a great deal to be learned (even about the most common species). To assist the beginner, we have included sections on how to find and observe various species, how to record your observations as field notes, how to photograph specimens, and how to collect and care for amphibians and reptiles.

Acknowledgments

THE AUTHORS wish to express their sincere appreciation to the following persons for providing information, guidance, encouragement, and in some instances reviewing parts of the text: Laurence E. Bayless, Maurice G. Brooks, Donald Cox, the late W. Gene Frum, Hal Harrison, Richard Highton, Michael Little, C. J. McCoy, James Meads, Robert Mount, M. Graham Netting, Neil D. Richmond, James Rutherford, Michael E. Seidel, the late Edward H. Taylor, Ralph Taylor, Edward Thomas, and the late Charles F. Walker.

For a wide variety of favors including the gift and/or loan of specimens, rendering assistance in the field, checking maps or reading parts of the manuscript or helping in other ways, we are indebted, in addition to those mentioned above, to Kraig Adler, Robert Baker, Rodney Bartgis, James Boso, Richard Bothner, Paul Brant, John Converse, Russ DeGarmo, David Dennis, Kenneth Dolan, Bernie Dowler, Mabel Hopwood Gorman, Mannie Griffith, Sharon Gross, James Handlan, Paul Heckert, Austin Henning, Corson Hirschfeld, David Huffman, W. H. Martin, Stan Mills, O. Kenneth Mittong, Tracy Morse, Gladys Murray, Beth Anne Pauley, Jeffrey Pauley, Robert Rowsey, Janice Russell, Ronald Sandy, Larry Sawyers, Arnold Schultz, Thomas Slator, Charles Smith, John Sowards, Charles Spencer, Donald Tartar, Maxine Thacker, Amy Varnum, Thomas Wilkerson, Wayne Wilson, Shirley Witt, and Richard Workman.

Ms. Vickie Crager, as secretary and typist for the Biology Department at Marshall University, has been helpful in many ways. We are very grateful to Ms. Elizabeth Pival and Ms. Linda Bredengerd for typing the manuscript. We are grateful for the drawings made by Steve Lawton for the keys, the drawing of maps by Ed Hopkins, and for the work submitted by the many photographers for use in this book.

Our families were helpful in many ways—the children for their aid in the field and our wives for their encouragement and patience during our periods of absence while in the field.

Acknowledgments

AMPHIBIANS

AND

REPTILES

IN

WEST VIRGINIA

Herpetology in West Virginia

MODERN HERPETOLOGY in West Virginia began with A. M. Reese, a vertebrate zoologist with an interest in reptiles, who in 1907 became head of the zoology department at West Virginia University, a position which he held until his retirement in 1946. In the early 1930s he asked a number of his graduate students to conduct herpetological surveys of their county of residence as their masters' theses. The students who completed these projects included R. K. Brown for Mercer County (1932), N. B. Green for Randolph County (1931), and Peter Zucchero for Lewis County (1933).

In 1929, Reese published a list of the state's amphibians and reptiles in the West Virginia Encyclopedia. The twenty-six species were based, for the most part, on specimens which had been added to the museum of the zoology department. The list included the eastern hellbender, the mudpuppy, the blunt-nose salamanders of the genus *Ambystoma* and several species of *Plethodon.* Among the frogs and the toads were the bullfrog, leopard frog, pickerel frog, the American toad and Fowler's toad, as well as two genera of frogs, *Hyla* and *Acris.* Three species of turtles were listed: the common snapping turtle, the eastern box turtle, and the spiny softshell. Poisonous snakes included three pit vipers, the timber rattlesnake, the northern copperhead, and the eastern cottonmouth. The nonpoisonous species included the eastern milk snake, eastern kingsnake, eastern garter snake, northern water snake, black racer, black rat snake, eastern hognose snake, northern ringneck snake, and the eastern smooth green snake. Among the lizards were the fence lizard and several skinks of the genus *Eumeces.*

In 1925 M. Graham Netting joined the staff of the Carnegie Museum of Natural History in Pittsburgh as its first full-time herpetologist. His arrival presaged a new era for herpetology in West Virginia. In addition to his many duties with the program at the museum and throughout Pennsylvania, he turned his attention to West Virginia, establishing relationships with some of the outdoor organizations in the area. One of these was the Oglebay Institute in Wheeling, which sponsored such activities as the Brooks Bird Club and the Oglebay Plant Club. The Brooks Bird Club held summer sessions on the shores of Lake Terra Alta in Preston County, offering programs in bird study, ecology, and plant study. Netting soon became an active participant in the group. Maurice Brooks, writing in the twenty-fifth anniversary issue of *The Redstart* (1957), commented that Graham Netting "tempered the natural enthusiasms of a group of beginners with the disciplines of a scientist. He was not content to have the club remain merely 'bird counters'; rather, he constantly raised the question of 'why?' to accompy the 'what?' and 'how many?' He never missed a chance to suggest further lines of inquiry and more careful study when new observations were made. Most important of all, perhaps, he took endless time to answer the beginner's questions, to identify his specimens, and to indicate the direction and purpose of additional work. A surprising number of younger biologists benefited from such guidance and such association." Graham Netting became active in the West Virginia Academy of Science and through that group was able to channel many young investigators into productive field work. His interest in West Virginia herpetology never lagged, he remained alert to every new range extension, each new addition to the checklist, and he frequently encouraged aspiring authors to submit their observations for publication. He also contributed articles to the magazine *West Virginia Wildlife,* thereby fostering a broad interest throughout the state which led to publication of many papers and expanded the knowledge of herpetology within West Virginia.

During the summer of 1931, Albert H. Wright of Cornell University taught a field zoology course for West Virginia University which involved traveling over the state collecting and studying the vertebrate fauna. Amphibians collected on that expedition served as the subject for a master's thesis in 1936 for Bertram Cadbury, a Cornell student.

In 1935 the West Virginia Academy of Science appropriated $100 to pay the expenses for Neil D. Richmond to travel with the West Virginia Biology Field Course throughout the state collecting specimens. Richmond, a native of Fairmont whose interest was herpetology, had studied at the University of Michigan, and he subsequently became curator of herpetology at Carnegie Museum. The specimens he collected in 1935, supplemented during the summers of 1937 and 1938, formed the nucleus for the West Virginia Biological Survey Collections, stored in the science hall at West Virginia University. Because Richmond was not a member of the university staff, there were no curatorial services available. No one on the faculty had an interest in herpetology, and the West Virginia Academy of Science was reluctant to invest any more money in the project. In order to protect the collections from threatened deterioration, they were moved in 1939 to Marshall College, where N. Bayard Green assumed their care. Between 1939 and 1971 the collections grew from approximately one thousand specimens to over five thousand. When Green retired in 1971 the collections came under the curatorship of Michael Seidel.

Although Neil Richmond was no longer involved in the Biological Survey collections, he continued his studies of the state's herpetofauna. In 1941 he collaborated with Grace Boggess to issue a *Key to the Reptiles and Amphibians of West Virginia* which recognized sixty-seven species.

In recent years there has been an upsurge of interest in field work in West Virginia. A number of higher educational institutions within the state now offer courses in herpetology. Thomas Pauley began teaching herpetology at Salem College in 1970 and at the Terra Alta Biological Station from 1972 to 1978. (This station, sponsored by West Virginia University, offered among its field courses one in herpetology; unfortunately the station has been discontinued.) Laurence Bayless has developed a program at Concord State College, and James Meads at Glenville State College teaches a course in vertebrate zoology which is oriented to herpetology. Michael Seidel at Marshall University has developed a research program that promises to clarify some of the more intriguing problems in turtle biology within the state.

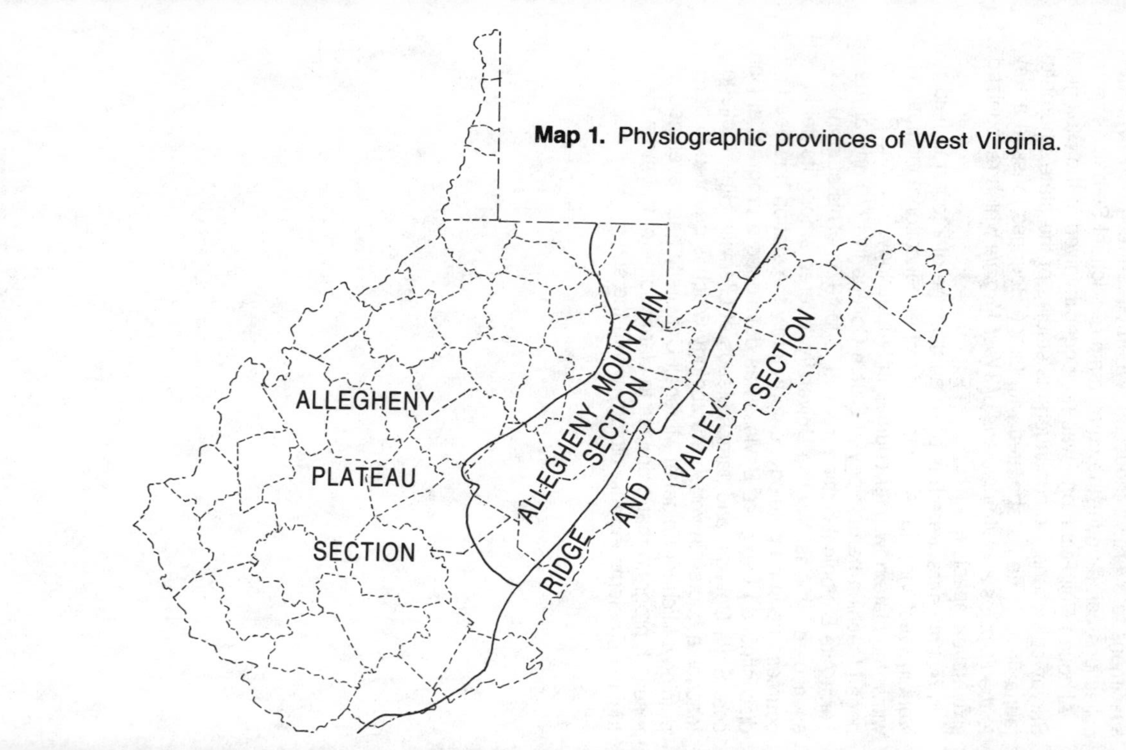

Map 1. Physiographic provinces of West Virginia.

Physiography and Climatology of West Virginia

WEST VIRGINIA is divided into five major physiographic provinces (see map 1). These provinces, which are named according to their predominant physiographic feature, are: (1) the *Allegheny Plateau,* an area of rolling foothills that extends from the western border of the state to the Allegheny Mountains; (2) the *Allegheny Mountains,* a chain of the Appalachian Mountains that reaches heights of over 4,000 feet (1,219 m); (3) the *Ridge and Valley,* an area east of the Allegheny Front (the eastward-facing edge of the Allegheny Mountains) that is composed of a series of steep-crested ridges and wide valleys; (4) the *Great Appalachian Valley,* a wide valley east of the Ridge and Valley province; and (5) the *Blue Ridge Mountains,* a mountain range at the tip of the Eastern Panhandle.

The mean elevation in West Virginia is 1,654 feet (504 m). Elevations range from 4,862 feet (1,482 m) at Spruce Knob in Pendleton County to 240 feet (73 m) at Harpers Ferry, Jefferson County. Lee *et al.* (1973) state that the mean elevation is greater in West Virginia than in any other eastern state. They also point out that the land rises from nearly 500 feet (152 m) at the western border (Allgeheny Plateau) to more than 4,000 feet (1,219 m) at the highest ridge of the Allegheny Mountains and decreases to less than 300 feet (91 m) at the eastern border (Ridge and Valley).

The climate of West Virginia is determined by its geographic location and topography. Its location, at a latitude of 37°12′ to 40°38′N and longitude of 77°43′ to 82°39′W, is such that most of its area is in the path of predominantly westerly winds which at this latitude are influenced by cold northern and warm southern air masses which can produce a considerable amount of precipitation (Lee *et al.* 1977). In addition the mountains cause prevailing winds to rise and cool, thus releasing higher precipitation to the west (windward) and lower precipitation to the east (leeward).

The annual average precipitation in West Virginia (U.S. Department of Commerce 1973) is 53.8 inches (136.6 cm) in the Allegheny Mountains, 43.4 inches (110.2 cm) in the Allegheny Plateau, and 36.6 inches (93.0 cm) in the Ridge and Valley province. The annual average precipitation for the entire state is 44.8 inches (113.8 cm)

Map 2. Counties of West Virginia.

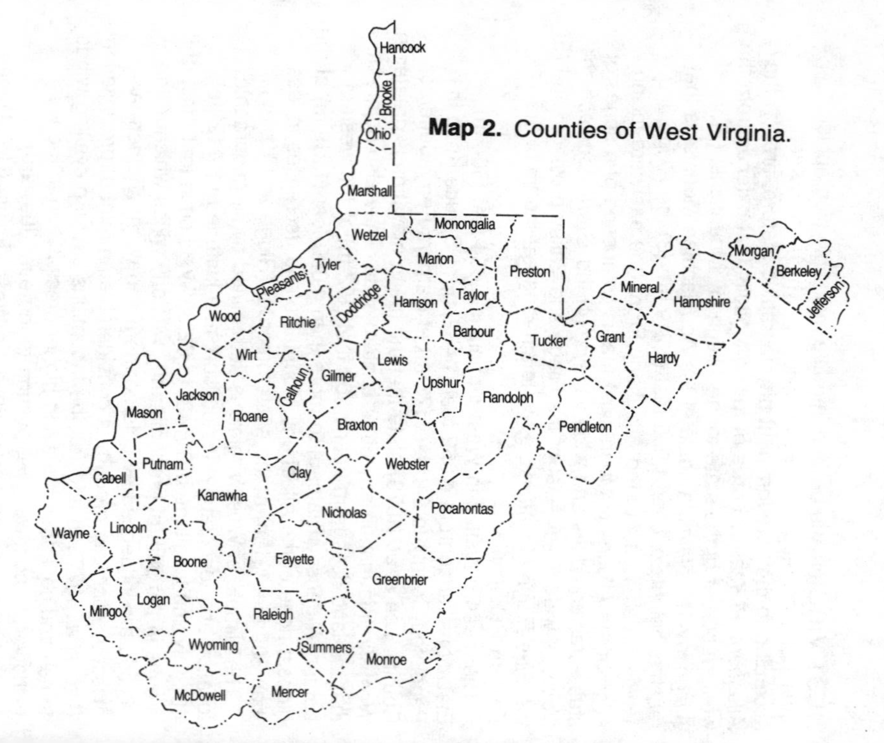

(Lee *et al.* 1977). The area of least precipitation (32.0 inches or 81.3 cm) is Franklin and Brushy Run, Pendleton County. The area of greatest precipitation (67.0 inches or 170.2 cm) is Pickens, Randolph County, a small community just west of the Appalachian Divide. Grafton and Dickerson (1969) demonstrated that elevation affects the annual average precipitation. Their studies showed that the annual average precipitation increases by 6.0 inches (15.2 cm) as the elevation increases from 2,000 to 3,000 feet (610 to 914 m) on the western side of the mountains. Conversely, due to the effects of the rain shadow, the annual average precipitation decreases by nine inches (22.9 cm) as the elevation decreases from 3,000 to 2,000 feet (914 to 610 m) east of the mountains.

The annual average temperature in West Virginia (U.S. Department of Commerce 1973) ranges from 49.4° F (9.7° C) in the Allegheny Mountains, to 52.8° F (11.5° C) in the Ridge and Valley province, to 53.6° F (12.0° C) in the Allegheny Plateau. Lee (1969) determined that the mean annual temperature decreases by 2.9° F (1.6° C) for each 1,000 feet (305 m) increase in elevation between the lower elevation provinces and the Allegheny Mountains.

PHYSIOGRAPHIC DISTRIBUTION

Three important factors regulate the physiographic distribution of West Virginia's amphibians and reptiles. First, they are "cold-blooded" vertebrates, meaning that their body temperature depends on the ambient temperature. Second, amphibians and reptiles are sensitive to the level of moisture. Lungless salamanders (Family Plethodontidae), for example, respire through the membrane lining of the mouth and skin. Since these membranes must remain moist for the diffusion of oxygen and carbon dioxide, it is essential that these salamanders inhabit a moist area. Finally, the anatomical characteristics of amphibians and reptiles limit their mobility, and they may be restricted to certain areas by natural barriers.

Because of the limitations imposed by temperature, moisture, and natural barriers, some species in West Virginia are known to occur in only one physiographic province. These are listed below.

Allegheny Plateau

AMPHIBIANS

Smallmouth Salamander
(*Ambystoma texanum*)
Kentucky Spring Salamander
(*Gyrinophilus porphyriticus duryi*)
Midland Mud Salamander
(*Pseudotriton montanus diastictus*)
Blanchard's Cricket Frog
(*Acris crepitans blanchardi*)
Ravine Salamander
(*Plethodon richmondi*)
Green Salamander
(*Aneides aeneus*)

REPTILES

Map Turtle
(*Graptemys geographica*)
Smooth Softshell
(*Trionyx m. muticus*)
Eastern Spiny Softshell
(*Trionyx s. spiniferus*)
Ground Skink
(*Scincella lateralis*)
Black Kingsnake
(*Lampropeltis getulus nigra*)

Allegheny Mountains

AMPHIBIANS

Cheat Mountain Salamander
(*Plethodon nettingi*)
Mountain Earth Snake
(*Virginia valeriae pulchra*)

Ridge and Valley and Great Appalachian Valley

AMPHIBIANS

Valley and Ridge Salamander
(*Plethodon hoffmani*)
White-spotted Salamander
(*Plethodon punctatus*)
Cave Salamander
(*Eurycea lucifuga*)
Upland Chorus Frog
(*Pseudacris triseriata feriarum*)
Northern Cricket Frog
(*Acris c. crepitans*)

REPTILES

Wood Turtle
(*Clemmys insculpta*)
Spotted Turtle
(*Clemmys guttata*)
Eastern Painted Turtle
(*Chrysemys p. picta*)
Corn Snake
(*Elaphe g. guttata*)
Eastern Kingsnake
(*Lampropletis g. getulus*)
Northern Pine Snake
(*Pituophis m. melanoleucus*)

There is a greater diversity of amphibians and reptiles in the Allegheny Plateau than in any other province in West Virginia. This is probably because it is the largest area and its temperature and precipitation ranges are less extreme. The smallmouth salamander (*Ambystoma texanum*), Kentucky spring salamander (*Gyrinophilus porphyriticus duryi*), midland mud salamander (*Pseudotriton montanus diasticus*), and Blanchard's cricket frog (*Acris crepitans blanchardi*) occur in the western and southwestern border counties of the Allegheny Plateau. The range of the ravine salamander (*Plethodon richmondi*) includes most of the forested area in the southwestern and western sections of this province, while the green salamander (*Aneides aeneus*) is found on stone outcroppings throughout the southwestern and central portions.

Reptiles that are known in West Virginia only from the Allegheny Plateau include the map turtle (*Graptemys geographica*) and the black kingsnake (*Lampropeltis getulus nigra*) in the western and central counties, the smooth softshell (*Trionyx m. muticus*) and the ground skink (*Scincella lateralis*) in the extreme western areas, and the eastern spiny softshell (*Trionyx s. spiniferus*), which is found throughout the plateau area.

Just two species in West Virginia are restricted to the wetter and cooler Allegheny Mountain province. The mountain earth snake (*Virginia valeriae pulchra*) is known to occur in the high elevations of Preston, Pendleton, Pocahontas, and Randolph counties and most likely in Tucker County. The Cheat Mountain salamander (*Plethodon nettingi*) is endemic to this province, limited to elevations above 3,150 feet (960 m) in the Cheat Mountains of Tucker, Randolph, Pendleton, and Pocahontas counties.

The number of species increases again in the Ridge and Valley and the Great Appalachian Valley provinces. The valley and ridge salamander (*Plethodon hoffmani*) is found in most counties in these provinces, while the white-spotted salamander (*Plethodon punctatus*) is restricted to the higher elevations of North and Shenandoah Mountains. The cave salamander (*Eurycea lucifuga*) is usually found at the twilight zones of limestone caves in the southeast part of the Ridge and Valley province.

The ranges of two treefrogs, the upland chorus frog (*Pseudacris triseriata feriarum*) and the northern cricket frog (*Acris c. crepitans*), are limited to the Ridge and Valley province. The upland chorus frog is found in the southeastern counties, and the northern cricket frog is found in the eastern panhandle.

There are three species of turtles and three species of snakes specific to the Ridge and Valley and Great Appalachian Valley provinces. The wood turtle (*Clemmys insculpta*) is one of the most terrestrial turtles, second only to the box turtle, in the state. While its range overlaps into the northern Allegheny Mountains, it is found more commonly in the eastern panhandle. The range of the spotted turtle (*Clemmys guttata*), not commonly found in West Virginia, is also limited to the eastern panhandle. Even though the range of the eastern painted turtle (*Chrysemys p. picta*) is very limited in West Virginia, this species is very common in most aquatic habitats in this area.

The corn snake (*Elaphe g. guttata*), eastern kingsnake (*Lampropeltis g. getulus*), and northern pine snake (*Pituophis m. melanoleucus*) are all indigenous to these eastern provinces. The corn snake was found as recently as 1975 in Morgan County, and it may be that more collecting will extend its range within the state. The eastern kingsnake is found near bodies of water throughout the eastern panhandle, and the northern pine snake is an uncommonly occurring species in dry pine woods in the southeastern county of Monroe.

Explanation of Species Accounts

PLANTS AND ANIMALS are divided into major groupings called *phyla* (sing. *phylum*). The Phylum Chordata includes all fishes, amphibians, reptiles, birds, and mammals. Phyla are divided into *classes.* Amphibians belong to the class Amphibia; reptiles to Reptilia. Classes are further divided into *orders,* orders into *families,* and families into *genera* (sing. *genus*). A genus is composed of one or more *species.* A species is a genetically distinctive group of populations which is isolated reproductively from all other species. A *subspecies* is a division of a species which occupies a distinct geographical area and has recognizable characteristics of the species. Ordinarily, only one subspecies may occupy a specific locality. Where the ranges of two adjacent subspecies come in contact, interbreeding may occur with the result that their distinctive characters become blended or intergraded. Such a situation is found in the case of the northern spring salamander and the Kentucky spring salamander (no. 21, 22).

Each species described in this guidebook is listed under both the common and the scientific name. Common or vernacular names are fully standardized. Although they may vary somewhat from region to region, they are widely used by both professionals and amateurs. Common names are handy and mean more to more people. In 1978 the Society for the Study of Amphibians and Reptiles published *Standard Common and Scientific Names for North American Amphibians and Reptiles* by Collins *et al.* This list, now in its second edition (1982), has served as the source for common names recognized in this guide. While common names are widely used, the scientific name provides a unique and universally understood name for each kind of animal.

The basic unit in classification is the species. Each species is designated by a name which usually consists of two words; first, the generic name (genus) followed by the specific name (species). The genus name is always capitalized while the species name is not. The entire name is italicized. A subspecies is a division of the population which makes up the species. Subspecies bear a three-word scientific name, the subspecies name is added to the name of the species. A complete scientific name also bears the name of the individual who described that species.

The Greek (Gr.), Latin (L.), or New Latin (NL.) roots are listed to enable the reader to understand the derivation of scientific names. The roots are from Jaeger (1966).

Description. This section provides a description to assist the reader in distinguishing the species from all others within the state. Size is given in both English and metric units, the former as estimates and the latter for more precise measurements. Lengths for toads and frogs are given as snout-vent length (i.e., from the tip of the snout to the vent). Turtles are measured from anterior to posterior margin of the upper shell in a straight line. Total length is given for salamanders, lizards, and snakes as measured from the tip of the snout to the tip of the tail. The measurements represent a size group into which the majority of those animals measured would fall. They derive either from work of the authors or from general sources such as Conant (1975). Color and pattern are also described, along with any other characteristics which might assist in identification. One should keep in mind that occasional individuals may not conform to the description.

Confusing Species. This category calls attention to features which help to distinguish similar species.

Habitat and Habits. The natural history of each species is discussed in this section, including habitat preferences, daily and seasonal activities, food, as well as unusual behavioral traits.

Breeding. This section gives information on courtship, mating, deposition of eggs, incubation, hatching, and care of the young. The breeding seasons of some species will differ in the extreme southern and northern parts of the state. In those cases where information was not available for species found within West Virginia, data from nearby states are used. Where specific studies are not cited the data are either those of the authors or from general references.

Range. The range of each species within the United States is included under this heading. These ranges are for the most part taken from Conant (1975). A map of West Virginia shows those counties in which each species has been collected, based upon the authors' examination of the collections at Marshall University, records from other museums, and reports in the literature. This may be referred to as the species' range in West Virginia, although it may occur in other counties for which specimens or published records are lacking.

Photographs. The color plates illustrate eighty-one of the species and subspecies found in West Virginia. The five not illustrated occupy restricted ranges and are less likely to be encountered in the field.

SOURCES OF LOCALITY RECORDS

The specimens in the collections of the West Virginia Biological Survey (WVBS) at Marshall University formed the principal source for the locality records. Although no major effort was made to contact every possible source for records, the following collections were consulted: the West Virginia material in the Carnegie Museum of Natural History (CM), Pittsburgh, made available through the courtesy of its curator, C. J. McCoy; the University of Michigan Museum of Zoology, through the courtesy of Arnold G. Kluge; the American Museum of Natural History, through the courtesy of Richard G. Zweifel; and those of the United States National Museum, through the late James A. Peters. Richard Highton made all his West Virginia field records available to the authors.

How to Locate and Photograph Amphibians and Reptiles

IF YOU LIKE to observe amphibians and reptiles, you will find many interesting species in the hills of West Virginia. Its rolling pastures, deciduous woodlands, swift mountain streams, humid ravines, and arid shale barrens provide a living habitat for the 80 species described in this book. While some species are easily seen at certain times of the year, others can be difficult to find unless special information about them is known. For example, searchers tore open decayed logs for years looking for the green salamander (with limited success) until Netting and Richmond (1932) found that their favored habitat was sandstone crevices.

Although some amphibians and reptiles are common, they often escape detection. Some remain motionless while others depend upon their coloration blending into the background. A good way to observe some amphibian species is to walk through the woods quietly and slowly, keeping a watchful eye out for any movement. For some species, you will need to turn over boards, rocks, pieces of tin, tarpaper, or other trash. Since these objects are shelters for a variety of organisms, be careful to return all overturned objects to their original position. Avoid destroying logs and stumps because they provide shelter to many invertebrates.

In the spring, visit ponds and swamps at night to observe the breeding of toads and frogs and some salamanders. A head lamp will provide a light while leaving your hands free. Your enjoyment will be increased if you record your observations in a notebook. Be sure to record the date, time of day, locality, weather conditions, description of the area, plants, and behavior of all animals observed. When you get back home you may want to transfer your notes to 4 x 6 cards for permanent reference.

Amphibian collecting is very good after the first rains in the spring or the fall. A headlamp or a flashlight held over your head will pick up the eyeshine of toads, frogs, and other animals that you ordinarily may not see. Driving slowly along a little-traveled, dark-paved road will reveal many specimens, especially during a rainfall.

If photography appeals to you, you may enjoy getting involved in this absorbing hobby. An artistic eye, an interest in the subject and a great deal of patience to wait for the right moment to release the shutter are necessary. The equipment you will need is more sophisticated and the techniques more demanding than the pictures you may be used to taking.

For close-ups you will need a single-lens reflex camera with extension tubes or macrolenses. The advantage of a single-lens reflex is that you can see exactly what you are working with and how the picture will turn out. Close-ups are also possible with extension tubes and a telephoto lens. Zoom lenses provide a great deal of adaptability. It is a good idea to start slowly and become familiar with each piece of equipment before buying something new. Try out your equipment on a still subject such as a flowering plant. Side lighting or back lighting pose certain advantages. For adequate depth of field you will need the smallest aperture (f/22 or f/32), and this necessitates using high ASA films or a supplemental flash. If an electronic flash is not used you can resort to reflectors such as mirrors, white cards, or shiny metal piepans to direct the light to the desired target.

Although many nature photographers prefer outdoor settings, you can construct an indoor background of mosses, rocks, or other material. When photographing such animals as salamanders, lizards, and snakes, it is a good idea to immobilize them for a short time by placing them in a sack or jar in a refrigerator. Keep a close eye on them or you may have some frozen specimens. When focusing on a snake or a salamander its eye nearest the camera should be the point of focus. Avoid busy backgrounds or other features in the picture which will distract attention from the subject.

Collecting and Caring for Amphibians and Reptiles

COLLECTING amphibians and reptiles should be for scientific study purposes only. If specimens are brought into the classroom, they should be kept for just a few days and returned to the original collection site. The state Department of Natural Resources prohibits collection of amphibians and reptiles without a valid collecting permit. You should be aware of the status of species before you collect them. Refer to the section in this guide on species of special concern and avoid disturbing these species.

Below is a list of good study species that can be easily captured.

Amphibians

Salamanders

Red-spotted Newt or Red Eft
Mole Salamanders and their larvae
Spring Salamanders and their larvae
Red Salamanders and their larvae

Frogs and Toads

Toads and their larvae
Ranid frogs such as the wood frog, green frog, bullfrog, and leopard frog and their larvae
Tree frogs such as the spring peeper, mountain chorus frog, cricket frogs, and gray treefrogs and their larvae

Reptiles

Turtles

Aquatic species such as the softshell, snapping, and painted turtles
Terrestrial species such as the box and wood turtles

Lizards

Fence lizard
Five-lined skink

Snakes (it is highly recommended that only harmless species be studied)
Black Racer
Black Rat Snake
Ringneck Snake
Hognose Snake
Milk Snake
Kingsnakes
Green Snakes
Brown Snake
Redbelly Snake
Garter Snake

COLLECTING METHODS

The first step in capturing a specimen is studying its habitat. Once the habitat is determined, persistence in searching will probably locate the species. The best time to collect amphibians is at night, particularly during or within 24 hours after a rainfall. A headlamp is useful because it frees both hands for capturing specimens. Most amphibians and reptiles can be caught by hand, although caution should be taken with large reptiles such as the two black snakes and the softshell and snapping turtles which can inflict painful bites. Of course, only experienced and well-trained field biologists should attempt to collect a poisonous snake.

Salamanders can be captured by hand with relative ease if one is quick enough. Care should be taken not to grasp it by the tail since it easily breaks off—and the animal escapes. After the specimen has been caught, be sure to keep it in a container that will guarantee a moist and cool environment during transportation. In collecting pond dwellers such as newts, a dip net is recommended. A tea strainer or aquarium fish net is ideal for collecting salamander larvae.

Toads can also be taken by hand, but frogs are more evasive. They usually retreat to water and may require a net.

Box and wood turtles can simply be grasped by the carapace. Painted turtles can be captured in the same manner, but these turtles can bite and they have long, sharp claws. Extreme care must be taken with softshell and snapping turtles; since both species have a long neck which can extend the head to the sides, they should be handled by the tail.

Turtle traps are usually required to catch aquatic species. One of the easiest to construct uses three or four boards about 18 inches long and 8 inches wide (45.7 and 20.3 cm). Nail these in the shape of a hollow triangle, or use four boards to form a box. Tack chicken wire across the bottom and drive 10-penny nails about one inch from the top completely through the boards, angling them so they point toward the center of the trap. Put some suitable bait (chicken entrails, etc.) in the middle and allow the trap to float (be sure to tie the trap to the bank or anchor it). Turtles enter the trap by climbing over the tops, and the inward projecting nails prevent them from climbing out. (To prevent possible injury, the points of the nails should be filed off.)

Funnel traps are the most common turtle traps used. One type (after Conant 1975) is constructed of four wire hoops 30.0 inches (76.2 cm) in diameter covered with fisherman's netting. Make one end closed and in the other end either a narrow slit or, preferably, a funnel-shaped structure. Hold the trap in place by driving metal rods through the ends into the bottom of the pond or lake. Make sure the top of the trap is exposed to allow trapped turtles to breathe. A good method for baiting either trap is to put the bait in a tin can with many holes in the top and sides and suspend the can in the center of the trap on a string.

Lizards are wary and very difficult to catch. The best method is to approach from the side or behind and quickly place your hand over it. Hold it by the body or you will end up with a wiggling tail while the lizard escapes. Tools to capture lizards include large rubber bands (those used by newspaper companies to bundle papers are ideal) used to "shoot" and stun specimens; long, flexible, whiplike branches used to slap the lizard thus stunning it; or a lizard noose. The latter can be made from a pole or stick 4 to 5 feet long (1.2–1.5 m), with a short length of string tied into a slip knot attached to the end. Use a somewhat stiff thread (or wire) to assure that the loop will remain open. Place the loop around the lizard's head and pull the pole quickly, but not so hard as to injure the lizard.

Snake sticks consist of golf putters or simple tools with a similar right-angle bend, forked sticks, and commercial snake tongs. The least desirable is the forked stick because it is difficult to match the size of the snake. If the forks are too large, it can escape, but if they are too small, they can damage the snake's neck. One tool frequently used is a wire noose which extends the length of a rod. The noose can be put around the snake's neck and the wire pulled to close the noose. This tool is not desirable either since it can easily cut the neck and permanently injure the specimen or possibly even sever the head.

Small snakes can simply be picked up. Larger specimens can also be captured easily by just picking them up. Some species can inflict a somewhat painful bite, so it is wise to hold the specimen down with your foot or a stick. To pick up a snake, grasp it behind the jaws with your thumb and middle finger, using the index finger to immobilize the head.

Most specimens can be kept in the field in collecting bags. These bags can be purchased commercially from biological supply houses or made of sturdy fabric. Plastic bags are sometimes used, but these do not always allow for air movement and can become too hot.

TRANSPORTING THE CATCH

The vessels most readily available to transport specimens are tin cans and glass jars. Both have advantages and disadvantages. Specimens cannot be observed in tin cans, but cans cannot be broken and injure the specimen. If a can is used, air holes should be punched from inside to outside to prevent injury to the specimen. If a jar is used, try a canning jar. Remove the lid and replace it with plastic mesh or screen wiring for air circulation. Amphibians must be in a moist environment, so it is recommended that wet paper towels be placed in their containers.

PREPARING A TEMPORARY INDOOR HABITAT

The most readily available cage for housing amphibians and reptiles is an aquarium, one large enough for the specimen to stretch out in. If an aquatic species to to be observed, an aquarium with gravel and some aquatic vegetation is ideal. Vegetation is very important for hiding and resting places fpr smaller species. It is also desirable to provide some cover objects or crevices for hiding and resting.

For semiaquatic specimens, partition the terrarium into a "dry" side and a "wet" side. The dry side can be constructed of gravel, sand, or sandy soil. A ramp of wood, bark, or stone should be put in the water for easy access.

For terrestrial specimens, an aquarium can also be used. Conant (1975) suggests filling the bottom with gravel to about 1.0 inch (2.5 cm), covering with 0.2–0.4 inches (0.5–1.0 cm) of charcoal chips, and topping this with 1.0 inch (2.5 cm) of sandy soil. He further recommends adding a few plants, kept in a small pot for easy removal and cleaning. As in other situations, provide hiding places by adding bark or stones.

Tops for aquaria and terraria will need to be used for most species, especially snakes. Such tops can be easily constructed of a wooden frame with heavy wire screening tacked to it. The top must be securely attached to the aquarium. Snakes can squeeze through the narrowest of cracks and force open loosely fixed covers.

Proper temperature, moisture, food, and water are essential for the good health of your specimens. Conant (1975) recommends that amphibians be kept below 70.0° F (21.1° C) and reptiles at a slightly higher temperature, 75.0°–85.0° F (23.9°–29.4° C).

The gathering of food can be a time-consuming activity and may be next to impossible in the winter. With the exception of tadpoles (which are herbivores) and some turtles that are omnivores, native amphibians, reptiles, and salamanders are carnivores and require either insects or other live animal food or some type of prepared animal food. Conant (1975) suggests using dog food or lean ground meat with a drop or two of a vitamin-mineral concentrate and a pinch of bone meal or oyster-shell flour (for calcium), formed into small pellets. Food should be placed at the water's edge to prevent the food from fouling the water. If food must be put into the water, observe the animal's eating frequency and do not put in more food than it will eat. Small live fish such as guppies, as well as chopped fish, earthworms, and various aquatic animals, can be included as food items.

If your amphibians or reptiles require live insects, it is easy to make an insect trap. One method is to place a gallon jar with a funnel in the mouth under a light bulb. Flying insects enter the jar through the funnel but cannot work their way out. Crawling insects can be captured by burying a can up to the rim and placing sweet syrup such as a mixture of sugar and water in it. Insects are attracted to the bait and fall into the can. It is best to have a screen wire platform above the bait to prevent the insects from falling in the syrup and drowning. Collecting insects around an outside light at night can also be very productive.

During the winter, live insects may be difficult to collect, but crickets and mealworms can be obtained commercially. It is not difficult to maintain a mealworm colony. When the original colony is obtained, simply put them in a gallon jar, or better a five-gallon pail, with newspaper, corn meal, and/or oats. The only attention required is to add a few drops of water weekly.

The diet of snakes varies according to the species. Food for captive specimens of different species is explained in the text.

Taxonomic Keys to Adult Amphibians and Reptiles in West Virginia

HOW TO USE A KEY

THE PURPOSE of a key is the identification of unknown specimens. The following keys are made up of couplets which are numbered on the left. Each couplet is a pair of alternative statements, of which one, but not the other, describes a characteristic of the amphibian or reptile to be identified. At the end of each statement (on the extreme right) there is either a name or a number leading to further couplets. To use the key, start at the beginning with couplet no. 1. Choose the half of the couplet (1a or 1b) which best describes the unknown specimen and note the number at the end of the couplet. Go to the couplet bearing that number and make a second choice. Continue until a selected half-couplet ends in a name. That is the name of the unknown specimen.

The accompanying drawings illustrate many of the characters mentioned in the keys. When a couplet contains a reference to a drawing (e.g., figure 1, no. 2) check the drawing to assist in the use of the key. Consult the glossary for definitions of scientific terms.

KEY TO THE MAJOR GROUPS

1a No scales on body, skin smooth or warty, no claws on toes → **Amphibians** 2
1b Body covered with scales or hard bony shell, claws present on toes → **Reptiles** 3

2a Tail present, hind legs about same size as front legs → **Salamanders**
2b Tail absent, hind legs much larger than front legs → **Toads and Frogs**

3a Body encased in hard bony or leathery shell, teeth absent → **Turtles**
3b Body not encased in bony shell, teeth present → 4

4a Legs present with claws, ear openings and eyelids also present → **Lizards**
4b Legs, ear openings, and eyelids absent → **Snakes**

KEY TO THE SALAMANDERS

1a Adults (total length to 17 in. or 43.2 cm) with three pairs of external gills; four toes on hind feet → **Mudpuppy,** ***Necturus m. maculosus***

1b Adults without external gills; four or five toes on hind feet → **2**

2a A thick wrinkled fold of skin between front and hind legs; one pair of gill slits. Body flattened dorsoventrally; total length to 20 in. or 51 cm; no eyelids → **Eastern hellbender,** ***Cryptobranchus a. alleganiensis***

2b No fold of skin along sides; no gill slits → **3**

3a Nasolabial groove absent → **4**

3b Nasolabial groove present (see fig.) → **8**

3b

4a Side of body between limbs without vertical grooves (costal grooves), a pair of distinct longitudinal ridges on top of head → **Red-spotted newt,** ***Notophthalmus v. viridescens***

4b Sides of body with vertical grooves (costal grooves) → **5**

5a Body with two rows of large, yellow spots down the back; ground color black or bluish black → **Spotted salamander,** ***Ambystoma maculatum***

5b Body without large yellow spots → **6**

6a Body with four to seven white or gray hourglass-shaped crossbars → **Marbled salamander,** ***Ambystoma opacum***

6b Body without large white or gray crossbars → **7**

7a Body bluish black with bluish-white flecks along the sides; two short rows of vomerine teeth bordering the nares posteriorly; no median groove on tongue; front and hind toes overlap when limbs adpressed along sides → **Jefferson Salamander,** **Ambystoma jeffersonianum**

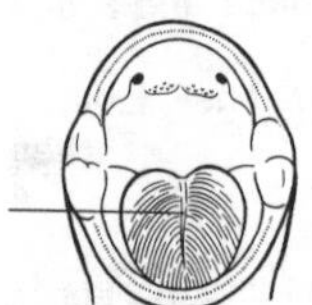
7b

7b Body grayish or brown with large silvery lichenoid flecks; lateral rows of vomerine teeth absent; plica of tongue diverging from a median furrow (see fig.) front and hind toes do not meet when limbs adpressed along sides → **Smallmouth salamander,** ***Ambystoma texanum***

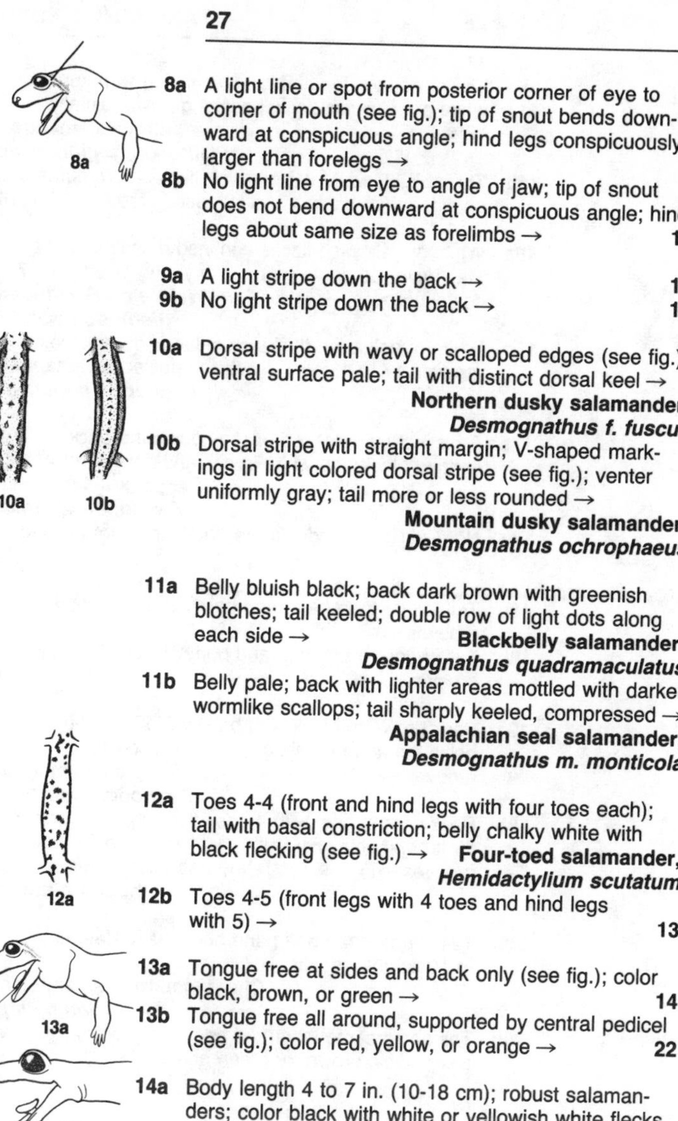

8a A light line or spot from posterior corner of eye to corner of mouth (see fig.); tip of snout bends downward at conspicuous angle; hind legs conspicuously larger than forelegs → **9**

8b No light line from eye to angle of jaw; tip of snout does not bend downward at conspicuous angle; hind legs about same size as forelimbs → **12**

9a A light stripe down the back → **10**

9b No light stripe down the back → **11**

10a Dorsal stripe with wavy or scalloped edges (see fig.), ventral surface pale; tail with distinct dorsal keel → **Northern dusky salamander, *Desmognathus f. fuscus***

10b Dorsal stripe with straight margin; V-shaped markings in light colored dorsal stripe (see fig.); venter uniformly gray; tail more or less rounded → **Mountain dusky salamander, *Desmognathus ochrophaeus***

11a Belly bluish black; back dark brown with greenish blotches; tail keeled; double row of light dots along each side → **Blackbelly salamander, *Desmognathus quadramaculatus***

11b Belly pale; back with lighter areas mottled with darker wormlike scallops; tail sharply keeled, compressed → **Appalachian seal salamander, *Desmognathus m. monticola***

12a Toes 4-4 (front and hind legs with four toes each); tail with basal constriction; belly chalky white with black flecking (see fig.) → **Four-toed salamander, *Hemidactylium scutatum***

12b Toes 4-5 (front legs with 4 toes and hind legs with 5) → **13**

13a Tongue free at sides and back only (see fig.); color black, brown, or green → **14**

13b Tongue free all around, supported by central pedicel (see fig.); color red, yellow, or orange → **22**

14a Body length 4 to 7 in. (10-18 cm); robust salamanders; color black with white or yellowish white flecks on dorsum and/or side → **15**

14b Body length 2 to 4 in. (5-10 cm), slender salamanders; black or dark brown predominating → **17**

15a Throat dark; sides and back sprinkled with numerous white or yellowish flecks; costal grooves usually 16* → **Slimy salamander, *Plethodon g. glutinosus***

15b Throat light; white or yellowish flecks more numerous on sides than back; 17 to 18 costal grooves → **16**

16a White or yellowish flecks confined mostly to sides; may have red spots on back in young or adults; 17 costal grooves → **Wehrle's salamander, *Plethodon wehrlei***

16b White or yellowish flecks on sides and back; costal grooves 17 to 18 → **White-spotted salamander, *Plethodon punctatus***

17a A distinct stripe of red or gray down the back; belly mottled black and white in salt-and-pepper effect → **Redback salamander, *Plethodon cinereus***

17b No distinct stripe down the back; belly not mottled → **18**

18a Tail longer than head and body; 20 to 22 costal grooves → **19**

18b Tail shorter than head and body; 17 to 19 costal grooves → **20**

19a Back brown to black with brassy or silvery flecks; belly, throat, and chin gray; 19 to 22 costal grooves → **Ravine salamander, *Plethodon richmondi***

19b Back deep brown with brassy flecking; belly gray, throat and chin with white mottling; 20 to 21 costal grooves → **Valley and Ridge salamander, Plethodon hoffmani**

20a Tail shorter than head and body; belly slate gray; 17 to 19 costal grooves → **Cheat Mountain salamander, *Plethodon nettingi***

20b Tail about same length as body; belly not slate gray; color black, brown, or green and gold → **21**

**Plethodon kentucki*, a species similar in appearance to *Plethodon glutinosus,* occurs on the Allegheny Plateau Physiographic Province west of the New River. See the species accounts for morphological differences between these two species.

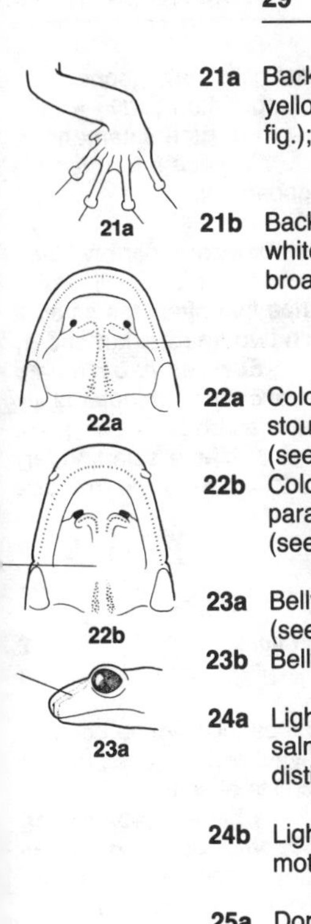
21a
22a
22b
23a

21a Back green, black, and bronze mottled; belly pale yellowish white; toe tips/square and expanded (see fig.); head broad and flattened → **Green salamander,** ***Aneides aeneus***

21b Back dark gray to black; belly speckled black and white; toe tips round and not expanded; head not broad and flattened (see 17a above) → **Redback salamander,** ***Plethodon cinereus***

22a Color red, orange, salmon, or yellowish brown; body stout; vomerine and parasphenoid teeth continuous (see fig.) → **23**

22b Color yellow or pink; body slender; vomerine and parasphenoid teeth separated by a gap (see fig.) → **27**

23a Belly pale cream; light line from eye to nostril (see fig.) → **24**

23b Belly reddish; no light line from eye to nostril → **26**

24a Light line from eye to nostril distinct, color dull salmon red; back and sides mottled or clouded, not distinctly spotted → **Northern spring salamander,** ***Gyrinophilus p. porphyriticus***

24b Light line from eye to nostril faint; back clear, not mottled → **25**

25a Dorsal color bright pinkish or orange; lateral color sharply set off from light belly, no mottling on back or sides; distinct spots on back or sides → **Kentucky spring salamander,** ***Gyrinophilus porphyriticus duryi***

25b Dorsal color flesh-colored with gray clouded reticulations; belly flesh-colored; two to three irregular rows of pale spots along sides → **West Virginia spring salamander,** ***Gyrinophilus subterraneus***

26a Color bright red with thirty to forty distinct black spots scattered over dorsal surface of head, body, legs, and tail; iris of eye brown → **Midland mud salamander,** ***Pseudotriton montanus diastictus***

26b Color red with numerous crowded irregular black dots which run together in older specimens; iris of eye yellow → **Northern red salamander,** ***Pseudotriton r. ruber***

27a

27a Lateral black bars on tail forming a herringbone pattern (see fig.); tail much longer than body → **Longtail salamander, *Eurycea l. longicauda***

27b Tail not marked with herringbone pattern → 28

28a Color yellow, tan, or greenish bronze; a narrow black line down each side of back from eye onto tail enclosing light middorsal stripe that often has small black dots → **Northern two-lined salamander, *Eurycea b. bislineata***

28b Color bright red or pinkish orange with irregular black spots and dashes; tail longer than body → **Cave salamander, *Eurycea lucifuga***

KEY TO THE TOADS AND FROGS

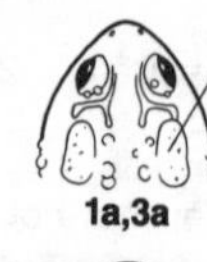
1a,3a

1a,3b

2a

2b

1a Parotoid glands present (see figs.) → 2

1b Parotoid glands absent → 4

2a Parotoid glands round; hind toes fully webbed and sole of hind foot with a horny tubercle at base of inner toe (see fig.); cranial crests absent → **Eastern spadefoot, *Scaphiopus h. holbrookii***

2b Parotoid glands oblong, kidney-shape; hind toes not fully webbed (see fig.); sole of hind foot without a horny tubercle at base of inner toe; cranial crests present → 3

3a Parotoid gland separated from postorbital ridge or connected by a spur (see fig.); each dorsal spot including one or two large warts; warts on upper surface of tibia large and spiny; belly sparsely spotted → **Eastern American toad, *Bufo a. americanus***

3b Parotoid gland touches the postorbital ridge (see fig.); each dorsal spot enclosing several small warts; warts on dorsal surface of tibia small; belly immaculate white → **Fowler's toad, *Bufo woodhouseii fowleri***

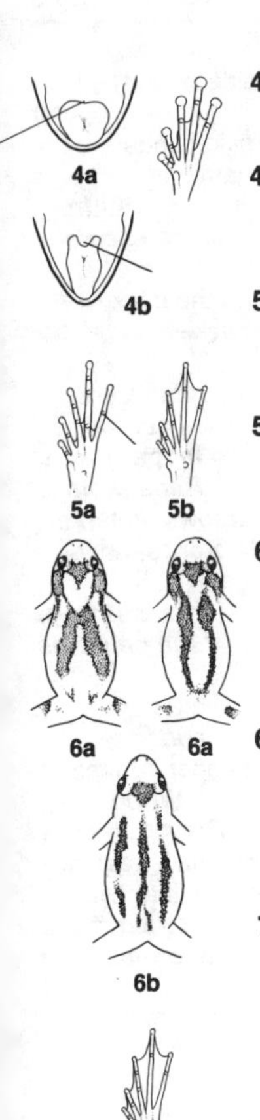

4a Posterior margin of tongue entire or with shallow notch (see fig.); tips of toes with expanded discs (see fig.); skin of belly granulated or pebbled → 5

4b Posterior margin of tongue with deep notch (see fig.); tips of toes not expanded into discs; skin of belly smooth, not granulated → 9

5a Toes less than one half webbed; web between fourth and fifth toe indented to a point below the level of the distal subarticular tubercle of the fifth toe (see fig.) → 6

5b Toes well webbed; indentation of web between fourth and fifth toes not extending inward beyond level of dorsal subarticular tubercle of fifth toe (see fig.) → 7

6a Legs long, heel reaching a point anterior to middle of the eye when leg is extended along side; dorsal pattern usually consisting of a pair of crescent-shaped bars which sometimes meet in the midline (see figs.) → **Mountain chorus frog, *Pseudacris brachyphona***

6b Legs short, heel reaching a point posterior to the eye when adpressed along body; dorsal pattern of three longitudinal stripes or rows of spots (see fig.) → **Upland chorus frog, *Pseudacris triseriata feriarum***

7a Toe discs indistinct (see fig.); one or two pairs of conspicuous light warts below anal opening; toes fully webbed (see fig.); a dark triangle between the eyes → **Cricket frogs: Northern cricket frog, *Acris c.crepitans* found in eastern part of the state; Blanchard's cricket frog, *Acris crepitans blanchardi* found in the Ohio Valley**

7b Toe discs distinct; anal warts absent → 8

8a A light spot below eye; fingers one-third webbed; concealed surface of thigh with a pattern of yellow and black; skin rough, greenish, brownish, or gray → **Gray treefrog complex, *Hyla versicolor or Hyla chrysocelis***

8b No light spot below eye; fingers not webbed; no yellow on groin; color tan to brown; dark X on back (see fig.) → **Northern spring peeper, *Hyla c. crucifer***

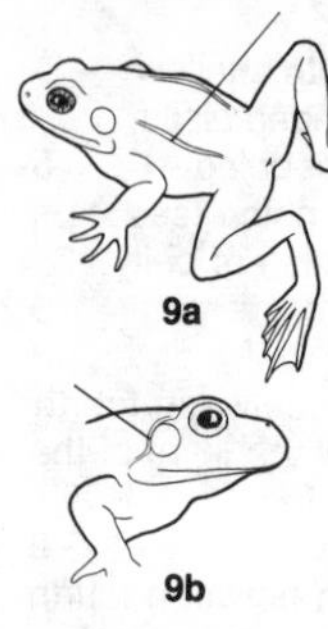

9a Dorsolateral folds extending along side of body toward groin (see fig.) → **10**

9b Dorsolateral folds absent; a fold of skin bends sharply downward along posterior margin of tympanum (see fig.) → **Bullfrog, *Rana catesbeiana***

10a Pattern of large conspicuous spots on the back → **11**

10b No large conspicuous spots on the back → **12**

11a Dorsal spots rounded, edged in white; dorsolateral folds light-colored; under surface of hind legs white; dorsal color green → **Northern leopard frog, *Rana pipiens***

11b Dorsal spots squarish in two irregular rows on tan or brown background, dorsolateral folds bronze; under surfaces of hind legs yellow or orange → **Pickerel frog, *Rana palustris***

12a Color brown, salmon, tan, or pinkish with a dark mask extending through eye and tympanum; dorsolateral folds extending to groin; upper surface of thigh with dark crossbars → **Wood frog, *Rana sylvatica***

12b Dorsal color green or gray with many small irregular spots; dorsolateral folds extending one-half to two-thirds to groin → **Green frog, *Rana clamitans melanota***

KEY TO THE TURTLES

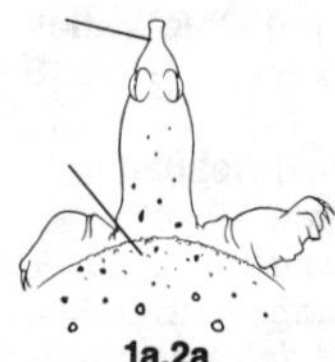

1a Carapace covered with skin; edge of carapace flexible; snout projected into a soft proboscis (see fig.) → **2**

1b Carapace covered with horny shields; edge of carapace not flexible; snout not projected into a soft proboscis → **3**

2a Anterior border of carapace with many small spines (see fig.); hind feet mottled with black; nostril crescent-shaped, with ridge projecting outward from septum (see fig.) → **Eastern spiny softshell, *Trionyx s. spiniferus***

2b Anterior border of carapace smooth; hind feet not mottled; nostrils round with no ridge projecting outward from septum (see fig.) → **Midland smooth softshell, *Trionyx m. muticus***

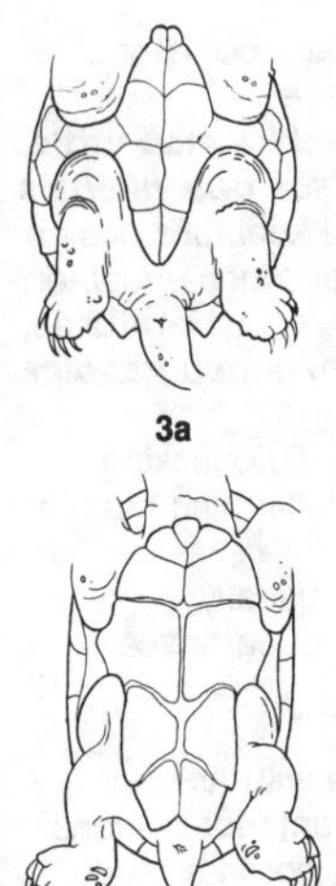

3a

4a

3a Tail almost as long as carapace with crest of large tubercles; plastron with fewer than eleven plates, cruciform (see fig.); posterior border of carapace serrate → **Common snapping turtle,** ***Chelydra s. serpentina***

3b Tail short, except in hatchlings; tail without crest of large tubercules; plastron with eleven or more plates → 4

4a Plastron with eleven plates or shields (see fig.); head usually with two yellow lines on each side; barbels on chin and throat → **Stinkpot,** ***Sternotherus odoratus***

4b Plastron with twelve plates or shields → 5

5a Plastron with movable hinge enabling turtle to close shell; carapace arched and dome shaped, mottled and streaked with yellow on brown → **Eastern box turtle,** ***Terrapene c. carolina***

5b Plastron solid, immovable, without hinge; incapable of closing shell; carapace not arched and dome shaped → 6

6a Each shield of carapace usually with one to several round yellow or orange spots on black background → **Spotted turtle,** ***Clemmys guttata***

6b Carapace without distinct yellow or orange spots → 7

7a Head and neck without yellow stripes; rear margin of carapace notched; plates of carapace deeply sculptured; soft parts red or orange → **Wood turtle,** ***Clemmys insculpta***

7b Head and neck with longitudinal stripes → 8

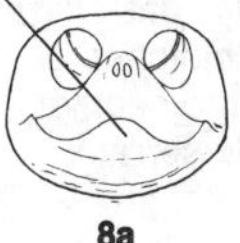

8a

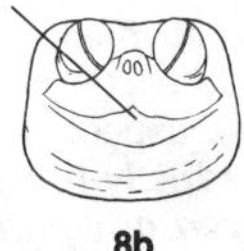

8b

8a Alveolar surface of upper jaw broad and smooth; cutting surface rounded at symphysis without notch (see fig.) → 9

8b Alveolar surface narrow or tuberculate; cutting surface of upper jaw angular at symphysis with notch (see fig.) → 10

9a Middorsal keel with knobs; postocular spot large, crescent-shaped, extending below eye → **Ouachita map turtle, *Graptemys pseudogeographica ouachitensis***

9b Knobs absent or weak on middorsal keel; postocular spot small, separated from eye by distance equal to diameter of spot → **Map turtle, *Graptemys geographica***

10a Carapace smooth, individual scutes dark, lacking a pattern; middorsal keel absent in adults; hind margin of carapace smooth → **11**

10b Carapace with longitudinal wrinkles; usually middorsal keel evident; hind margin of carapace serrate → **12**

11a

11a Anterior margins of costals alternate with anterior margins of the vertebrals (see fig.); anterior margins of costals and vertebrals usually not bordered with yellow; a dark central figure on plastron → **Midland painted turtle, *Chrysemys picta marginata***

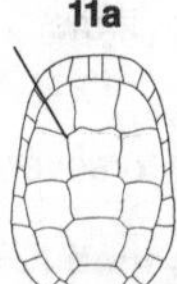

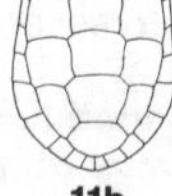

11b

11b Anterior marginals of costals line up with anterior margins of the vertebrals (see fig.); anterior margins of costals and vertebrals usually bordered with yellow; plastron clear without central figure → **Eastern painted turtle, *Chrysemys p. picta***

12a

12a A dark circular blotch on each plastral scute; cutting surface of upper jaw angular at symphysis with v-shaped notch not flanked by cusps (see fig.); wide red stripe back from eye in all but melanistic males → **Red-eared slider, *Trachemys scripta elegans***

12b Plastron marked with indistinct smoky blotches or dendritic (branching) pattern following the seams; lower cutting surface of jaw prominently serrate; tubercles prominent on alveolar surface of jaw → **13**

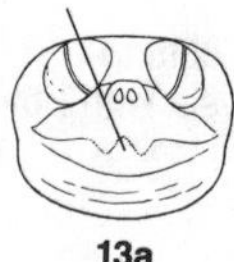

13a

13a Deep notch in upper jaw with prominent cusp on each side (see fig.); plastron shaded with pink or coral; nuchal scute deep (long) in ventral aspect → **Redbelly turtle, *Pseudemys r. rubriventris***

13b

13b Cusp not prominent on upper jaw (see fig.); plastron yellow or pale orange; nuchal scute shallow (short) in ventral aspect → **River cooters, *Pseudemys c. concinna* and *Pseudemys concinna hieroglyphica***

KEY TO THE LIZARDS

1a Scales pointed and keeled; scales around middle of trunk in rows of thirty-five or more, differing in size and shape → **Northern fence lizard, *Sceloporus undulatus hyacinthinus***

1b Scales smooth and glossy, scales around middle of trunk in rows of thirty or less, all of uniform size and shape → 2

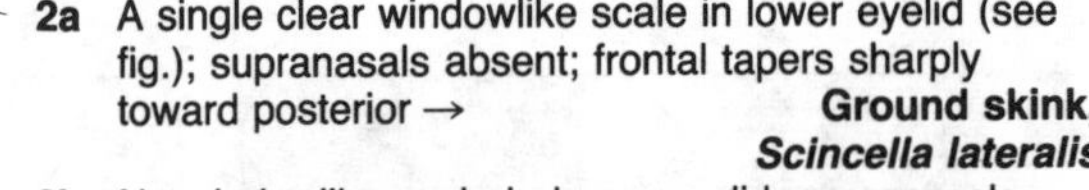

2a

2a A single clear windowlike scale in lower eyelid (see fig.); supranasals absent; frontal tapers sharply toward posterior → **Ground skink, *Scincella lateralis***

2b No windowlike scale in lower eyelid; supranasals present; frontal about as broad in front as behind → 3

3a

3a Sides jet black; back bronze to yellow; a single postmental scale under chin (see fig.) → **Northern coal skink, *Eumeces a. anthracinus***

3b Color of back same as sides → 4

4a

4a No postlabials, or one or two of small size (see fig.); eight upper labials, usually five preceding subocular; adult males are large and brown with wide heads; juveniles black with five yellow stripes and bright blue tail; 30 to 32 rows of scales around center of body → **Broadhead skink, *Eumeces laticeps***

4b

4b Two postlabials of large size (see fig.); seven upper labials, four usually preceding subocular; black or brown with five broad light stripes; old males may lose pattern and become uniform brownish in color; 26 to 30 rows of scales around center of body → **Five-lined skink, *Eumeces fasciatus***

KEY TO THE SNAKES

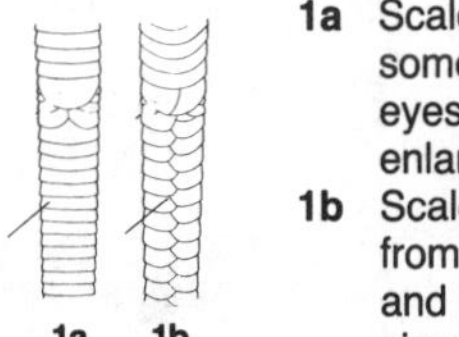

1a 1b

1a Scales on ventral surface of the tail in one row for some distance back of vent (see fig.); a pit between eyes and nostrils; two front teeth in upper jaw enlarged into fangs → 2

1b Scales on ventral surface of the tail in a double row from vent to tail tip (see fig.); no pit between eyes and nostrils; teeth in upper jaw small and uniform in size → 3

2a Tail terminates in horny rattle or button; color sulphur yellow or black with black chevron markings (see fig.) → **Timber rattlesnake, *Crotalus horridus***

2b Tail terminates in horny tip, no rattle; color copper brown with darker hourglass markings across back and onto the sides (see fig.); ventral surface pinkish with dark markings (see fig.) → **Northern copperhead, *Agkistrodon contortrix mokasen***

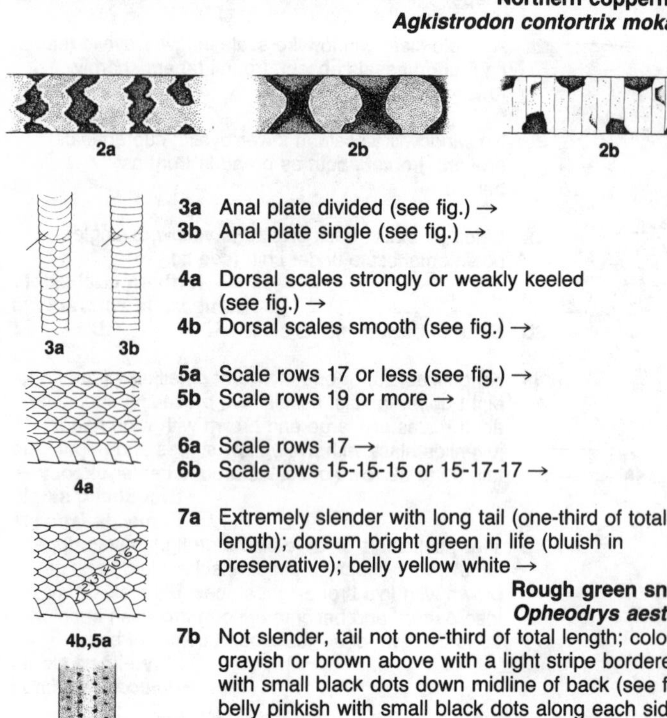

2a 2b 2b

3a 3b

4a

4b,5a

7b

3a Anal plate divided (see fig.) → **4**
3b Anal plate single (see fig.) → **17**

4a Dorsal scales strongly or weakly keeled (see fig.) → **5**
4b Dorsal scales smooth (see fig.) → **13**

5a Scale rows 17 or less (see fig.) → **6**
5b Scale rows 19 or more → **9**

6a Scale rows 17 → **7**
6b Scale rows 15-15-15 or 15-17-17 → **8**

7a Extremely slender with long tail (one-third of total length); dorsum bright green in life (bluish in preservative); belly yellow white → **Rough green snake, *Opheodrys aestivus***

7b Not slender, tail not one-third of total length; color grayish or brown above with a light stripe bordered with small black dots down midline of back (see fig.); belly pinkish with small black dots along each side at ends of the ventrals → **Northern brown snake, *Storeria d. dekayi***

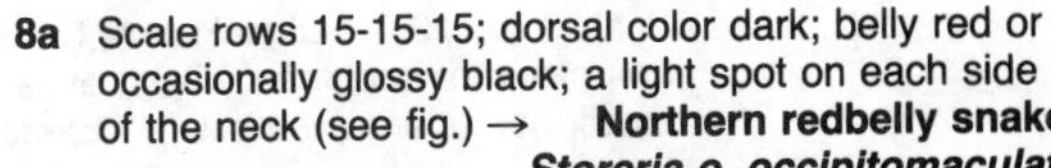

8a

8a Scale rows 15-15-15; dorsal color dark; belly red or occasionally glossy black; a light spot on each side of the neck (see fig.) → **Northern redbelly snake, *Storeria o. occipitomaculata***

8b Scale rows 15-17-17; dorsal surface reddish brown to dark gray with no pattern; ventral color uniform whitish; no light spot on each side of the neck; found in high altitudes of the Alleghenies → **Mountain earth snake, *Virginia valeriae pulchra***

9a

9a Tip of snout turned up into shovellike projection; underside of tail conspicuously lighter than rest of venter; twenty or more dark squarish blotches with light interspaces (see fig.), varies from brown, tan, yellow, red, to orange; occasionally all black → **Eastern hognose snake, *Heterodon platirhinos***

9b Tip of snout not upturned → **10**

10a Dorsal scales strongly keeled → **11**

10b Dorsal scales weakly keeled, lower rows without keels → **12**

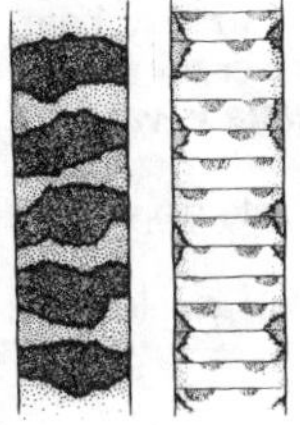

11b

11a Maximum number of scale rows 19; back gray or brown, a light stripe along the side of the first and second row of scales; two dark stripes down the middle of the belly → **Queen snake, *Regina septemvittata***

11b Scale rows 21 to 25; heavy bodied brownish or gray snakes with many dark brown blotches down the back (see fig.); belly yellowish with many brown or red crescent-shaped marks (see fig.) → **Northern water snake, *Nerodia s. sipedon***

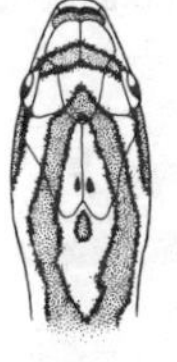

12b

12a Glossy black or brownish back; juveniles have conspicuous gray or brown blotches on a lighter ground color; scales in 25 to 33 rows → **Black rat snake, *Elaphe o. obsoleta***

12b Gray or tan with large black-edged red or brown blotches down middle of back; two alternating rows of smaller blotches along each side; dark "spear-point" mark on top of head (see fig.) → **Corn snake, *Elaphe g. guttata***

13a Scale rows 13; small pinkish or brown snakes with no pattern or spots; belly light; eyes small; head small, not tapering to neck → **Eastern worm snake, *Carphophis a. amoenus***

13b Scale rows 15 or more → **14**

14a Dorsal color black → **15**

14b Dorsal color brown or green → **16**

15a

15a Small snakes with glossy black back; yellow ring around neck (see fig.); belly yellow or orange → **Northern ringneck snake, *Diadophis punctatus edwardsii***

15b Long, slender black snake with a bluish belly and white throat; juveniles with a row of reddish blotches down a gray back, dark spots on flanks and venter → **Northern black racer, *Coluber c. constrictor***

17a

16a Small bright green snake with yellowish-white belly → **Eastern smooth green snake, *Opheodrys v. vernalis***

16b A small snake with a gray or tan back, sometimes with four rows of small black dots; belly whitish; head small → **Eastern earth snake, *Virginia v. valeriae***

17a,17b

17a Dorsal scales smooth (see fig.), anal plate single (see fig.) → **18**

17b Dorsal scales keeled (see fig.), anal plate single (see fig.) → **20**

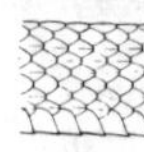

17b

18a Dorsal color brown or tan with 30 to 60 reddish blotches edged with black (see fig.), belly white-checkered with small black squares (see fig.) → **Eastern milk snake, *Lampropeltis t. triangulum***

18b Dorsal color black with yellow bands or spots; belly yellow with black markings → **19**

18a

18b

19a

19a Dorsal color black with narrow yellow crossbands that fork on the sides (see fig.) and formed of yellow scales, not yellow dots on black scales as below → **Eastern kingsnake,** ***Lampropeltis g. getulus***

19b Dorsal color black with indistinct pattern of crossbands formed of yellow spots on black scales → **Black kingsnake,** ***Lampropeltis getulus nigra***

20a Dorsal pattern consisting of 25 to 35 large black blotches on a dull white or gray background; belly white → **Northern pine snake,** ***Pituophis m. melanoleucus***

20b Dorsal pattern consisting of a longitudinal stripe or series of longitudinal dots → **21**

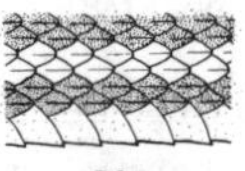

21a

21a Tail length about one-third of total length; slender with three bright yellow stripes on a rich brown background; the lateral stripes on the third and fourth scale rows (see fig.) → **Eastern ribbon snake,** ***Thamnophis s. sauritus***

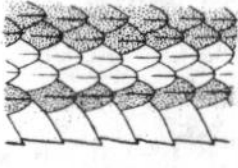

21b

21b Tail length less than one-third of total length; ground color may be various shades of brown, blue, green, or red; lateral stripes on the second and third rows of scales (see fig.) → **Eastern garter snake,** ***Thamnophis s. sirtalis***

KEY TO THE TADPOLES

Tadpoles are larval stages of toads and frogs and have several distinctive characteristics, such as body shape and the absence of external gills and forelimbs (these develop beneath the skin and do not "break through" until transformation). The highly specialized mouth parts (oral disc) are useful in identification: the mouth is framed by an upper and lower "beak"; above and below the beak are several rows of minute comblike "teeth" comprising the labial tooth formula. Laterally, and often ventrally, are a series of short and rounded fleshy papillae. In the identification of tadpoles, one should use specimens with hind limb buds showing. In working with the mouth parts, it is essential to use a binocular microscope or a good magnifying glass.

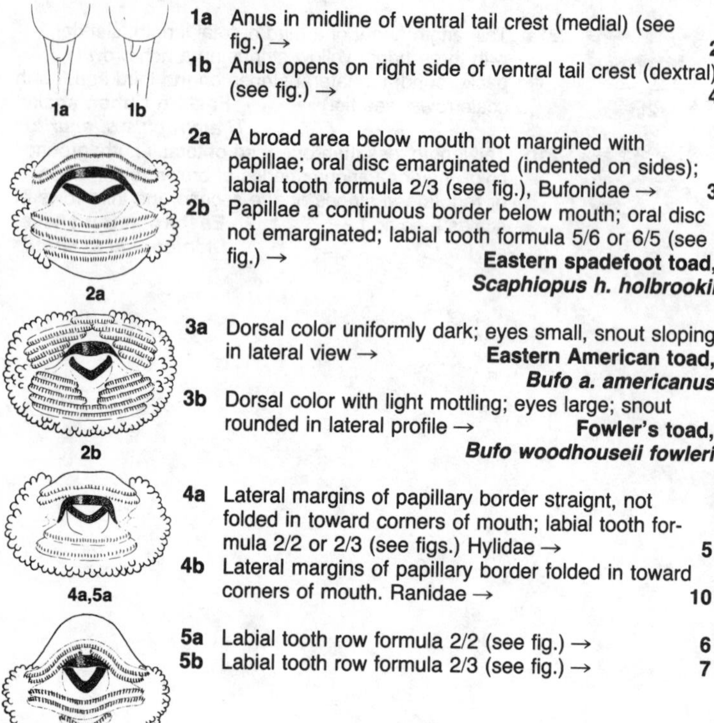

1a Anus in midline of ventral tail crest (medial) (see fig.) → **2**
1b Anus opens on right side of ventral tail crest (dextral) (see fig.) → **4**

2a A broad area below mouth not margined with papillae; oral disc emarginated (indented on sides); labial tooth formula 2/3 (see fig.), Bufonidae → **3**
2b Papillae a continuous border below mouth; oral disc not emarginated; labial tooth formula 5/6 or 6/5 (see fig.) → **Eastern spadefoot toad, *Scaphiopus h. holbrookii***

3a Dorsal color uniformly dark; eyes small, snout sloping in lateral view → **Eastern American toad, *Bufo a. americanus***
3b Dorsal color with light mottling; eyes large; snout rounded in lateral profile → **Fowler's toad, *Bufo woodhouseii fowleri***

4a Lateral margins of papillary border straignt, not folded in toward corners of mouth; labial tooth formula 2/2 or 2/3 (see figs.) Hylidae → **5**
4b Lateral margins of papillary border folded in toward corners of mouth. Ranidae → **10**

5a Labial tooth row formula 2/2 (see fig.) → **6**
5b Labial tooth row formula 2/3 (see fig.) → **7**

6a Found in western area of state, along Ohio River counties → **Blanchard's cricket frog, *Acris crepitans blanchardi***

6b Found east of the Allegheny Front → **Northern cricket frog, *Acris c. crepitans***

7a Tail reddish and heavily mottled with black; total length 2 inches (5 cm) → **Gray treefrog complex, *Hyla versicolor* and Hyla chrysocelis**

7b Tail not reddish; total length less than 2 inches (5 cm) → 8

8a Tail fin blotched, musculature area clear → **Northern spring peeper, *Hyla c. crucifer***

8b Tail fin not blotched → 9

9a Lower half of tail musculature with a light band in which dark pigment is absent; dorsal fin lower than ventral, terminates behind spiracle → **Mountain chorus frog, *Pseudacris brachyphona***

9b Lower half of tail musculature pigmented; dorsal fin higher than ventral → **Upland chorus frog, Pseudacris triseriata feriarum**

10a Labial tooth formula 3/4 or 4/4 (see fig.) → **Wood frog, *Rana sylvatica***

10b Labial tooth formula 2/3 or 1/3 → 11

10a

11a Beak narrowly pigmented; the lower mandible dark for less than half its width; belly densely pigmented → 12

11b Beak broadly pigmented; the lower mandible dark nearly to its base; belly lightly pigmented → 13

12a Tail with small, sharply defined black dots, most numerous on upper half → **Bullfrog, *Rana catesbeiana***

12b Tail with moderate to large spots or blotches which are not sharply outlined, as abundant on lower as on upper half of tail → **Green frog, *Rana clamitans melanota***

13a Tail crests usually light with small scattered spots; papillae below mouth small (see fig.) → **Northern leopard frog, *Rana pipiens***

13b Tail crests dark with large diffuse blotches of black which coalesce; papillae below mouth large, ten or fewer present → **Pickerel frog, *Rana palustris***

13a

Amphibians

AMPHIBIANS form the class of backboned animals that is evolutionarily between the fishes and reptiles in the vertebrate classification. The term *amphibia* was introduced by Linnaeus and derives from two Greek words which literally mean "both life." Most amphibians hatch from gelatinous eggs which are laid in or near water into an aquatic larval form that breathes through gills. In others, the aquatic larval form remains in the gelatinous egg. In both types, the larva undergoes a metamorphosis into an air-breathing form. Some amphibians spend their entire lives in water, while others live in moist places on land.

The amphibians have no unique characteristics such as a body covering of feathers, hair, or scales which are found in other vertebrates. They usually have four limbs which bear from two to five toes without claws. The skin in most species is smooth and moist but some forms, such as toads, have a dry, warty skin. Numerous glands in the skin secrete a mucous that may be irritating or poisonous. A variety of respiratory structures are present within the group such as gills, lungs, skin surface, and throat membranes. The heart usually has three chambers (plethodontids have two).

Amphibians probably derived from crossopterygian fishes early in the Devonian age. They share with the crossopterygians a great many anatomical features while possessing numerous distinguishing characteristics that are, for the most part, adaptive for a life on land.

The Class Amphibia is divided into nine orders, of which six are represented solely by fossil forms. Two of the three remaining orders are represented by forms occurring in West Virginia.

ORDER CAUDATA (URODELA)—SALAMANDERS

The members of this order are characterized by the presence of a tail throughout their lives. The body is elongate, lizardlike, with two pairs of limbs (except sirens) which bear four toes on the front feet and usually five toes on the hind feet. Within West Virginia, they are referred to as spring lizards, waterdogs, mudpuppies, and occasionally as grampuses. Most salamanders are terrestrial as adults, but even then must remain in a moist environment to prevent dessication. Most are also nocturnal and remain hidden under logs, rocks, or in their burrows during the day. Their food usually consists of small worms, insects, and other invertebrates. Many are brightly colored, but are rarely seen because of their secretive nature. They range in size from the hellbender, which grows to 20.0 inches (50.8 cm), to the diminutive four-toed salamander of 4.0 inches (10.2 cm). Salamanders are commonly confused with lizards, which have a scaly body covering and claws on their toes. Neither feature is ever found in salamanders.

Many of the salamanders mate on land, even though some of them may return to water to deposit their eggs. Some species mate in the spring, others in late summer or fall, even though they may not deposit their eggs until the following year. The mating process is preceded by a distinctive courtship, called the *liebesspiel,* in which the male excites the female by rubbing the sides of his head and chin against her as he swims or walks around her. The skin of these parts of his body contains glands that secrete substances which further excite the female and stimulate her to continue this nuptial activity. While the male is involved in this *liebesspiel,* he deposits spermatophores (minute packets of sperm supported on a gelatinous base) which he attaches to the vegetation if in the water, or the substrate if on land. The female, who has become excited, follows the male and pinches off the sperm-bearing tip of the spermatophore with the lips of her cloaca. The sperm remain within her cloaca in blind sacs, the spermathecae, until the extrusion of the eggs from the ovaries which brings the sperm and egg cells together in the oviducts. This type of fertilization is found in all West Virginia salamanders except the hellbender, which has external fertilization. In this species, the male covers the eggs with seminal fluid after they are laid.

Female salamanders deposit their eggs in a variety of arrangements and locations. The eggs may be deposited singly, or in a cluster held together by gelatinous envelopes, or in masses. Locations include underground burrows, rotten logs, sandstone crevices or caverns, sphagnum bogs, ponds, and streamside debris or tunnels.

Most West Virginia salamanders have an aquatic larval stage when gills function as the respiratory structures. Exceptions are the species of the genus *Plethodon* and the green salamander (*Aneides*). In these salamanders, the eggs, which are deposited on land, develop into gill-bearing larvae which remain within the egg capsules. By the time the larva is ready to break out of the egg capsule, the gills have regressed and the subadult has taken on adult form.

Salamanders occur in the North Temperate Zone of the Old World, in South America, Central America, and in North America. There are 9 families, about 60 genera, and about 300 living species recognized. In West Virginia there are 5 families, 11 genera, and 28 species known.

Family Cryptobranchidae

This family contains two genera of large, permanently aquatic salamanders, one of which occurs in the Orient and the other in the eastern United States. The oriental genus, *Andrias,* has two species, the largest of which attains a length of nearly 5 feet (1.5 m) and is the world's largest salamander. Adults of this family lack eyelids, have a pair of open gill slits, external fertilization, and a wrinkled, fleshy fold of skin along each side between the fore and hind limbs.

Genus *Cryptobranchus* Leuckart • Hellbenders

One species, *Cryptobranchus alleganiensis,* which includes two subspecies, is recognized. One subspecies occurs in West Virginia and surrounding states, and the other is confined to streams in southeastern Missouri and adjacent Arkansas.

1 **Eastern Hellbender** *Cryptobranchus alleganiensis alleganiensis* (Daudin)
Gr. *kryptos,* hidden; *branchia,* gill; *alleganiensis,* in the Allegheny Mountains

Description: The hellbender is a large aquatic salamander with a flat head that is rounded in dorsal view, and small, beady, lidless eyes. It may attain a total length of 20.0 inches (50.8 cm). A wrinkled fold of skin lies along each side between the fore and hind limbs.

There are five toes on the hind foot (the mudpuppy has four). The tail is strongly compressed, with a high dorsal keel. A large, conspicuous, persistent gill slit that opens into the throat lies just in front of each forelimb. Hellbenders are generally brown with numerous irregular, dark spots on the back. The belly is a uniform dark brown or gray and is lighter in color than the rest of the body.

Habitat and Habits: Hellbenders live in permanent streams throughout the Ohio river drainage. They are more frequently found in cool, clear mountain streams such as those of the Cheat River system. They spend much of their time under flat rocks in river beds and emerge at night to forage for food. Hillis and Bellis (1971) found that they defend the area under their cover rocks against other hellbenders. They may occasionally be seen moving slowly on river bottoms.

Hellbenders are held in disrepute because of their alleged habit of feeding on game fish and their eggs, but Green (1935) has shown that they subsist primarily on crayfish. From a survey of the stomach contents of 34 specimens collected from Shavers Fork of Cheat River in Randolph County, Green reported that 20 of the stomachs (59 percent) contained crayfish remains, 35 percent contained remains of fish, 21 percent contained insects and tadpoles, while 53 percent contained extraneous matter such as leaves, sand, pebbles, and sticks, apparently because hellbenders grab their food from the river bottom. Although Shavers Fork is a well-known trout stream, there was no evidence of trout in these stomachs.

Breeding: The mating season begins the last of August and continues for about two weeks with egg-laying taking place from late August to early November. The male excavates a nest under rocks or logs in the stream bed where the female lays marble-sized eggs which are connected in a string, like beads. She may deposit more than 400 eggs. Topping and Ingersol (1981) projected that over 1,100 eggs may be deposited. The male covers the eggs with seminal fluid. The eggs may complete development in eight weeks, depending upon the temperature of the water. Hatchlings resemble the parents except they bear gills. The gills are absorbed toward the end of the second year when the salamander is about 5.0 inches (12.7 cm) long. Sexual maturity is attained by the end of the third or fourth year, and by this time the salamander has reached a length of approximately 13.4 inches (34.0 cm) (B. Smith 1907). For a detailed review of the natural history of hellbenders see Nickerson and Mays (1972).

Remarks: Hellbenders are often caught by fishermen, who cut the line and throw the salamander upon the bank. Many people believe that it is poisonous and that a fish will not bite a hook which has caught one of these creatures. Hellbenders are harmless amphibians which seldom attempt to bite.

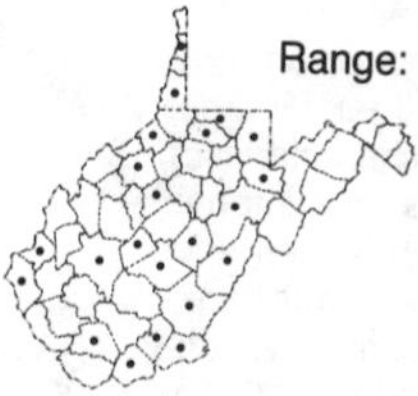

Range: Eastern hellbenders range from southern New York south through Pennsylvania, southeastern Ohio, West Virginia, and Kentucky to northern Georgia and Louisiana. They occur throughout West Virginia west of the Allegheny Front. No records are available from the Potomac drainage.

Family Proteidae

The members of this family retain certain larval characteristics permanently: three pairs of bushy external gills and reduced eyes with no eyelids. Two genera are recognized. The first is the genus *Proteus* (restricted to southeastern Europe) which has just one species, a slender white cave salamander with bright red gills and three fingers and two toes on the limbs. The other genus is *Necturus.*

Genus *Necturus* Rafinesque • Waterdogs and Mudpuppies

The mudpuppies or waterdogs are relatively large salamanders which may attain a total length of 17.0 inches (43.2 cm). They have three pairs of bushy gills which are retained throughout life. The two pairs of well-developed limbs bear four toes each. They may be found in a variety of permanently aquatic habitats including streams, rivers, ponds, and lakes.

The genus inclues five species that are found only in eastern North America. They range from near the Atlantic Coast through southern Quebec, westward into Manitoba, south to Texas, Louisiana, Alabama, and Georgia.

Three subspecies are recognized, one of which occurs in West Virginia.

2 Mudpuppy *Necturus maculosus maculosus* (Rafinesque)

Gr. *nekton,* swimming; L. *macula,* spotted

Description: The mudpuppy is a large aquatic salamander which may attain a length of 17.0 inches (43.2 cm). The head is flattened and truncate and broadly swollen behind the eyes. The eyes are small and lidless. The dorsal coloration is rusty brown to bluish black with numerous irregular dark spots which may extend on to the grayish belly. It has bushy gills which are bright red in life. The tail is compressed, with a strong dorsal keel. There are four toes on the hind feet (the four-toed salamander is the only other West Virginia salamander to have this characteristic).

Habitat and Habits: Mudpuppies live in streams, rivers, and impoundments. During the day they remain hidden under rocks and debris and in furrows or under bank overhangs. They become active at night as they forage over the floor of the stream for food. The usual foraging method is a slow, leisurely crawl over the bottom, although they are capable of swimming rapidly when alarmed. Mudpuppies are active throughout the year. Food consists of any animal matter which they can swallow. Stomach contents reveal crayfish, small fish, amphibians, molluscs, worms, and aquatic insects and their larvae (Hamilton 1932).

Breeding: Mating takes place in the fall. Following courtship, the male deposits spermatophores which are secured by the female. In the early spring, the salamanders move upstream to spawn. In mid March 1961, fishermen reported a large movement of these salamanders in Mud River, Cabell County, and also in Twelvepole River, Wayne County. Egg-laying takes place in June. The female attaches the eggs, individually, to the undersurface of boards, flat rocks, and other available substrate. Development within the egg may take up to 50 days depending upon the temperature of the water. Cochran and Lyons (1985) found a female in the company of 30 to 40 young. Stomach analysis showed she had not eaten, which suggests that she remained with the eggs during incubation. Sexual maturity is reached by the end of the fifth or sixth year.

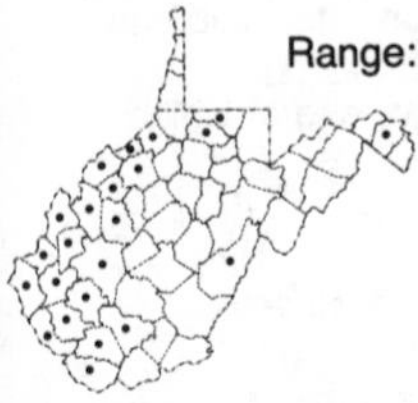

Range: Mudpuppies are found in southern Quebec and eastern New York to southeastern Manitoba, and south to eastern Kansas, Missouri, and northeastern Mississippi, northern Alabama, and northwestern Georgia. They occur throughout West Virginia, with the greatest concentration of records in the Ohio Valley. Bond (1931) reported the species to be common in the Monongahela and Cheat rivers, and Strader (1936) reported it from the South Branch of the Potomac below Romney.

Family Ambystomatidae • Mole Salamanders

This family contains medium-sized terrestrial salamanders that spend most of their time in underground burrows and, as a consequence, are rarely encountered outside the breeding season. They are predominantly black or dark brown in color but may have markings of yellow, silver, or bluish gray. Their prominent eyes have lids, the trunk bears distinct costal grooves, and the rounded snout lacks nasolabial grooves. Most species emerge in the spring, migrate in large numbers to spawning pools and deposit clusters of gelatinous-coated eggs. Some deposit eggs in the fall on land. This family contains two living genera, one of which occurs in the United States.

The principal genus, *Ambystoma,* occurs throughout the range of the family. Family Ambystomatidae ranges from the southern corner of Alaska, James Bay, and southern Labrador, south to the southern border of the Mexican plateau and to the northern half of Florida, but is apparently absent in northern Mexico and most of the southwestern United States.

Genus *Ambystoma* Tschudi • Mole Salamanders

This genus has 26 species, and 4 of these occur in West Virginia. The gilled larvae pass through an aquatic phase before transforming into the adult stage.

3 **Jefferson Salamander** *Ambystoma jeffersonianum* (Green)
Gr. *ambyx,* the rounded top of a cup; from type-locality at Jefferson College, Pa.

Description: This is a slender, dark brown or gray salamander which may reach a length of 7.0 to 8.0 inches (17.8–20.3 cm). It can be distinguished from other *Ambystoma* by its extremely long toes. There are 14 costal grooves. Small bluish flecks occur along the sides of the head, trunk, limbs, and tail. The belly is lighter gray, especially around the vent.

Confusing Species: The smallmouth salamander's toes are much shorter, and the silvery lichenoid spots are much larger than in the Jefferson salamander. The slimy salamander has a groove from each nostril to the upper lip (nasolabial groove).

Habitat and Habits: Adults spend most of their lives underground or in stacks of wet leaves where they frequently aggregate in sizeable numbers. Green and Brant (1966) reported this species from caves in Greenbrier and Pendleton counties. They are most frequently observed during early spring when they leave their underground burrows and move in a massive migration to the breeding pools. During migration, many are mashed by cars on the highways. Occasional specimens are collected at night while out foraging for food. Throughout the day they remain hidden under logs, stones, or leaves.

Their food consists of variety of invertebrates such as snails, earthworms, centipedes, millipedes, insects, and spiders (Judd 1957). Ambystomatid larvae feed on small tadpoles, small fish, and can be cannibalistic.

Breeding: Early in the spring, in response to a warming trend and rainfall, the adults emerge from their winter seclusion and move toward the breeding pools. Thompson *et al.* (1980) found that *A. jeffersonianum* in Maryland selected breeding pools isolated from streams and surrounded by forest with a dense border of trees and shrubs. They found that breeding sites contained a great amount of living, emergent vegetation as well as dead plant debris. Many of the adults, along with some subadults, or those which have not reached sexual maturity, enter the breeding ponds before all the ice has melted.

Following a brief courtship in which several salamanders swim back and forth through the water, the male grasps the larger female with his forelegs just behind hers. Later the male releases his hold, swims in front of the female, and attaches a spermatophore to some debris in the water. As she follows, she secures the spermatophore with the lips of her cloaca. This procedure will be repeated before the female starts laying eggs. She deposits her eggs in masses of 25 to 30 along a twig or weed stem until the full complement (up to 200 eggs) is reached. As the egg envelopes absorb water and swell, the entire mass assumes a transparent, gelatinous appearance. Courtship and egg-laying take place at night but may continue after daylight if the day is cloudy and overcast. The eggs hatch in about two weeks, more or less, depending upon the temperature.

Although the Jefferson salamander has been cited as an early breeder (Mohr 1931; Bishop 1941; Gatz 1971), observations in southwest West Virginia indicate that the breeding season may occur later than has been reported. On February 22, 1981, Ralph Taylor collected the first breeding specimen of this species. On April 5–6 there occurred a mass migration which lasted from about 10:00 P.M. until around 3:00 A.M. the next morning. Many of the salamanders appeared to be making their way to a large swamp between the highway (W. Va. Rt. 2) and the Ohio River. No eggs were observed although several gravid females were collected.

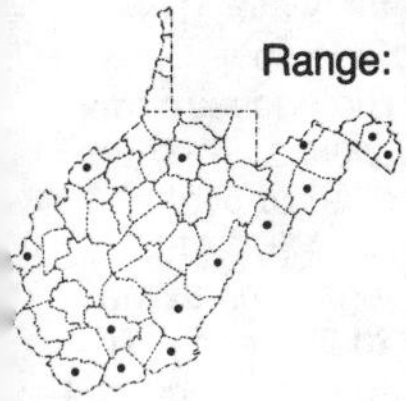

Range: The Jefferson salamander is found from western New England through western New York, southwestward to central Virginia, Kentucky, and Indiana. In West Virginia its distribution is probably statewide, although most records are from the eastern panhandle and the southeastern counties.

4 Spotted Salamander *Ambystoma maculatum* (Shaw)
Gr. *maculatus,* spotted

Description: The spotted salamander is slate-colored or black with two irregular rows of rounded yellow dorsal spots extending from the head onto the tail. It may attain a length of 8.0 inches (20.3 cm). There are numerous silvery or white flecks over the body. The belly is dark gray. There are usually 12 costal grooves.

Habitat and Habits: Spotted salamanders are creatures of deciduous forests where they are occasionally found wandering over the forest floor during rainy nights. They are diggers, and most of their life is spent underground. They may be found under logs, piles of damp leaves, or trash, or in newly plowed fields. Most of their above-ground activity is limited to the breeding season in the spring months. They eat a variety of invertebrates such as earthworms, snails, slugs, pill bugs, crustaceans, and insects and their larvae.

Breeding: Breeding takes place usually in February or March. Factors affecting the breeding activities of most ambystomatids have been studied by such researchers as Wright and Allen (1909), Blanchard (1930b), Bishop (1941), and Baldauf (1952). Baldauf found that a temperature of 55.0° F (12.8° C) was necessary to initiate the breeding stimulus, although such factors as rain, disappearance of snow, thawing of the ground surface, and the rapid runoff of snow water were correlated to the temperature.

During warm rainy nights, both sexes of spotted salamanders migrate en masse to the breeding pools where they swim vigorously back and forth rubbing and nosing one another. Spotted salamanders may be observed around the borders of the breeding pools or crossing highways en route to such pools.

Shoop (1965) observed that spotted salamanders tend to use the same route entering and leaving breeding ponds. Forester and La Pasha (1982) found that spotted salamanders do not migrate to breeding pools in response to frog calls. During breeding, the males deposit spermatophores on weed stems, grass, leaves, and other debris in the water. The females pinch off the sperm cap of the spermatophore with their cloacal lips. The eggs are then fertilized as they pass through the cloaca. They are deposited in irregular masses, rounded or oval in shape and measuring 2.0 to 4.0 inches (5.1–10.2 cm) in diameter, which adhere to vegetation in the water. Each mass may contain 12 to 250 eggs. The individual egg is pigmented dark brown to black and is surrounded by several gelatinous envelopes. The entire egg mass is frequently cottony white in color. It has a jellylike but firm consistency and may be lifted from the water without breaking apart. The mass is usually several inches below the surface, and it is not unusual for a pond to contain many egg masses. According to Bishop (1941) the larvae hatch in 45 to 50 days at which time they are 0.47 to 0.51 inch (1.2–1.3 cm) long. The length of the larval period varies greatly and seems to be dependent upon temperature, food, and water conditions. The larvae range from 1.6 to 2.8 inches (4.0–7.2 cm) at transformation. The adult pattern is attained shortly after metamorphosis.

Range: The range of the spotted salamander extends from Nova Scotia, Prince Edward Island, and mainland New Brunswick west to central Ontario and south to the Gulf Coast. On the western periphery of its range it is known in eastern and central Wisconsin, the forested parts of Illinois, the southern two-thirds of Missouri, extreme southeastern Kansas, eastern Oklahoma and Texas. It is less common in the coastal plain. Spotted salamanders occur throughout West Virginia, and records are available for almost every county.

5 **Marbled Salamander** *Ambystoma opacum* (Gravenhorst)

L. *opacus,* shaded, dark

Description: The marbled salamander is a short, stout-bodied salamander which may attain a total length of 5.0 inches (12.7 cm). Its dorsal pattern consists of alternating light and dark crossbands down the back. The lighter bands are silvery white in males and grayish in females and are usually narrow on the back and broader on the sides forming an hourglass pattern. There are 12 costal grooves. The belly is black.

Habitat and Habits: Marbled salamanders are nocturnal and spend most of their time underground. During the day they may be found under bark, wet leaves, logs, or trash in flood plains, deciduous woods, swamp borders, and stream banks. Occasionally they may be collected at night with the aid of a headlamp while they are out foraging for food. At other times they are fossorial, burrowing through the soil. They are slow and lethargic and if exposed lie quietly instead of trying to escape as do many other salamanders. They are more likely to be found close to the surface under debris than are the other West Virginia ambystomatids.

Several studies have been made of the food of these salamanders. Earthworms, insects, snails, slugs, crustaceans, and spiders have been found in their stomachs.

Breeding: The breeding habits of the marbled salamander differ in two important respects from those of other West Virginia ambystomatids. Breeding takes place in the fall, and on land. Toward the end of September both males and females migrate, males preceding females by a few days. This migration brings the sexes together in the breeding area, which may be a dried vernal (summer) pond area, the edges of an oxbow pond, or a depression destined to fill with water from fall or winter rains. Males initiate the courtship by nudging and pushing each other around with their snouts. Following this activity, the females, having secured spermatophores deposited by the males on vegetation and debris around the breeding area, seek a nesting site. In many cases, soil around the bases of black willows (*Salix nigra*) at the edge of the pond is selected for the nests. The nest is usually a small depression in the ground beneath a sheltering object such as drift debris along the margin of a woodland stream, or leaf mold, logs, bark, or pieces of wood board on a dry pond bottom. Petranka and Petranka (1981) found that females usually avoid nesting sites in the shallowest or deepest depressions because the shallowest areas are quick to dry up and the deepest areas may receive enough rainfall for the eggs to hatch but, unless there is a second rainfall, not enough to support the larvae. Each female deposits 50 to 150 eggs. The eggs may adhere to one another and to the soil of the burrow as the female moves around in the nest. She usually remains with the eggs until they are submerged when fall rains raise the level of the pond.

The eggs hatch in the fall or early winter months, depending upon the flooding of the burrows. In some cases under observation, freshly laid eggs hatched within 15 days due to early flooding, while in other cases the eggs remained in the burrows until late winter or early spring. When they hatch, the embryos are 0.75 inch (1.9 cm) long. The newly hatched larvae are relatively inactive until the temperature begins to warm up and more food becomes available. Balancers may be present at hatching although they are usually lost by the time the forelimbs appear. The broad tail fin emerges and elongate gills are noticeable. Larvae, by this time, have assumed the form of a typical pond-dweller. Larvae remain active throughout the spring, feeding on fairy shrimp and other invertebrates as well as on smaller ambystomatid larvae and tadpoles, especially those of the spring peeper and wood frog. They are dark brown or almost black in color with numerous light spots over the body and tail. As transformation approaches, the keel of the tail is lost before the gills are greatly reduced. Metamorphosis is completed during the summer. Recently transformed juveniles have been collected from dried swamps and other breeding areas in July and August.

The presence of larvae in a pond in the spring serves as an indication of the presence of the species in the area. Adult marbled salamanders are rarely encountered, and frequently their breeding area is unknown.

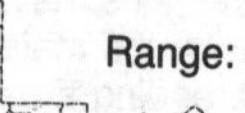

Range: The range of the marbled salamander extends from New England to northern Florida, and west to southern Illinois, eastern Oklahoma, and eastern Texas. Its distribution is probably statewide in West Virginia.

6 **Smallmouth Salamander** *Ambystoma texanum* (Matthes)

Texanum refers to the state of Texas, where it was first found

Description: The smallmouth salamander is a medium-sized salamander that may attain a length of 6.0 inches (15.2 cm). The head and mouth are both proportionately small in relation to the heavy body. The color is black or dark brown, with numerous bluish gray or silvery gray lichenlike markings along the sides of the body and tail. The toes are short and do not touch when the legs are extended along the sides. There are 14 costal grooves.

Habitat and Habits: The smallmouth salamander spends most of the year underground, emerging early in the spring to breed before it returns to its subterranean habitat. Throughout the breeding season it may be found under logs, bark, leaves, stones, and trash around the breeding area. When a smallmouth salamander is exposed in its hiding place, it often reacts by elevating its tail and waving it from side to side. This may be interpreted as a defensive posture to divert attention of the predator away from the anterior end of the animal.

The food of the smallmouth salamander differs little from that of the other ambystomatid salamanders. They are voracious, cannibalistic, and insectivorous. In fact their diet, which consists almost entirely of animal food, is limited only by prey size and availability. Their burrowing habits through layers of leaves and under objects in contact with the soil provides them with a large selection of invertebrates such as earthworms and insects. For a detailed study of the foods of the smallmouth salamander see Whitaker *et al.* (1982).

Breeding: The smallmouth salamander breeds in late winter or early spring, usually in February or March. The breeding area may be either standing or running water such as a drainage ditch, swamp, river flood plain, or small stream. The late winter and early spring rains may serve as the stimulus to emerge from hibernation and migrate to the breeding area. Brown *et al.* (1982) found that temperature may have an influence on migration but precipitation probably does not. Petranka (1984) observed that breeding occurs more or less independently of rainfall and temperature conditions. Wyman (1971), Garton (1972), and Petranka (1982) describe the courtship behavior of the smallmouth salamander. It begins with the males moving among the arrivals and nudging them with their noses and the sides of their heads. After attracting the attention of a female the males wander among the vegetation in the pool and deposit their spermatophores. The accompanying female follows and pinches off the spermatophore. This may continue for some time before the female begins to deposit eggs. The female lays several hundred eggs, singly or in clutches of 6 to 8 eggs each. Petranka (1984) found that the number of eggs per mass ranged from 8 to 1,142. Occasionally eggs are attached singly to the undersurface of stones, logs, or other debris in the water. In one instance, discarded crossties along a railroad drainage ditch served for concealment of the salamanders and their eggs. Within a few weeks the eggs hatch. The enclosed embroys are about 0.5 inch (1.2 cm) in length. The adults may remain in the area for several weeks before returning to shelter. The larvae transform within two months and can be found near the breeding site until late August.

Remarks: Green and Richmond (1940) reported a single specimen of the smallmouth salamander from Buffalo, Wayne County (CM 17578) which established this salamander's presence in West Virginia. Green (1961) described a colony of this species breeding on a flooded high school athletic field in west Huntington. Since then other breeding colonies have been located at Shoals, Wayne County, near Point Pleasant, Mason County, and in Wood County.

Range: The smallmouth salamander is found from the Ohio Valley west to the southern part of Wisconsin, south through Kansas, Oklahoma, and eastern Texas to the Gulf of Mexico. In West Virginia, it appears to be confined to the counties along the Ohio River.

Family Salamandridae • Newts

This is a widespread family occupying Europe, Asia, northern Africa, and North America. It includes 15 genera with about 50 species. Only 2 genera of newts, *Notophthalmus* in the east and *Taricha* in the west, occur in North America. The members of this family metamorphose completely, and most spend at least part of their lives on land. Larvae of the eastern newt typically metamorphose into bright red efts that may live on land for as long as seven years, after which they return to the water and become sexually mature. Newts have a rough, granular skin, lack costal grooves, and possess lungs.

Genus *Notophthalmus* Rafinesque • Eastern Newts

The genus *Notophthalmus* contains three species, all found in eastern North America (the range of one species extends into northern Mexico). One species (*Notophthalmus viridescens*) contains four subspecies and is represented in West Virginia by the following.

7 Red-spotted Newt (Red Eft) *Notophthalmus viridescens viridescens* (Rafinesque)
Gr. *notos,* the back; Gr. *ophthalmos,* the eye;
L. *viridescens,* greenish

Description: The adult is a small aquatic salamander about 4.0 inches (10.2 cm) long. Pauley collected a gravid female in Hardy County that measured just 2.3 inches (5.8 cm) (personal observation). The dorsal color is greenish brown with a scattering of black dots and a series of small, black-bordered red spots along each side. The ventral surface is lemon yellow with many scattered, small black spots. The male has enlarged horny excresences on the lower surface of the hind legs and a strongly compressed tail with a sharp keel. Costal grooves are lacking. There is a pair of longitudinal ridges on top of the head.

In West Virginia, there are three distinct stages during its life history: a larva; a terrestrial, sexually immature subadult; and an aquatic, sexually mature adult. The immature or eft stage has rough, granular skin that is bright orange-red with a row of black-bordered red spots along each side. The eft wanders over the forest floor and is most conspicuous following warm summer rains. After a period of three to seven years (Healey 1974), the subadult returns to the water and takes on the adult coloration described above.

Habitat and Habits: Adult newts are found in a wide range of aquatic habitats, particularly in quiet pools, ponds, and swamps. While they may occur in streams, they are seldom abundant there. Gates and Thompson (1982) found that pools selected by newts generally contained sparse amounts of vegetation, except around the edge. The mature adults can be seen floating or drifting near the surface of the pond at any hour of the day or night. They are active throughout the year and may be observed swimming beneath the ice during winter months. During late summer and fall, when their ponds may dry up, they burrow into the mud and remain there until the water level is restored.

A mass migration of the red-spotted newt was witnessed by Ralph Taylor and his students on the evening of February 18, 1981, while they were observing the behavior of the smallmouth salamander in a water-filled ditch along the railroad tracks at Shoals, Wayne County. The newts, all in breeding condition, were moving in the same direction along the roadbed apparently toward a large swamp where newts are known to breed in the spring. (For a detailed study on the migrations of the red-spotted newts and red efts, see Hurlbert 1969.)

A fully transformed eft may be 1.8 inches (4.7 cm) long (Bishop 1941). The length of its sojourn on land varies considerably. For example, Noble (1926) found that newts of the coastal plain on Long Island, as well as those in the Wood's Hole area, did not pass through the terrestrial eft stage. Bishop (1941) indicates that sexual maturity may be attained at the end of the second year although many individuals do not return to the water until the end of the third year. Brandon and Bremer (1966) describe a population of *Notophthalmus viridescens louisianensis* in Illinois which became sexually mature while still in the larval stage.

The food of the newt, like that of most salamanders, is limited only by size and availability. Throughout most of the season it consists of various worms, insects, insect larvae, crustaceans, slugs, snails, and small vertebrates. In the early spring, the cycles of the various animals in the area may determine the newt's diet. Thus it may feed on the eggs of the spotted salamander, then shift to the fairy shrimp as they increase in number, then to mosquito larvae, and finally to eggs of one of the frogs breeding at this season. Wood and Goodwin (1954) report newts eating their own embryos. Burton (1976, 1977) and MacNamara (1977) present detailed studies of the food habits of adult and immature newts. Ries and Bellis (1966) studied the spring food habits of the red-spotted newt.

Breeding: Mating generally occurs in the spring, although there may also be a fall mating period. During mating periods the male develops a broadly keeled tail and horny excresences along the rear margins of the hind legs. Spring mating includes a variety of movements of the male which may begin when he clasps the female around the neck with his hind legs. Throughout this period of clasping, twisting, and turning, which is often violent, the male vibrates or fans his tail from side to side. Following his release of the female he moves forward and waits for the female to follow. If she does, and presses her head lightly against his tail and cloacal region, he deposits a spermatophore which she picks up. This may continue for some time until she begins oviposition. She deposits eggs one at a time, attaching them to leaves and stems of aquatic vegetation. The eggs are pigmented and may number 300 or more. Eggs are deposited in April in West Virginia, and usually hatch within two or three weeks. Newly hatched larvae soon develop gills, balancers, and limbs. Transformation into the red eft stage occurs in late summer or early fall. During the fall mating period, the male noses and clasps females and may deposit spermatophores, but there is no evidence that the female deposits eggs.

Remarks: Newts are avoided as prey by most animals since their skin secretions are toxic and irritating. As a result, they are not ordinarily used as fish bait, as are many other salamanders. They are ideal aquarium animals and many classrooms use them to good advantage. Students may enjoy providing them with food such as cut-up earthworms, although they will thrive on dog food.

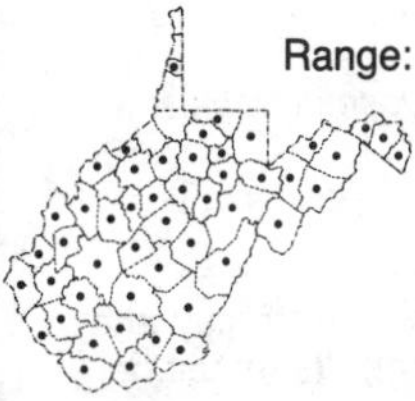

Range: The red-spotted newt is found from the Maritime Provinces of Canada to the Great Lakes region and south to central Georgia and Alabama. They are widely distributed throughout West Virginia and are one of the most common salamanders in the state.

Family Plethodontidae

This is the largest and most successful group of salamanders. There are about 220 species in 27 genera worldwide. All but 2 species are found in the New World. In the United States and Canada there are about 80 species in 16 genera. Plethodontids range from small to medium size and vary in color from dull to bright. They occupy a wide variety of habitats such as mountain brooks, rock crevices, and forests. Several species live in caves and underground streams.

All members of the family are lungless and depend upon the skin and lining of the mouth and throat for gaseous exchange. Plethodontids can be identified by the presence of a nasolabial groove which extends from each nostril to the upper lip. In some species this groove may be difficult to see. If this is the case, squeeze the upper lip. This usually causes a fluid to exude and renders the groove more visible.

West Virginia has 7 genera and 21 species of plethodontids.

Genus *Desmognathus* Baird • Dusky Salamanders

The genus *Desmognathus* as well as the genera *Leurognathus and Phaeognathus* belong to the subfamily Desmognathinae. The names of these genera end in the suffix *-gnathus* because in all three the lower jaw is held in position by ligaments joining it to the upper part of the backbone. As a result the mouth is opened by raising the upper jaw as well as the skull (Goin, Goin, and Zug 1978). This arrangement produces large jaw muscles which are obvious in side view, a trait frequently used in identifying this genus. Other key characteristics include a light line from the eye to the angle of the jaw, and hind legs that are noticeably larger than the front ones.

Desmognathus is the only genus of these three with representatives in West Virginia. Four species occur within the state. Members of this genus contain many perplexing forms. Individuals vary widely in coloration and pattern.

8 **Northern Dusky Salamander** *Desmognathus fuscus fuscus* (Green)
Gr. *desma,* band, ligament; Gr. *gnathos,* jaw; L. *fuscus,* brown

Description: This is a medium-sized salamander which may attain a total length of 5.0 inches (12.7 cm). Its robust body may be various shades of brown or gray. There is usually a reddish brown stripe down the back with darker wavy or scalloped borders. The dorsal pattern is extremely variable, and beginners frequently arrive at an identification only through the elimination of other recognized species. Juvenile dusky salamanders have five to eight pairs of reddish spots down the back between the front and hind legs. As the salamander grows older these spots coalesce to form the scalloped dorsal band of the adult. Older specimens are darker, and most of the pattern may be obscured. There is usually a light streak extending from the posterior corner of the eye to the angle of the jaw. Belly color is variable, but usually mottled with gray or brown. There is a sharp dorsal keel down the compressed tail and there are 14 costal grooves.

Habitat and Habits: Dusky salamanders are creatures of very damp areas such as margins of streams and brooks where they seek shelter during the day under leaves, rocks, and logs. Like most salamanders, they are more active at night than during the day. They are quick, agile, and difficult to capture, and their slimy covering often enables them to elude the grasp of a would-be captor. They are active burrowers and dig tunnels in the soft soil of the stream bank into which they may escape. They also climb well and at night may be found on the sides of stones and in low vegetation.

Many studies have been made on the food habits

of the dusky salamanders (Burton 1976; Sites 1978). Stomach contents reveal a diet of earthworms, snails, slugs, soft-bodied insects, larvae, mites, spiders, as well as some salamanders and their larvae.

Breeding: Inasmuch as the dusky salamander spends most of its life in the same area, there is no mass migration from its habitat to the breeding spot. The deposition of spermatophores has been noted in the fall as well as in the spring. They are deposited on leaves and other available material near the stream and secured by the female with her cloacal lips. She lays a cluster of 10 to 20 pale yellow, pigmentless eggs, held together by their thin outer envelopes. The eggs are usually attended by the female and are frequently lying within a coil of her body. The nests are generally located in cavities under debris, logs, and stones close to a small woodland stream. Egg-laying occurs from June to early August (Danstedt 1975) with hatching taking place in late summer or early fall. Krzysik (1980) suggests July as the peak month for egg deposition and the first half of September as the peak time for hatching in western Pennsylvania. The newly hatched larvae make their way into the stream by following tunnels or crevices in the soil until they reach water level. Usually the egg mass is situated so that the hatchlings drop into the water as they escape from the egg envelope. Throughout their larval period, approximately one year, they swim in shallow pools or lie beneath flat stones and leaves in woodland streams. Transformation may take place in late spring or early summer (Danstedt 1975) depending upon temperature, availability of food, and other factors. Males mature at two years of age and females at three years (ibid.).

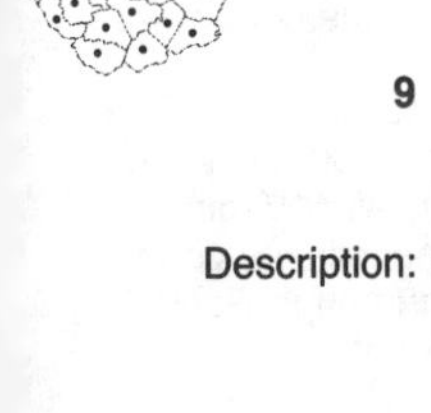

Range: The range of the dusky salamander extends from New Brunswick to central Kentucky and western South Carolina. It is found throughout West Virginia, from the lowest elevations to an altitude of 3,900 feet (1,189 m) on White Top, Randolph County.

9 Mountain Dusky Salamander *Desmognathus ochrophaeus* Cope

Gr. *ochra,* yellow, pale; Gr. *phaeios,* dusky, dark

Description: The mountain dusky salamander is a small salamander which may attain a total length of 4.0 inches (10.2 cm). There is usually a dorsal pattern (especially in juveniles and small adults) consisting of a light yellow, reddish, or tan stripe bordered by straight dark stripes on each side. There may be several dots or chevron markings within the dorsal stripe. In older individuals, especially at higher altitudes within the state, the light line from the eye to the angle of the jaw may be obscured, and the overall color may be dark brown or almost black. The tail is rounded, without a dorsal keel, and there are 14 costal grooves.

Confusing Species: The northern two-lined salamander (no. 27), which may have a similar dorsal pattern, has a bright yellow belly; a more slender, streamlined form; lacks the diagonal bar from eye to jaw angle; and has a laterally compressed tail.

The redback salamander (no. 12) has hind legs about the same size as the forelegs, lacks the bar from eye to jaw angle, and has a salt-and-pepper belly pattern.

Habitat and Habits: The mountain dusky salamander is more terrestrial than the northern dusky or any other *Desmognathus* in West Virginia and often strays far from water, especially during the summer. It may be found under leaf litter, bark, and stones, and in crevices of cliffs and rock formations throughout the Alleghenies. The mountain dusky is an active, elusive salamander which runs, twists, and leaps to avoid capture. It is nocturnal and is seldom encountered in the daytime unless its place of concealment is uncovered. As colder weather approaches, it seeks more aquatic sites. During the winter it is active around mountain springs, seepages, and bogs where it hides between debris and the saturated ground. It feeds on invertebrate animals such as earthworms and a variety of insects (Keen 1979).

Breeding: Mating and egg-laying probably take place in spring or fall (Tilley and Tinkle 1968; Fitzpatrick 1972; Tilley 1973; and Forester 1977). The female watches over 19 or more unpigmented eggs which she has deposited in a grapelike cluster beneath a log or rock in seepages or other wet areas. The larval period probably extends from one to eight months (Keen and Orr 1980), depending upon whether the eggs were laid in the spring or fall.

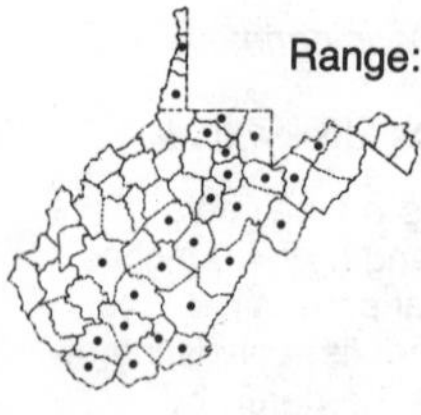

Range: The mountain dusky salamander occurs west of the Hudson River in New York and into northeast Georgia and northeast Alabama. Within West Virginia it extends mainly throughout the mountainous counties of Monongalia and Preston, south through Randolph, Monroe, Mercer, and McDowell counties.

10 Appalachian Seal Salamander *Desmognathus monticola monticola* Dunn
L. *mons,* a mountain; L. *colo,* inhabit.

Description: The Appalachian seal salamander is a stout-bodied brown salamander which may attain a length of 5.5 inches (14.0 cm). The dorsal pattern consists of a background of tan or brown with darker wormlike markings. The belly is pale gray and there are 14 costal grooves. The tail is compressed, sharply keeled, and has a pointed tip.

The dorsal pattern of larvae and juveniles consists of four pairs of reddish orange spots arranged in two rows on the back between the front and hind legs. The spots may remain as part of the adult pattern on the tail.

Habitat and Habits: The seal salamander prefers the cool mountain streams of Appalachia where it tunnels in the banks of wet moss or lives under rocks in the stream bed. It is more aquatic than other members of the genus. During the day it can be found by turning stones within a stream or peeling away moss along the stream bank. At night it will perch atop a rock splashed by the spray of a tumbling brook or lie at the entrance to a burrow in the bank with only its head exposed. It is quick, elusive, and slippery. A dip net held in the stream bed as rocks above are moved is one way to capture it. Like other dusky salamanders, it feeds on a variety of aquatic invertebrates.

Breeding: The yellowish eggs are deposited in seepages or moist areas along a stream, attached individually to the undersides of leaves or stones. As many as three dozen eggs may comprise a complement. Eggs are laid from June through September and are guarded by the female. They hatch in September. Little is known about the late larval stages and transformation. Organ (1961) estimates the larval stage to be 12 to 13 months in the southern Appalachians.

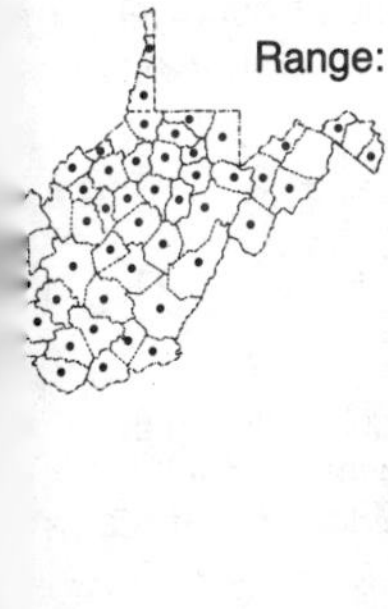

Range: The Appalachian seal salamander occurs from southwestern Pennsylvania southwest through the uplands to central and southwestern Alabama. In West Virginia it probably occurs throughout the state with the possible exception of the western counties of Cabell, Jackson, Mason, and Putnam. It has been taken in the mountains up to 4,470 feet (1,362 m) (Pauley 1980a).

11 Blackbelly Salamander *Desmognathus quadramaculatus* (Holbrook)
L. *quadrus,* fourfold, four; L. *macula,* spot

Description: This is a large, robust salamander of swift mountain streams that may reach a length of 8.0 inches (20.3 cm). It is dark brown or black above with greenish or light brown blotches. There are two rows of light dots along each side. The tail is sharply keeled on top. The top of the head and snout are often brownish; the snout is usually paler than the rest of the head, especially in older specimens. The belly is uniformly black. There are 14 costal grooves.

Habitat and Habits: Blackbelly salamanders favor swiftly flowing mountain streams with numerous boulders and waterfalls. They tunnel into the moist soil above the stream and lie at the mouth of the burrow waiting for passing prey. The beam of a flashlight will reflect the shine of their eyes at night.

This salamander is a good swimmer. When discovered in its rocky retreat, it is quick and elusive. It may be seen resting on a rock in a stream, occasionally in bright sunlight, bathed in the spray of the cascading current.

Breeding: The unpigmented eggs are deposited individually to a support, such as a stone, log, or leaf in the streambed. A normal egg complement contains 20 to 40 eggs. The female remains with the eggs until they hatch in late summer or early fall. The larval period lasts for about 24 months (Martof *et al.* 1980).

Remarks: According to local fishermen within the area of the state where this salamander is found, the blackbelly makes ideal fish bait. It therefore may not exist in many streams where it was once found. One fisherman of the area is said to have remarked that 50 years ago he had collected 200 to 300 "large black lizards" from a hollow in an hour's time.

Range: The blackbelly salamander is found from southern West Virginia throughout the mountains to northeastern Georgia. It occurs in Fayette County (Green 1967) through Raleigh, Summers, Mercer, and Monroe in West Virginia.

Genus *Plethodon* Tschudi • Woodland Salamanders

The genus contains twenty-six species, five in the Pacific Northwest, one in New Mexico, and the remainder in the eastern portion of the United States and Canada. Members of the genus are referred to as "woodland salamanders." They are entirely terrestrial and nocturnal. The eight species which occur in West Virginia hide under debris, in logs, and in burrows in soil throughout the day and emerge at night to search for food. Occasionally they climb low bushes or tree trunks. They spend their larval stage within the enclosed aquatic environment of the egg capsule.

12 **Redback Salamander** *Plethodon cinereus* (Green)
Gr. *pleth,* to be full; L. *odon,* teeth; L. *cinic,* ashes, ash-colored

Description: This is a small, slender salamander which may attain a length of 4.0 inches (10.2 cm). It usually has a straight-edged red stripe down the back that may extend onto the tail. The color of this stripe varies from bright to deep red; it may be suffused with gray, or absent (the lead-backed phase). The belly is sprinkled black and white. The tail is round in cross section and there are usually 18 to 19 costal grooves.

Confusing Species: The valley and ridge salamander, *Plethodon hoffmani* (no. 14), is the only small species of *Plethodon* whose range overlaps that of the redback salamander in the Eastern Panhandle. It differs in having a higher costal groove count (20–21), a whiter throat, and a darker belly with less speckling.

The ravine salamander (no. 13) and the redback salamander both occupy the eastern portion of the Appalachian Plateau province. The ravine salamander is more attenuated, has 19 to 22 costal grooves, and a plain dark belly.

At higher elevations (3,150 feet [960 m] or higher) where it occurs, the Cheat Mountain salamander, *Plethodon nettingi* (no. 15), may be confused with the redback salamander. It is a small black or dark brown species which may grow to 4.0 inches (10.2 cm) and has 17 to 19 costal grooves. The belly and throat are uniformly dark gray to black.

Habitat and Habits: The redback salamander inhabits cool, moist forests of coniferous, deciduous, or mixed types up to an elevation of 4,800 feet (1,463 m) (Pauley 1980a). It hides under bark, rocks, logs, leaves, and debris during the day and emerges from concealment to forage for food at night. When exposed in its hiding place it often remains coiled and motionless unless prodded, when it rushes away with leaping movements of the body and tail.

The stomach contents of this species have been studied by numerous investigators. In what appears to be one of the most complete studies, Surface (1913) reported that the stomach contents of 260 specimens included "snails, earthworms, spiders, mites, millipedes, insect larvae and adult insects, of which ants formed a large part." Pauley (1978) studied the stomach contents of 86 *P. cinereus* and found ants and mites to be the major food items. Other studies are those of Jaeger (1972) and Burton (1976).

Breeding: Mating occurs in fall and spring (Blanchard 1928; Sayler 1966) and egg-laying from May to July. Eggs have been collected as early as May 23 at an elevation of 4,400 feet (1,341 m) on Barton Knob, Randolph County. Five to 12 eggs are deposited in a grapelike cluster usually in a crevice within a rotting log or stump. Other nest cavities are depressions under stones, crevices under bark (on a fallen tree trunk), or under moss. The egg cluster, usually attached to the roof of the crevice, is encircled by the female, who protects the eggs against desiccation. Hatching probably occurs in August or September in West Virginia. Eggs containing embryos which appeared ready to hatch have been collected in late August at an elevation of 2,200 feet (671 m). In several years of field work in elevations above 3,500 feet (1,067 m), Pauley found several females with eggs from June 6 to August 20 (unpublished data). The number of eggs per nest ranged from four to ten. He found two females with young, one with four on August 4, 1981, and one with eight on September 4, 1976. The young ranged in size from 0.6 to 0.7 inch (1.5–1.8 cm). Breeding age is attained at the end of the third season, and the first eggs are laid in the spring of the fourth year (Blanchard 1928; Sayler 1966; Nagel 1977).

Range: Their range extends from southern Quebec and Nova Scotia south to southern North Carolina and southern Missouri. In West Virginia they are probably statewide except for the Ohio Valley counties from Wayne north to Pleasants.

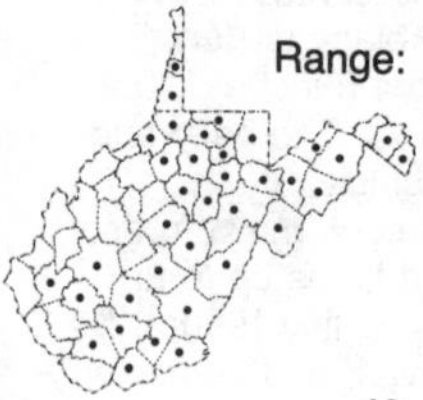

13 Ravine Salamander *Plethodon richmondi* Netting and Mittleman

Named for Neil D. Richmond, who collected the holotype

Description: The ravine salamander is an extremely elongate, slender salamander with short legs and a slender head. It may attain a length of 5.0 inches (12.7 cm). The dorsal color is brown to black with numerous gold and silver flecks; occasionally small white speckles appear on the sides. The belly and throat are uniformly dark, finely mottled with white. Costal grooves range from 19 to 22. Twelve costal folds remain between the toes when the front and hind feet are pressed along the sides.

Habitat and Habits: The ravine salamander inhabits the wooded slopes of valleys and ravines. It may be found along benches of hillsides but is less common on hillsides or valley floors. During the day it hides under leaves and stones.

Ravine salamanders become active above ground toward the last of September and remain so until the latter part of May. Throughout these months they may be exposed by removing the debris which constitutes their cover. At night they are active except when weather conditions are too severe. They have been collected in the winter by removing snow from their leaf cover and exposing them. When uncovered, they remain coiled in an immobile condition. From early June to late September the salamander is very difficult to find because it burrows deep underground to avoid the warmer temperatures. In Harrison County on August 17, 1949, a specimen was unearthed 4 feet (1.2 m) below the surface by a worker digging a cistern. Specimens collected in the spring prior to their "forced aestivation" have tails noticeably greater in diameter than those of recently emerged specimens in the fall. Netting (1939) comments on this phenomenon, as does Duellman (1954).

Duellman also summarizes the results of two food studies on the ravine salamander. Ants predominated, and together with sow bugs comprised over 50 percent of the food items of the specimens examined. The remainder of the food consisted of small ground beetles, earthworms, snails, small crustaceans, and spiders.

Breeding: Little is known about reproduction of the ravine salamander, or of any other *Plethodon* that spends the summer months underground when egg deposition takes place. Wallace (1969) examined the ovarian eggs in 137 females in Kentucky between March and November. His findings suggested that egg deposition occurs in May or early June. Barbour (1971) reports finding a female containing four ovarian eggs with two newly laid eggs and two hatchlings on

August 23 under a flat rock on a steep slope. Duellman (1954) reports on a clutch of 12 unattached eggs with no common external envelope in a depression under a limestone slab. Although the eggs bore a strong resemblance to *Plethodon* eggs, there was no attending female to confirm the identification. Hatching apparently occurs in later summer. Wallace and Barbour (1957) found two adult *P. richmondi,* two eggs, and two newly hatched young on August 23 in Mason County, Kentucky. A juvenile (CM 14212), 0.9 inch (2.3 cm) in length, was collected in Ritter Park, Huntington, Cabell County on October 15, 1938. The site was a rocky ledge on a steep hillside which had an accumulation of leaf litter and duff that sheltered several adult ravine salamanders.

Remarks: Prior to 1938, all small dark *Plethodon* were considered to be the lead-backed phase of *Plethodon cinereus* (no. 12). In 1938 the ravine salamander and the Cheat Mountain salamander (no. 15) were described, and in 1972 the valley and ridge salamander (no. 14) was described. To verify the identifications and the ranges of these species in West Virginia, we reexamined all specimens of the small *Plethodon* in the West Virginia Biological Survey Collection.

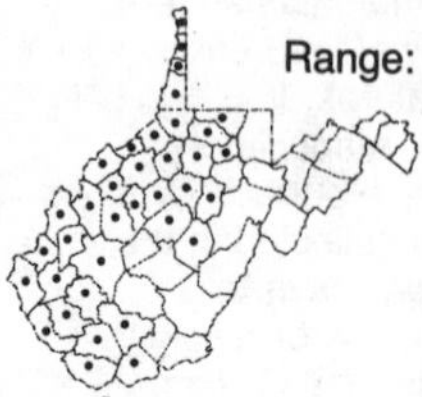

Range: The ravine salamander ranges from western Pennsylvania south to northeastern Tennessee and northwest North Carolina, and west to southeastern Indiana. In West Virginia it occupies the Allegheny Plateau west of the Allegheny Mountains in the north and west of the New River in the south. It overlaps with *Plethodon cinereus* in the northwestern part of the state, the northern panhandle, and the southernmost counties of Summers and Raleigh.

14 **Valley and Ridge Salamander** *Plethodon hoffmani* Highton

Named for Richard L. Hoffman, who collected the holotype

Description: This is a slender salamander similar to the ravine salamander but with a whiter throat and some white mottling on the belly. It may attain a total length of 5.0 inches (12.7 cm). The back is dark brown. Costal grooves vary from 20 to 21.

Habitat and Habits: In West Virginia, *P. hoffmani* is restricted to the Valley and Ridge province (Highton 1972; Pauley 1980a). It inhabits hillside slopes of mixed deciduous forest with flat stones and other cover objects. The soils in this region are generally dry and well drained;

it is therefore best to observe this salamander in the early spring when the soil is moist. For additional information on the ecology of *P. hoffmani* see Fraser (1974).

Fraser (1974) examined 94 stomachs of adult *P. hoffmani* and found the major food items to be hymenopterons, springtails, centipedes, mites, and flies.

Breeding: Angle (1969) studied the reproductive cycle of *P. hoffmani* in the Valley and Ridge province of Pennsylvania and Maryland. He found that courtship and mating probably occur in the spring, with egg deposition in April and May. He observed an average of 4.6 ovarian eggs per female. Fraser (1974), in a study of *P. hoffmani* in Virginia, found the average number of deposited eggs to be 4.6 for five females.

Remarks: Before Richard Highton described the valley and ridge salamander in 1972, this species was thought to be the ravine salamander (*P. richmondi,* no. 13). All studies of *P. hoffmani* prior to 1972 were published in reference to *P. richmondi.*

Range: Its range extends from the West Branch of the Susquehanna River Valley in central Pennsylvania, southwest in the Appalachians to New River in southwestern Virginia. Its range in West Virginia is confined to the Ridge and Valley province in the eastern part of the state. *P. hoffmani* has a broad elevation range, occurring from 1,600 feet (488 m) near Seneca Rocks to 4,400 to 4,599 feet (1,341–1,402 m) on Allegheny Mountain (Pauley 1980a).

15 Cheat Mountain Salamander *Plethodon nettingi* Green

Named for M. Graham Netting, curator of herpetology at Carnegie Museum of Natural History, Pittsburgh

Description: This is a small black or very dark brown salamander that may reach a length of 4.0 inches (10.2 cm). The back is usually sprinkled with many brassy or silvery flecks, and the belly and the throat are uniformly dark gray to black. There are 17 to 19 costal grooves.

Habitat and Habits: The Cheat Mountain salamander lives in forested areas above 3,150 feet (960 m), elevations that are, or were, occupied by red spruce (*Picea rubens*) and yellow birch (*Betula alleghaniensis*). Brooks (1945, 1948b) states that the habitat appears to be pure stands of red spruce or forests in which red spruce is a prominent species. Recent studies by Pauley reveal that the Cheat Mountain salamander also occurs in mixed deciduous forests.

The Cheat Mountain salamander is found in the interior of well-decayed spruce logs or under flat rocks and fallen limbs during the day. It emerges at dusk and crawls over the forest floor, occasionally climbing the trunks of spruce or other trees for a short distance. Nocturnal activity is probably limited by the dew point; on cool dry evenings it remains out for a short time, but on warm humid evenings it may remain active for several hours.

No definitive study of the food habits of this salamander has been published. Pauley (1980b), who has devoted a large amount of research to the biology of the Cheat Mountain salamander, performed a food analysis on 42 salamanders and listed these items in order of occurrence: mites, 42.1 percent; springtails, 17.8 percent; beetles, 16.4 percent; flies, 9.3 percent; ants, 4.3 percent; others, 10 percent.

Breeding: There are no reported observations on the mating of this salamander. The eggs are attached by short pedicels to the roof of a small crevice in a well-rotted spruce log or under rocks. Brooks (1948b) reports that egg masses of 4 to 17 eggs have been collected from May 28 to August 25. They are frequently attended by one, and sometimes by two individuals. Pauley (unpublished data) observed a female attending 10 eggs (ranging in size from 0.193 to 0.196 inch, or 0.49 to 0.50 cm) on July 23, 1976, on Shavers Mountain. The eggs were brought into the laboratory, and four hatched between August 21 and 23. The total length of the young ranged from 0.67 to 0.71 inch (1.7–1.8 cm). Pauley also found a female with eight juveniles (averaging 0.71 inch, or 1.8 cm, in total length) on September 4, 1976, on McGowan Mountain, Tucker County.

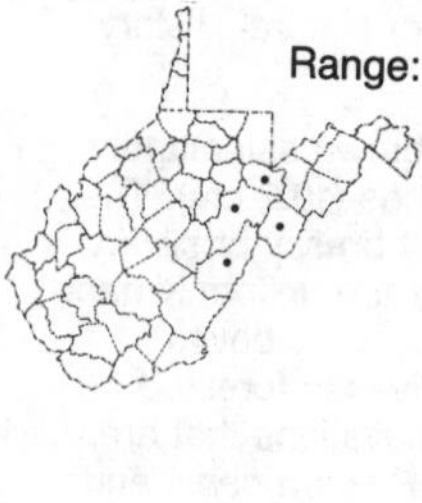

Range: The Cheat Mountain salamander is endemic to West Virginia. Pauley (1981) defines the limits of its range as "extending east from McGowan Mountain through Mozark Mountain to Dolly Sods, south through Roaring Plains to Spruce Knob, southwest to Thorny Flat and north through Barton Knob to McGowan Mountain, an area of 18.7 x 50 miles (30 x 80 km)." Recent field surveys have extended the northern limit of its range to Backbone Mountain just north of Blackwater Canyon, Tucker County (Pauley, unpublished data). The total range is included within the counties of Tucker, Randolph, Pocahontas, and Pendleton.

16 Slimy Salamander *Plethodon glutinosus glutinosus* (Green)

L. *gluten,* glue, sticky

Description: This is a large salamander which may grow up to 8.0 inches (20.3 cm) long. It is shiny black in color and usually generously sprinkled with white flecks. The amount of brassy flecking in the white spots varies and in some instances may be characteristic of a local population. In rare cases the flecking may be confined to the sides, reduced, or absent (very rare). There may be minute brassy flecks sprinkled among the silvery white spots. The throat and belly are slate gray. There are 16 costal grooves.

Confusing Species: Wehrle's salamander (no. 18) has a white throat or white mottling which may extend onto the breast, while the slimy salamander's throat is gray, never white, except in the young. Wehrle's salamander usually has 17 costal grooves. The Cumberland Plateau salamander (no. 17) has a lighter throat, cheeks, and breast, and fewer and smaller dorsal white spots.

Habitat and Habits: The slimy salamander may occur at heights up to 4,592 feet (1,400 m) (Pauley 1980a). It is a woodland species that may be found in a wide variety of terrestrial habitats including moist ravines, shale banks, flood plains, cave entrances, and under piles of leaves.

They emerge from underground retreats in late February or early April, depending on elevation. As the earth warms they become more active at night or in late afternoon following a warm rain, remaining hidden under loose logs or stones during the day. During the hotter summer months slimy salamanders retreat underground at lower elevations, returning to the surface as the temperature lowers and moisture increases. At higher elevations they are active throughout the summer. When encountered in a rotting log or other place of concealment, slimy salamanders are quick to escape by twisting and bending their bodies.

Their food consists of mites, spiders, centipedes, millipedes, earthworms, insects, and snails (Davidson 1956; Powers and Tietjen 1974).

Breeding: Noble and Brady (1930) describe their mating activity as essentially similar to that of other *Plethodon* species. Highton (1962) discusses egg-laying at the latitude of West Virginia. The season for oviposition is late spring through midsummer. Eggs are deposited in clusters in underground burrows, rotting logs (Fowler 1940), or rock crevices (Smith 1961).

Hatching takes place in late summer or early fall, but newly hatched young are usually found above ground the following spring. Sexual maturity is reached in four or five years (Pope and Pope 1949; Semlitsch 1980). In Maryland and Pennsylvania, only about half of the mature females oviposit each year, and each individual probably deposits eggs every two years (Highton 1962).

Remarks: When handled the slimy salamander exudes a whitish secretion from the skin. The slime becomes sticky as it dries, and when dry it adheres to the skin and is very difficult to remove even with vigorous scrubbing. It does disappear after a few days. One should be careful about rubbing the eyes after handling this, or any other salamander, as the secretions are very irritating to mucous membranes.

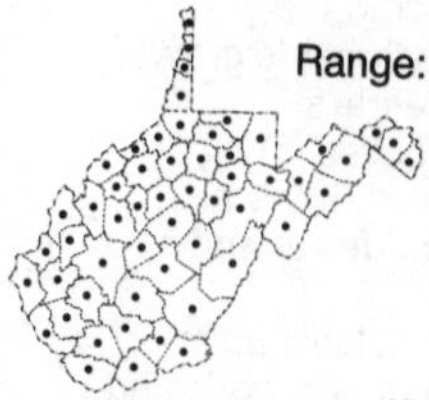

Range: Its range extends from central New York south to central Florida and west to eastern Oklahoma and Louisiana. The species occurs statewide in West Virginia.

17 Cumberland Plateau Salamander *Plethodon kentucki* Mittleman

Description: The Cumberland Plateau salamander resembles the slimy salamander, *Plethodon glutinosus* (no. 16), but it is smaller: sexually mature females range from 1.8 to 2.0 inches (4.6–5.1 cm) snout-vent length, and males from 1.7 to 2.4 inches (4.3–6.1 cm). It is further characterized by a lighter throat, breast, and cheeks, and fewer and smaller dorsal white spots (the brassy flecking found in the white spots of *P. glutinosus* are less evident in *P. kentucki*). The mental glands of breeding adult male *P. kentucki* are noticeably larger than those of *P. glutinosus*.

Habitat and Habits: Habitat preference is similar to that of the slimy salamander.

Remarks: *Plethodon kentucki* was described by Mittleman (1951) on the basis of specimens from four southeastern Kentucky localities. Clay *et al.* (1955) examined Mittleman's material and concluded that this salamander was morphologically indistinguishable from *P. glutinosus*. Until recently, *kentucki* was therefore regarded as a junior synonym of *P. glutinosus*. However, an electrophoretic analysis by Highton and MacGregor (1983) confirmed that *P. kentucki* is distinct from *P. glutinosus* and all other species of the genus *Plethodon*. Their study also found a great deal of geographic genetic variation among the populations of *P. kentucki.* They suggested the common name Cumberland Plateau woodland salamander for *P. kentucki.* Immunological studies by Maha, Maxson, and Highton (1983) provided additional evidence to support the validity of *P. kentucki* as a separate species from *P. glutinosus.*

Range: It ranges from the New River in West Virginia southwest to western Virginia and eastern Kentucky in the Cumberland Plateau section of the Appalachian Plateau physiographic province. At 14 of the 15 localities, it was found to be sympatric with *P. glutinosus.*

18 Wehrle's Salamander *Plethodon wehrlei* Fowler and Dunn

Named for R. W. Wehrle of Indiana, Pa., who collected the first specimen

Description: This is a medium-sized, dark brown to black salamander which attains a length of 5.0 to 6.0 inches (12.7–15.2 cm). Dorsal red spots are often present, especially on the young. The sides are liberally marked with white or cream-colored flecks which often coalesce to form sizeable blotches. The throat is white or blotched with creamy white which may extend onto the chest. The belly is slate gray. The costal groove count is 17. The toes of the hind feet are partially webbed, the webbing extending nearly to the tips of the first two toes.

Confusing Species: Wehrle's salamander and the white-spotted salamander (no. 19) may be confused. The white-spotted salamander is known only from Shenandoah and North mountains along the Virginia border. Spotting is usually sprinkled over the back and not confined to the sides as in *P. wehrlei.* The white-spotted salamander usually has 18 costal grooves.

Habitat and Habits: Wehrle's salamander inhabits the higher elevations of the Allegheny Mountains (up to 4,800 feet [1,463 m], Pauley 1980a), as well as the lower elevations of the Allegheny Plateau. At the higher elevations it occurs in red spruce forest mixed with yellow birch, while at lower elevations it is found in mixed deciduous woodlands. Throughout its range, it spends the day under logs, stones, and leaves; emerging at dusk to forage for food. Its habitat at the higher elevations is in rotting spruce logs, deep rock crevices, and "ice caves" (Netting 1936a). At lower elevations it is found under rocks and debris on hillsides in mixed second growth deciduous forest and in cave entrances. In the caves of Greenbrier, Pocahontas, and Pendleton counties, it forms a major component of the cave fauna (see Remarks, below).

Wehrle's salamander is nocturnal. Shortly after dusk it emerges from its shelter and wanders over the forest floor, occasionally climbing the trunk of a tree. At lower elevations it emerges from its tunnel in a road bank or under a stone.

The seasonal activity pattern varies according to elevation. In the high spruce forests, the salamanders emerge from hibernation in late April, are active throughout the summer, and retreat to their burrows by mid-October. At lower elevations, they are active from late September until the temperatures are too severe, and from March to late May or early June. Toward the end of May they become unusually hard to find and by early June they have disappeared from the surface to remain underground throughout the summer.

Netting *et al.* (1946) mention a specimen of Wehrle's salamander which regurgitated a centipede. Other food items cited by Bishop (1941) are ants, beetles, aphids, mites, crickets, and various insect larvae. Hall and Stafford (1972) add lepidopterous larvae, craneflies, and hymenopterons as food items. Pauley (1978), in a study of the stomach contents of 61 adults found that their food consisted of 56.1 percent ants, 12.7 percent beetles, 9.1 percent mites, 4.5 percent spiders, 1.8 percent springtails, and 15.6 percent other material.

Breeding: Johnson (1961) observed the mating and spermatophore deposition of captive *P. wherlei* in September and October and determined that in New York the eggs were deposited in March or April. In Pennsylvania specimens, Hall and Stafford (1972) found that mating occurs in September and October and egg deposition in January to March. Pauley and England (1969) determined that in West Virginia spermatophores were deposited in March and April and eggs deposited prior to May. Their conclusions were based on dissection and histological study of gonads from 111 specimens collected from October through June from seven West Virginia localities. It is evident that Wehrle's salamander deposits eggs underground in burrows or crevices during late spring and summer. This is apparently true at higher elevations also. At Barton Knob, Randolph County (elevation 4,400 feet or 1,341 m), where numerous rotting spruce logs provide shelter for *P. cinereus* and *P. nettingi* along with their egg masses, all efforts to locate a *P. wehrlei* guarding eggs have been fruitless.

Remarks: On October 1, 1932, A. M. Reese visited Arbuckle's Cave, which is located 0.3 mile (0.48 km) east of Maxwelton in Greenbrier County. He collected three salamanders which were identified as *P. wehrlei*. On subsequent visits to the cavern by numerous investigators the salamanders were collected in the twilight zone where they hid under strips of wood, bark, shale, and other debris. The Arbuckle Cave population differs from typical *P. wehrlei* in several respects. The costal groove count matches that of typical *P. wehrlei* from other areas, but they have a large, robust body form, and paired red spots on the dorsum. The latter character is said to occur in *P. wehrlei* near the southern end of its range (Behler and King 1979); juvenile *P. wehrlei* may have paired red spots throughout their range. The robust body may be attributed to the effect of the cave environment: an abundance of food, uniform temperature, and other factors. The cave was closed in the late 1960s by the owner who feared that livestock or humans would enter and suffer injury.

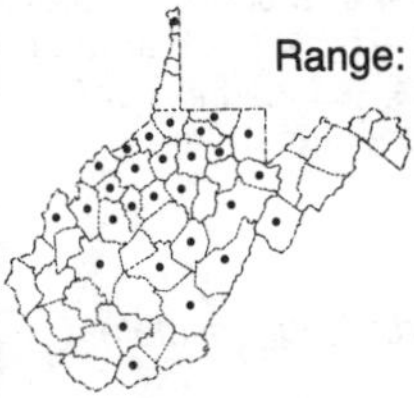

Range: *Plethodon wehrlei* ranges throughout the Appalachian Plateau from southwestern New York to northwestern North Carolina. In West Virginia *P. wehrlei* ranges from the western edge of the Ridge and Valley province throughout the Alleghenies and the Appalachian Plateau province with the exception of the Cumberland portion. There are records from Mercer and Raleigh counties as well as the Northern Panhandle.

19 **White-spotted Salamander** *Plethodon punctatus* Highton

L. *punctatum,* pointed, dotted (finely spotted)

Description: This is a medium-sized salamander which may attain a total length of 6.0 inches (15.2 cm). The back is black with numerous small white or yellowish spots or flecks. The belly is dark, with the throat light and sharply set off from the dark belly at the gular fold. It lacks the brassy flecking and paired red spots of *P. wehrlei* (no. 18). In preservative, the white spots disappear as in *P. glutinosus* (no. 16), although some specimens retain the white spots along the sides as in *P. wehrlei*. The white-spotted salamander has 17 or 18 costal grooves, while there are usually 17 in Wehrle's and 16 in the slimy salamander.

Habitat and Habits: This species occurs in mixed deciduous forest interspersed with Virginia pine and hemlock in which there are numerous rock outcrops. Fraser (1974) studied the ecology of *P. punctatus* and compared the feeding habits of *P. punctatus* and *P. hoffmani* (no. 14), listing hymenopterons, springtails, centipedes, mites, flies, and various larvae as the major food items for *P. punctatus*.

Breeding: Little is known of its reproductive habits. Fraser (1976) notes that it reaches maturity in three years.

Range: The species is known from only two mountains along the Virginia border, the higher elevations of Shenandoah Mountain, Pendleton County, over 3,000 feet (914 m), and North Mountain, Hardy County, 2,800 feet (853 m) (Highton 1972).

Genus *Hemidactylium* Tschudi • Four-Toed Salamanders

The genus contains only one species, which is predominantly northern in distribution. The life cycle includes a free-swimming larva with a conspicuous dorsal fin and a terrestrial adult. There are four toes on each hind foot. The tongue is attached in front, and the vomerine and parasphenoid teeth are separated.

20 Four-toed Salamander *Hemidactylium scutatum* (Schlegel)

Gr. *hemi,* half; Gr. *daktylos,* finger, toe; L. *scutum,* scalelike

Description: This is a small salamander which may attain a length of 4.0 inches (10.2 cm). The dorsal color is rusty brown and the belly is enamel white with many scattered black markings which extend onto the tail. There is a distinct constriction at the base of the tail; the hind feet have four toes.

Habitat and Habits: Adults live in hardwood forests where they seek shelter under logs, stones, and leaf litter. During spring females migrate to sphagnum bogs and deposit eggs. Other mossy areas may be utilized if sufficient moisture is available.

When disturbed or exposed the four-toed salamander throws itself into a tight coil, dorsal surface uppermost. With a background of similar rusty brown color, the posture could be protective. The constriction at the base of the tail also could serve the animal as a protective device. The tail is readily severed when the animal is under stress, as was the case when a collecting bag was inadvertently left in the sun for over an hour. By the time the bag was discovered, most of the specimens had discarded their tails. Bishop (1920) reports that a specimen gave a single violent wrench which separated its tail when a drop of acetic acid was touched to the back close to the constriction.

No studies of the food habits of the four-toed salamander are known, but scattered notes on stomach contents are available from various authors. Johnson (1977) says that it preys on molluscs and arthropods. Bishop (1920) lists larvae of microlepidoptera, beetles, spiders, mites, and bristletails, as well as leaf litter.

Breeding: The life history of the four-toed salamander has been described in detail by Blanchard (1923, 1933, 1934a, 1934b). Mating takes place in September and October, and the following spring females ready to lay eggs seek nesting sites in hummocks of sphagnum moss in bogs (Blanchard 1923). Wood (1955) observed a few nests in mounds of pine needles inside logs and under bark. A female may deposit up to 40 eggs (possibly more) in the nest, attaching them singly to stalks and rhizoids of the moss. More than one female may deposit her eggs in a nest (Blanchard 1923; Wood 1953; and Breitenbach 1982). Blanchard (1934b) found one nest with 1,110 eggs. Although several females may contribute to the nest contents, only one remains to guard it. In West Virginia the females' migration may take place in early March. Wilson and Friddle (1950) collected a female with eggs on March 1 at Rock Oak, Hardy County. Green (1937) reports finding two females in a bog near Elkins, Randolph County, with eggs. Both were dead, apparently drowned by rising water in their nest. Blanchard (1923) states that the period from egg-laying to hatching is about five weeks, and the larval lifespan is six weeks. Sexual maturity is reached in two and one-half years (Barbour 1971).

Range: The four-toed salamander's range extends from Nova Scotia through Wisconsin, south to Alabama. There are disjunct populations in the south and west. In West Virginia it probably occurs throughout the state.

Genus *Gyrinophilus* Cope • Spring Salamanders

These are large salamanders that may be either pinkish, reddish, or brownish in color. They are semi-aquatic and are associated with cool springs, caves, or rapidly flowing mountain springs. The genus is defined by a combination of characters which include the tongue free all around, vomerine and parasphenoid teeth continuous, a light line between the eyes and nostrils, and an aquatic larval stage. They range throughout the Appalachians from southern Quebec and Maine south into Alabama and Georgia. Three species are recognized, two of which are represented in West Virginia: *Gyrinophilus porphyriticus* (Green), with two subspecies, and *Gyrinophilus subterraneus.*

21 **Northern Spring Salamander** *Gyrinophilus porphyriticus porphyriticus* (Green)
Gr. *gyrinos,* tadpole; Gr. *philos,* loving; Gr. *porphyros,* purple

Description: The northern spring salamander is one of the largest of the lungless salamanders. Its robust body may attain a total length of 8.0 inches (20.3 cm). Its dorsal coloration varies from salmon pink to brownish orange. Younger specimens have dark reticulations, which are carried over from the larval pattern. These reticulations become indistinct and clouded in older individuals. The ventral surface is flesh pink. The most obvious distinguishing feature is the presence of a light line edged in black which extends from the inner corner of the eye to the nostril. A knifelike keel extends dorsally along the distal third of the tail. The costal grooves number 17.

Habitat and Habits: The spring salamander inhabits cool springs and rushing mountain streams, boggy areas and caves, and can be found under logs, flat stones, and piles of damp leaves near streams. They are rarely far from water. Spring salamanders are agile, elusive, and difficult to capture. Their slippery skin, wriggling, and proximity to escape routes all aid in their retreat. Experienced collectors coat the palms of their hands with sand to assist in catching these salamanders.

Spring salamanders feed on a variety of animals, including earthworms, other salamanders, and aquatic insects. When roughly handled they will frequently disgorge their most recent meal, which may consist of a two-lined or dusky salamander. Because of their predaceous habits, collectors soon learn to keep spring salamanders separate from other species in their collecting bags.

Breeding: According to Organ (1961), the eggs are attached individually to the undersides of large rocks partly buried in the muddy banks of mountain streams. An egg mass may contain from 40 to 100 eggs and is attended by the female. Two egg masses discovered by Organ (1961) on August 6 and July 14 led him to conclude that *G. porphyriticus* has a fall hatching period with little, if any, growth occurring during the first winter. Bruce (1972) states that in North and South Carolina females oviposit during the summer months at lower elevations and during the fall months at high elevations. Transformation probably occurs after the third year (Bruce 1980), with maturity being attained within another year (Bishop 1941). Bruce (1969) found that sexual maturity for females is attained at 5 years.

Range: The northern spring salamander ranges from southwestern Maine and southern Quebec to northern Alabama. It ranges throughout West Virginia up to an elevation of 4,198 feet or 1,279 meters (Pauley 1980a).

Gyrinophilus p. porphyriticus
Gyrinophilus porphyriticus duryi
Zone of intergradation

22 Kentucky Spring Salamander *Gyrinophilus porphyriticus duryi* (Weller)

Named for Ralph Dury, former director of the Cincinnati Society of Natural History.

Description: The adult Kentucky spring salamander is less robust than the northern spring (no. 21); it is slimmer and reaches a maximum length of only 6.5 inches (16.5 cm). The dorsum is a clear, dull salmon or pinkish color, and the belly is immaculate; the light line from the eyes to the nostrils is indistinct. Small dark spots occur along the sides and occasionally are scattered over the back. The cloudy reticulations seen in the larger northern spring salamander are absent. There are no melanophores on the ventral surface except along the chin.

Remarks: The breeding habits, ecology, and food are presumably similar to those of the northern spring salamander. This salamander interbreeds with the northern spring salamander where their ranges contact. The intergrades which result may possess some of the characters of both parents or, as is often the case, bear a stronger resemblance to one or the other parent. Brandon (1966) suggests an index of intergradation as follows: The absence of spots on the sides, back and tail, a distinct line from the eye to the nostril, a dark mottling or reticulated dorsal pattern, and flecked bellies in specimens over 3.0 inches (7.6 cm) long are used as criteria for genetic influence from *G. p. porphyriticus.*

Range: According to Brandon (1966), *G. p. duryi* occurs in northeastern Kentucky, a small corner of southwestern West Virginia (Mingo County), and southcentral Ohio. Intergrades occur throughout the central portion of West Virginia, while *G. p. porphyriticus* occurs in the eastern portion of West Virginia.

23 **West Virginia Spring Salamander** *Gyrinophilus subterraneus* Besharse and Holsinger

L. *sub,* under, below; L. *terra,* earth

Description: The West Virginia spring salamander differs from the northern spring salamander (no. 21) in retaining the pale, reticulated color pattern of the larvae, in having an indistinct line from eye to nostril, and in having reduced eyes. This salamander was described in 1977 by Besharse and Holsinger and is known only from General Davis Cave, Greenbrier County.

Remarks: Nothing has been discovered about its life history or reproductive behavior to indicate that its habits are different from those of *Gyrinophilus p. porphyriticus.* Blaney and Blaney (1978) maintain that the species is invalid and represents only one extreme in a highly variable population of *G. p. porphyriticus.* In cave populations of *Gyrinophilus,* there is a wide range in color pattern from dark to extremely light, and eyes range from normal to reduced, nonfunctional eyes. Blaney and Blaney believe that such extremes in individual variation must be considered when making taxonomic evaluations.

Howard *et al.* (1984) established electrophoretically that the population identified as *Gyrinophilus subterraneus* is different from other populations of *G. p. porphyriticus.* However, Howard (personal communication) has said that his sample sizes were very small and additional study must be conducted before *Gyrinophilus subterraneus* can be definitively determined a separate species.

Genus *Pseudotriton* Tschudi • Red Salamanders

Members of the genus *Pseudotriton* have a robust body; a short, keeled tail; and short, sturdy legs. They may attain a total length of 8.0 inches (20.0 cm). They are strikingly colored salamanders ranging from brownish to orange to bright coral red with scattered black dots, but no other pattern. The tongue is free at its margins and protrusible. The genus is confined to North America east of the Mississippi River.

Two species of the genus are recognized, both of which are found in West Virginia. The larval stage is aquatic, and the adults are aquatic or terrestrial.

24 Midland Mud Salamander *Pseudotriton montanus diastictus* Bishop

Gr. *pseudes,* false; Gr. *triton,* newt; L. mont, belonging to a mountain; Gr. *dia;* throughout; Gr. *stiktos,* dotted

Description: The midland mud salamander is a brilliant red color with numerous (30–40) distinct black spots scattered over the upper surface of the head, back, and dorsum of the tail. The undersurface is unmarked except for an occasional dark line on the edge of the lower jaw. The adults are stout and short-legged, with a short, slightly keeled tail. Total length may reach 6.0 inches (15.2 cm). There are 17 costal grooves.

Habitat and Habits: These salamanders inhabit muddy springs, sluggish brooks, and swampy forested areas. They may be found under logs and stones close to muddy streams where they burrow into the banks. During heavy rains in early spring and fall they may be seen in large numbers crossing highways and along stream banks. No reports are available on their food habits, but it is presumed that they feed on small invertebrates.

Breeding: Courtship and spermatophore deposition occur in late fall and early winter. About 100 eggs are deposited in the fall, each attached separately to the undersides of dead leaves in a quiet pool. Larval life probably lasts from 18 to 30 months. Bruce (1974) determined that the larval period in western South Carolina varied from 14 to 32 months. Males probably mature in three years (Bruce 1975). Bruce (1969, 1975) states that females mature in four or five years and reproduce every other year, while males mate every year.

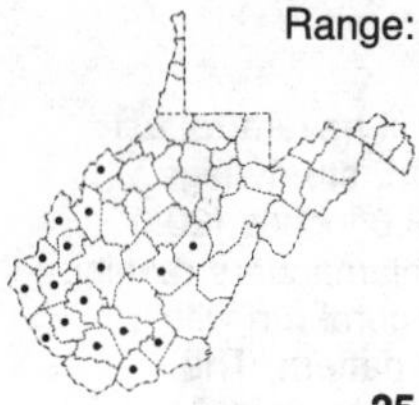

Range: The range extends from southern Ohio and West Virginia through western Virginia, Kentucky, and Tennessee. In West Virginia, it ranges from Webster County to Wood County and southwest to the Ohio and Big Sandy rivers.

25 Northern Red Salamander *Pseudotriton ruber ruber* (Latreille)
L. *rubeo,* to be red

Description: These salamanders are stout-bodied animals with a short, fleshy tail. They may attain a total length of 6.0 inches (15.2 cm), and there are 16 or 17 costal grooves. Their color varies from bright coral red in recently transformed juveniles to dark or cloudy red in older individuals. Both juveniles and adults have many distinct black dots on the upper surface, but in older individuals the dots tend to run together. The iris is yellow, compared to the brown iris of the midland mud salamander (no. 24).

Confusing Species: Both species of *Pseudotriton* and the two subspecies of *Gyrinophilus* are confusing, not only to inexperienced students, but occasionally to experienced herpetologists. *Pseudotriton* lacks the light line between the eyes and nostrils. *Pseudotriton* has 16 or 17 costal grooves; *Gyrinophilus* has 17 to 20. The dorsal color of *Pseudotriton* is much redder, while *Gyrinophilus* are more purple or smoky pink.

Habitat and Habits: Red salamanders inhabit springs and small streams in either open or wooded situations where they may be found under logs, stones, mosses, and piles of damp leaves. They are active at night and are often found on roads during spring rains. They feed upon earthworms, snails, slugs, spiders, insects, and smaller salamanders.

Breeding: Several dates for courtship and spermatophore and egg deposition are found in the literature (Organ and Organ 1968; Bruce 1969; Bruce 1978). In West Virginia courtship and spermatophore deposition occur in summer and early fall. The eggs, which number about 70 in a clutch, are deposited in the fall. The female attaches them to the undersurface of a rock, which may be deeply embedded in the soil at the edge of a spring or small stream. The eggs are yellowish but unpigmented. They hatch within eight to ten weeks depending upon water temperature. Newly hatched larvae measure 0.9 inch (2.3 cm). Larval life lasts for about 30 months. Bell (1956) suggests a larval period of 36 to 48 months in

Pennsylvania, and Bruce (1974) determines the period to be 28 to 32 months in western South Carolina. The larvae transform at an average length of 2.7 inches (7.0 cm). Males probably mature in three years. Bruce (1969) suggests that females mature in five years.

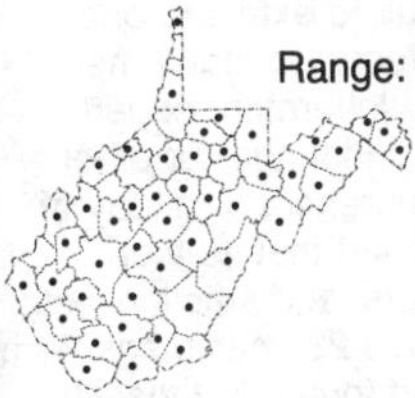

Range: The northern red salamander ranges from southern New York west to southeastern Indiana and southward east of the Mississippi River to northern Alabama and Georgia. It is widely distributed throughout West Virginia.

Genus *Aneides* Baird • Climbing Salamanders

Members of the genus *Aneides* have the posterior portion of the maxilla sharply edged without teeth, vomerine and parasphenoid teeth separated, tips of the phalanges Y-shaped, and the tongue attached in front. The larval stage occurs in the egg. The genus includes five species, only one of which is found east of the Mississippi River.

26 Green Salamander *Aneides aeneus* (Cope and Packard).

Gr. *aneides,* shapeless;
L. *aeneus,* bronze or coppery

Description: The green salamander is a small to medium-sized salamander which may attain a total length of 5.0 inches (12.7 cm). The dorsal color is dark brown with golden green, lichenlike patches over the body, head, legs, and tail. The ventral surface is pale and unmarked. There are 14 or 15 costal grooves. The flattened head and body and the expanded toe tips are modifications for its mode of life.

Habitat and Habits: The green salamander was first found in a cave in Tennessee (Cope and Packard 1881). Pope (1928) described the habitat as under bark strips of fallen logs. Netting and Richmond (1932) revealed its presence in sandstone crevices; Walker and Goodpaster (1941) found it in limestone solution pockets; and Gordon and Smith (1949) found it in granite crevices. It is evident that the green salamander's optimum habitat is crevices in rock faces, the nature of the rock formation being immaterial. In the absence of such habitat, the salamander will live under bark on trees, in rotting logs, and so forth. Inhabited rock faces are usually well-shaded and moist, but not wet.

Although they may be seen on cloudy days, the salamanders are most active at night when they emerge from the crevices and climb over the rock surfaces in search of food. They lie with their heads at the mouth of the crevice, but retreat rapidly to the rear when disturbed. It is difficult to extricate one from a crevice, and collectors resort to many methods to do so. Cupp (1980), in a laboratory experiment, found that males are territorial against other males. Gordon (1952), in a comprehensive study of the salamander's life history, found that its food consisted of snails, slugs, spiders, and small insects. Lee and Norden (1973) examined 23 specimens from West Virginia for food items and found that insects predominated (coleopterons, dipterons, and hymenopterons).

Breeding: Gordon (1952) suggests that "mating in *A. aeneus* occurs in late May or early June." Brooks (1948a) reports on a courting pair on a cliff face between midnight and 1:00 A.M. on June 13, 1941. Cupp (1971) reports courtship and spermatophore deposition on October 17, 1970, and goes on to comment, "even though spring mating as suggested by Gordon probably takes place, my observations demonstrate that at least some mating takes place during the fall dispersal and aggregation period of this species." Clusters of up to 20 unpigmented eggs held together and to the roof of a crevice by strands of mucus are deposited by the female in late spring or early summer. Pauley observed several clusters of *A. aeneus* eggs in rock crevices at Holly River State Park in Webster County on July 4, 1976. Hatching occurs within 12 to 13 weeks. Woods (1968) found the eggs require 82 days to hatch in Mississippi. The hatchlings, about 0.9 inch (2.3 cm) long, remain in the crevice and resume activity with the onset of spring.

Range: The range of the green salamander extends from southwestern Pennsylvania, western Maryland, and southern Ohio to west central Alabama and northeastern Mississippi. There is an isolated population in southwestern North Carolina and adjacent states. In West Virginia the green salamander's range is concentrated in the central counties of the Allegheny Plateau from Monongalia and Preston counties in a southwesterly direction to the Big Sandy River.

Genus *Eurycea* Rafinesque • Brook Salamanders

Members of the genus *Eurycea* are confined to eastern and south central North America. The characters of the genus include a tongue that is free at the margins, separate vomerine and parasphenoid teeth, a slender body in which yellow pigment predominates, and males with swollen snouts that may have cirri. There is an aquatic larval stage. The genus contains twelve species, of which three are found in West Virginia.

27 Northern Two-lined Salamander *Eurycea bislineata bislineata* (Green)
Gr. *eurys,* wide; L. *bis,* twice; L. *lineola,* a line

Description: This is a small, slender salamander which may reach a total length of 4.0 inches (10.2 cm). The dorsal color varies from dull greenish yellow, to bright orange yellow, to light brown. There is a light, median dorsal stripe bordered on each side by dark lines which originate at the eyes and extend the length of the trunk and tail. The dorsal stripe may contain many small black dots or flecks. The sides, legs, and underparts are yellow or orange yellow. Costal grooves are 15 or 16.

Habitat and Habits: Two-lined salamanders live in or near small streams with rocky bottoms, seepages, flood plains, or forests where they hide under logs, rocks, or in other moist situations. They are agile and scramble rapidly to escape when disturbed. They may be found throughout the year lurking under rocks along a stream's edge or under logs and leaves at a considerable distance from water. Under a heavy snow cover, they may be exposed by raking away the leaves. Ashton and Ashton (1978) found that two-lined salamanders continued to be active during the winter. Food items consist of springtails, hymenopterons, mites, beetles, and flies (Burton 1976). As spring approaches, the females become swollen with yellowish eggs that can be seen through the body wall.

Breeding: Noble (1929) reported that courtship occurs on land as soon as weather conditions in the spring permit terrestrial activity. Large numbers of two-lined salamanders may be seen crossing highways at night in early March on their way to a brook. The female deposits eggs singly on the lower surface of a rock or other object and remains with them until they hatch. Although the number of eggs deposited by a single female is commonly 40, it is not unusual to find egg masses of over 200 with one accompanying female. Frequently the complements of several females are found in the same nest (Baumann and Huels 1982). Egg-laying in southern West Virginia usually begins by mid March and continues through the middle of April. Development depends upon water temperatures, but usually takes place in about 50 days. The larvae are about 0.5 inch (1.3 cm) long at hatching, and transformation takes place within one to two years (Bruce 1985).

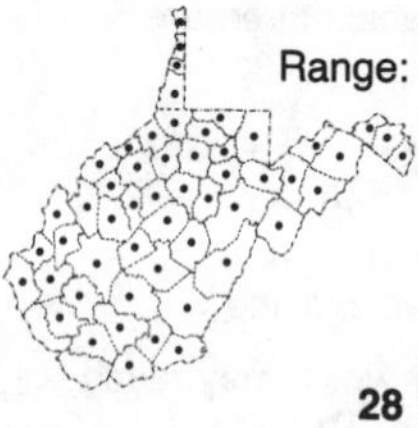

Range: The two-lined salamander ranges from Quebec to Virginia and eastern Illinois, south to northern Alabama. It is widely distributed in West Virginia and is one of our more common salamanders.

28 Longtail Salamander *Eurycea longicauda longicauda* (Green)
L. *longus,* long; L. *cauda,* tail

Description: The longtail salamander is a slender, speckled, yellow, salamander with a tail that comprises about 60 percent of its total length. The maximum length may exceed 6.0 inches (15.2 cm). The yellow to deep-orange dorsum is covered with numerous black flecks on the back, sides, and tail. The wavy vertical black bars down each side of the tail form a herringbone pattern, the most distinctive feature of this salamander. There are 13 to 14 costal grooves. During the breeding season the male can be distinguished from the female by the presence of cirri.

Habitat and Habits: Longtail salamanders are found along streams, seepage areas, springs, in stacks of firewood, piles of debris, and in caves. Large aggregations have been reported from abandoned coal mines (Mohr 1943). They are frequently found in association with northern dusky and two-lined salamanders and in rock crevices with green salamanders (nos. 8, 27, 26). Longtail salamanders are active at night and usually terrestrial. They feed on small terrestrial insects, mites, spiders, centipedes, snails, and earthworms (Anderson and Martino 1967).

Breeding: The life history of the longtail salamander is poorly known. Behler and King (1979) reported breeding from October to March with eggs deposited in underground crevices associated with springs, temporary pools, and streams. Hutchison (1956) determined by the size of ovarian eggs that egg deposition occurs in July or August. Mohr (1943) reported that larvae measured 0.6 inch (1.5 cm) at hatching, and Bishop (1941) reported larvae of 1.8 inches (4.5 cm) prior to transformation. Hutchinson (1956) reports that he observed 60 larvae in Turner's Cave, Greenbrier County, on June 9, 1956, that ranged in size from 0.6

to 1.2 inches (1.5–3.0 cm). He judged that the small ones had just recently hatched. Behler and King (1979) reported larvae transforming in three and one-half to seven months at 1.6 inches (4.1 cm) and becoming sexually mature within one to two years. Franz and Harris (1965) reported on a mass transformation and movement of larval longtail salamanders in which the total lengths of the transformed individuals ranged from 1.3 to 1.7 inches (3.3–4.4 cm). Large numbers of juveniles have been collected in late September under leaf litter in Cabell County (Green, unpublished data).

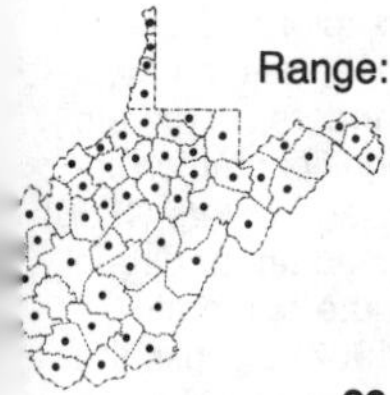

Range: The species ranges from southern New York and most of Pennsylvania, southwestward to northeastern Alabama, thence north and west into northeastern Arkansas and southeastern Illinois. It is distributed throughout West Virginia.

29 **Cave Salamander** *Eurycea lucifuga* Rafinesque

L. *lucis,* light; L. *fugio,* to flee

Description: The cave salamander is a medium-sized salamander which may attain a length of 7.0 inches (17.8 cm). The body is slender, and the tail may account for 63 percent of the total length in adults. The head is broad and flat and the eyes are well developed. The dorsal color may vary from shades of orange to red. Distinct dark brown or black spots cover much of the dorsal surface of the head, back, and tail. Costal grooves number 14 or 15. Cirri may be present in both sexes, but are more pronounced in the males.

Confusing Species: Cave salamanders are frequently confused with longtail salamanders (no. 28), but may be easily separated by color (the longtail is yellowish and the cave reddish) and by the tail pattern which, in the longtail, always consists of wavy vertical bars that form a chevron or herringbone pattern. In the cave salamander the black dots are scattered over the tail and do not merge into any form of pattern.

Habitat and Habits: The cave salamander's most frequented habitat is within limestone caverns where it may be found in rock crevices and on the shelves and faces of the rock formations, as well as wandering over the floor or under rock fragments on the floor. It is usually near the mouth or within the twilight zone, but may occasionally be deeper in the cave or on the surface near springs or streams which originate in the cave. Banta and McAtee (1906) quote from a letter from W. P. Hay concerning this point: "In 1899 and 1900 I found *Spelerpes maculicaudus* [*Eurycea lucifuga*] in considerable numbers in West Virginia, both in limestone caverns and in the forest under logs. In the caverns, *Spelerpes longicaudus* [*Eurycea longicauda*] was much more common, while in the woods the two species occurred in about equal numbers." The cave salamander responds slowly to strong light, but when touched reacts quickly and escapes by long leaps. In walking over the roof of a chamber the salamander uses its tail to maneuver.

Hutchison (1958) found that helomyzid flies make up a large percentage of its diet; it also eats mites, ticks, lepidopterons, and pseudoscorpions. Cave salamanders feed by extending their tongues to catch prey (as do other terrestrial salamanders, frogs, etc.).

Breeding: Hutchison (1956, 1958) provides significant information on the ecology and life history, and Myers (1958) describes the eggs and newly hatched larva. Organ (1968) describes the courtship and the spermatophore. Green, Brant, and Dowler (1967) discuss the results of a study conducted in several caves in Greenbrier County, West Virginia. The eggs are deposited in rimstone pools on the floor of caves from September through January. Larvae remain in the pools until winter and early spring when the pools begin to overflow. The small streams thus formed carry the larvae into larger streams where they remain until transformation at a length of 1.97 to 2.2 inches (5.0–5.6 cm).

Range: The cave salamander is found from western Virginia and West Virginia south to northwestern Georgia and central Alabama and west to central Missouri, extreme southeastern Kansas, and northeastern Oklahoma. The species occurs in West Virginia from Pocahontas County south along the southeastern border of the state through Greenbrier, Monroe, Summers, and Mercer counties, where limestone outcrops and the subterranean strata have dissolved to form caves and underground tunnels.

ORDER SALIENTA (ANURA)—TOADS AND FROGS

The members of this order are amphibians characterized by short, tailless bodies and long hind legs which contain a fourth segment by virtue of an elongation of the tarsal bones. The tail vertebrae are fused to form the urostyle. The head and trunk are fused; the neck is absent. Anurans have a middle ear cavity and a voice box. There are no universal characteristics that separate toads and frogs. In general, toads have parotoid glands, a warty skin, and short legs.

There is wide variation in reproductive habits, but in general fertilization is external; the eggs are deposited in water and hatch into a larval stage called a tadpole. The reproductive cycle is initiated by (1) migration of males to a breeding site, (2) calling by males, (3) appearance of females and species-specific response to the calls, (4) amplexus, in which the male clasps the female during mating.

There are two principal types of amplexus: axillary (pectoral) in which the male holds the female behind the forelimbs, and inguinal (pelvic) in which the male holds the female just in front of the hindlimbs. During amplexus the female deposits eggs and the male releases sperm over them. Within about 30 days, the eggs hatch into tadpoles with external gills. The gills are soon covered by body tissues except for one or two spiracles (openings). After the spiracles form, water passes through the mouth, over the gills, and out through the spiracles.

Tadpoles are herbivores. They transform into froglets or toadlets in a few days to two years (possibly three years in the higher elevations).

Anurans exhibit a variety of sex differences such as size, leg length, vocal pouches, thumb pads, diameter of tympana, and skin pigmentation.

Adult toads and frogs are all predaceous carnivores. In most species the diet consists mainly of insects, but larger species, such as the bullfrog, are known to eat small birds, mammals, crayfish, snakes, and other frogs.

Taxonomically, anurans are the most diverse group of amphibians with over 3,000 species. It is also the most widespread, occurring on all continents except Antarctica. Anurans are represented in West Virginia by four families, six genera, and 14 species.

Family Pelobatidae • Spadefoot Toads

The spadefoot toads include nine genera with over 80 species. Representatives are found in Europe, Asia, northern Africa, and North America (including Mexico). The name spadefoot derives from a specialized, dark-rimmed, cornified spur along the base of the inner toe. The toad uses this spur to burrow in soil. Only one genus occurs in the United States.

Genus *Scaphiopus* Holbrook • Spadefoot Toads

Six species belonging to this genus occur in the United States and Mexico. All known species of spadefoots are characterized by having explosive breeding patterns, loud voices, inguinal amplexus, fossorial existence, and abbreviated larval periods. Most members of the genus appear to be better adapted to a dry arid habitat. One species, the eastern spadefoot, has invaded the moister environment of the east while retaining the breeding pattern of its ancestors. This is the only species of the genus which occurs east of the Mississippi River.

Two subspecies are recognized, one of which occurs in West Virginia.

30 Eastern Spadefoot *Scaphiopus holbrookii holbrookii* (Harlan)

Gr. *scapheus,* a spade, pus, foot; named for John Edward Holbrook, a famous herpetologist of the early 1800s

Description: The spadefoot toad is a stout amphibian which may attain a snout-vent length of about 2.5 inches (6.3 cm). It characteristically has large, bulging eyes, vertical pupils, and short legs. The parotoid glands are round and inconspicuous. A pair of pectoral glands are usually present, more conspicuous in juveniles. The ground color of the back is olive to brown, with a pair of yellowish stripes extending back from the eyes and curving in toward the midline of the back. Some specimens may be uniformly dark brown or black. Tubercles on the soles of the feet are absent except for the horny, black "spade" on the inside of the inner toe of the hind foot. The vocal sac in males is median and subgular.

Habitat and Habits: Spadefoot toads live where they can burrow into the ground. They will be found in sandy soil or the loose soil of wooded areas, and on one occasion a colony was observed along the cinder bed of a railroad track. The site is usually adjacent to a low-lying area which will retain water after heavy summer storms.

The eastern spadefoot spends most of its time underground. When temperature and humidity are favorable, it emerges from its temporary burrow and forages for insects; it may remain active for several hours. When the temperature approaches 50.0° F (10.0° C) (Pearson 1955), it digs a burrow and sinks into the sand by means of a shuffling motion of the hind legs, leaving no trace of its presence. Thus, for years the idea prevailed that spadefoot toads only make an appearance during and following periods of heavy rainfall. Actually, they are active at night throughout most of the summer months. Their food includes a variety of insects such as coleopterons, hymenopterons, orthopterons, as well as arachnids (Pearson 1955).

Breeding: The reproductive cycle is initiated by heavy rainfall at any time from March through October. Large numbers of spadefoots congregate in shallow, temporary pools where the males call loudly day and night. Amplexus is inguinal and eggs are deposited in strings or bands intertwined with grass and other vegetation. The eggs develop rapidly, sometimes hatching within two days. The larval period varies from two to nine weeks. Observations of a colony at Ceredo, Wayne County, revealed that eggs laid on June 23, 1960, transformed on July 9, 1960. A second complement of eggs deposited on July 1, 1960, transformed on July 16, 1960 (Green, unpublished data).

Green (1963) reports on a study of the activities of three colonies in the Huntington area over a 25-year period. Judy (1969) discusses the influence of meteorological factors upon emergence.

Larval spadefoots are plankton feeders as well as occasionally being cannibalistic (Richmond 1947). Spadefoot tadpoles were observed feeding on the jelly of *Hyla versicolor* eggs in one of the Ceredo pools on July 2, 1960 (Green, unpublished data).

Remarks: The eastern spadefoot was first recorded in West Virginia on April 16, 1939, following five inches of rainfall over a three-day period (Green and Richmond 1940). To find it at night, shine the beam of a flashlight over a likely area to reflect the ruby-red eyes. The observer may walk to the toad and pick it up without it attempting to escape.

A loud chorus of calling males may also announce their presence. Within a short time after a severe thunder storm the voices begin. Various authors have described the call. Behler and King (1979) describe it as like the low-pitched complaint of a young crow. It is loud, and a chorus may be heard for over a mile. Spadefoots are also known to call from their burrows or even under water.

The skin secretion has a musty, peppery odor according to some authors (Martof *et al.* 1980).

Range: The eastern spadefoot occurs from eastern Massachusetts and Albany, New York, southward through Florida and westward to eastern Louisiana, southeastern Missouri, and southwestern Illinois. In West Virginia it occurs in the Ohio River counties from Wayne to Wood and east to Kanawha. A Hardy County record indicates its intrusion into the eastern part of the state through the Potomac drainage from the eastern population.

Family Bufonidae • Toads

This family includes the true toads, which are the rough skinned, "warty," squat-bodied, and short-legged amphibians that most people think of when they hear the word "toad." Parotoid glands are present and maxillary teeth are lacking. There are 25 genera and approximately 300 species. The family is worldwide in distribution except for New Guinea, Polynesia, Australia, and Madagascar. Only one genus, *Bufo*, occurs in North America.

Genus *Bufo* Laurenti • Toads

Bufo is by far the largest bufonid genus, containing more than 200 species. Its range is essentially the same as that of the family. The genus is represented by 18 species and several subspecies in the United States and Canada. Two species occur in West Virginia.

31 Eastern American Toad *Bufo americanus americanus* Holbrook

L. *bufonis,* a toad

Description: The American toad may attain a head-body length of 4.2 inches (10.8 cm), although most specimens range from 2.0 to 3.5 inches (5.1–8.9 cm). The distinctive features include: (1) only one or two warts in each large dark dorsal spot, (2) chest and forward part of the abdomen usually mottled with dark pigment, (3) warts of the tibia enlarged and with spiny tips, (4) parotoid glands oval or kidney-shaped and either separate from the ridge behind the eye or connected to it by a short spur.

Confusing Species: American toads are more reddish or rusty colored than Fowler's toad (no. 32). Review the species account of Fowler's toad for comparison of distinctive features with those of the American toad listed above.

Habitat and Habits: After a brief spawning period in the spring, adult toads become terrestrial and wander into upland areas far from bodies of water. Individuals may be found in dense woodlands, but they are more frequently encountered in open areas such as farmlands, pastures, and gardens. Adults have been collected at elevations over 4,000 feet (1,219 m) in the peaks of the Alleghenies. Toads are notorious insect predators and farmers generally consider them among the most valuable animals in this regard. They also consume spiders and other small invertebrates. Hamilton (1930, 1954) discusses the economic value of the toad in connection with a series of food studies. The type of food is known to vary with the size of the toad, the season, and the locality.

Breeding: American toads emerge from hibernation early in March and may be heard calling shortly afterward. Emergence may be later at higher elevations, and breeding is frequently interrupted by recurring cold weather. The call is a high-pitched musical trill usually lasting for several seconds. The clasping impulse is strong in toads, and males clasp any object of sufficient girth which offers no resistance. Spawning takes place in shallow pools, swamps, roadside ditches, tire tracks, and imprints of horses' hoofs, in the mud. The eggs are laid in long gelatinous strings containing several thousand eggs arranged in a twisted, double strand deposited either among vegetation or on the muddy bottom. The egg tube is made up of two layers with the eggs arranged in a single file within the tube, separated from one another by partitions across the inner tube. The rate of development is determined by the temperature, and the eggs may hatch in less than a week. The tadpoles are small and black and for some time after hatching swim in a dense mass. Transformation may occur as early as mid May. The toadlets grow rapidly and attain sexual maturity by the end of their second summer.

Remarks: The skin secretions of all toads are harmless to the human skin, but are irritating to mucous membranes. One should avoid rubbing the eyes after handling a toad. That they cause warts is an unsubstantiated folktale. Toads are distasteful to some animals, and dogs have become violently ill, some fatally, from merely picking up a toad in their jaws. Toads are consumed by several species of snakes, especially the hognose snakes.

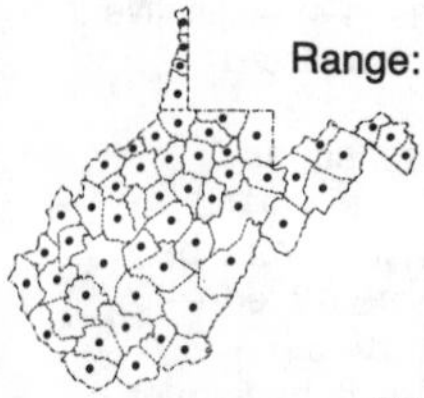

Range: The eastern American toad ranges from the Canadian Maritime Provinces and southeastern Manitoba, south to Mississippi and northeastern Kansas. It is widely distributed in West Virginia and has been collected in all fifty-five counties.

32 Fowler's Toad *Bufo woodhouseii fowleri* Hinckley
Named for S. W. Woodhouse and S. P. Fowler, two American naturalists of the 1800s.

Description: Fowler's toad is on average slightly smaller than the American toad (no. 31), attaining a snout-vent length of 2.0 to 3.3 inches (5.1–8.4 cm). It may be distinguished from the American toad in having three or more warts in each large dorsal dark spot, no greatly enlarged warts on the tibia, parotoid glands touching the cranial crests behind the eyes, and a light mid-dorsal stripe. The chest and abdominal skin are usually immaculate. The color is usually gray or greenish gray without reddish or rusty colors.

Habitat and Habits: Fowler's toad frequents sandy flood plains and river bottoms, as well as brushy thickets and woodland borders. They occur in almost every terrestrial habitat. They lie in their burrows during the day and are active chiefly at night. During humid and cloudy days they may also be active. Like other species of toads, they are voracious insect eaters, mainly ground-dwelling insects (Brown 1974).

Breeding: Fowler's toad usually does not emerge from hibernation until several weeks after American toads have completed their mating. At lower elevations in West Virginia, they emerge in mid April. Occasionally the call, which is a loud, discordant, nasal "w-a-a-a-h" may be heard with the musical trill of the American toad. Fowler's toad breeds in more permanent bodies of water such as streams and along lake shores where as many as 8,000 eggs may be deposited in long double-row strings. The egg tube is single-walled, without partitions separating the eggs. The small black tadpoles and the newly transformed toadlets are difficult to distinguish from those of the American toad.

Remarks: It is not unusual to encounter toads with a combination of *B. w. fowleri* and *B. americanus* characteristics. Hybridization between these species takes place in nature, as demonstrated by Blair (1941), who obtained fertile hybrids that were then backcrossed with *B. americanus* females. Jones (1973) and Green (1984) have also studied hybridization between these two species.

When two closely related species occupy the same geographic area, interbreeding is usually prevented by innate reproductive isolating mechanisms. Thus the American toad breeds earlier in the season than Fowler's toad, the selection of breeding sites is usually different, and the calls are species specific. However, in West Virginia the extremes of altitude cause considerable temperature variations which may interrupt or accelerate breeding cycles, bringing the two species together. For example, a late spring may retard the breeding activities of American toads so that they mate simultaneously with Fowler's toad; and flooding caused by heavy spring rains may so disarrange breeding sites that the two species are brought together.

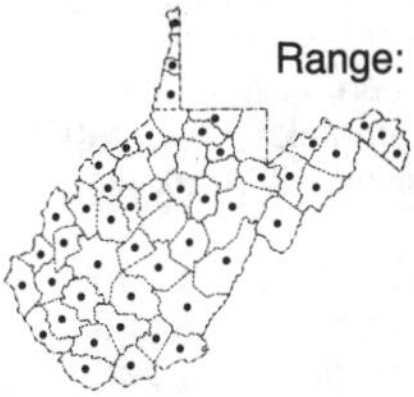

Range: Fowler's toad ranges over most of the eastern United States from southern New Hampshire west to Michigan, south through Illinois and Missouri to Louisiana, and east through Mississippi, Alabama, central Georgia, and South Carolina. In West Virginia it is widely distributed throughout the state.

Family Hylidae

The hylids are small- to large-bodied frogs. Most have expanded digit tips and are arboreal or semiarboreal in habit. They all possess intercalary cartilages that lie between the two most distal phalanges.

The family contains about 37 genera and about 600 species. Although the greatest center of diversification lies in Middle America, South America, and North America, representatives also occur in Europe, Asia, North Africa, New Guinea, and Australia. Although most hylids are treefrogs, a few are aquatic or terrestrial. The family is divided into four subfamilies of which the Subfamily Hylinae is the largest and has the same distribution as the genus *Hyla*. The family is represented in West Virginia by three genera and six species.

Genus *Acris* Duméril and Bibron • Cricket Frogs

The cricket frogs are small, rough-skinned frogs found among aquatic plants in swamps, lakes, and sluggish streams. They are often encountered on thick mats of algae that cover pasture ponds. They are very active creatures which defy capture by enormous leaps. Three subspecies of *Acris crepitans* are recognized; two of these occur in West Virginia.

33 Northern Cricket Frog *Acris crepitans crepitans* Baird

Gr. *akris,* a locust; L. *crepito,* to rattle

Description: The northern cricket frog is one of our smallest species of frogs. It may attain a maximum snout-vent length of 1.5 inches (3.8 cm). Its distinctive features include a dark triangle between the eyes, a longitudinal dark stripe along the rear surface of the thigh, extensive webbing between the hind toes (reaching the tip of the first toe and the next-to-last joint of the longest toe), and one or two pairs of white tubercles below the cloacal vent. Its dorsal color varies but usually includes splashes of green, yellow, and brown. The belly is a clear cream color. The male's vocal sac is usually yellow, flecked with dark pigment.

Habitat and Habits: Cricket frogs may remain active throughout a mild winter. They frequent aquatic vegetation around ponds, swamps, and sluggish streams where they rest on algal mats or leaves of spatterdock. Their diminutive size and coloration, coupled with their activity, make them very difficult to locate and capture. It is much easier to collect them when they are in chorus at night because their vocal sacs reflect the beam of a flashlight. Their leaps are phenomenal—they can leap vertically more than 35.0 inches (88.9 cm). Their major food items are dipterons, formicids, collembolons, and coleopterons (Labanick 1976).

Breeding: Cricket frogs usually emerge from hibernation in mid March, although their chorus is not heard until April or May. The call consists of a series of sharp, clicking notes similar to the sound of striking two pebbles or marbles together. Their choruses may be heard throughout the hottest part of the day in June and July. They are the last of the local species to breed, and pairs in amplexus have been recorded as late as the middle of July. The eggs are deposited singly or in small clumps attached to aquatic vegetation. The tadpoles have distinctive black-tipped tails and attain a much larger size in proportion to the metamorphosed frog than do other tadpoles. Unlike other frogs which vacate the breeding area after reproduction, the cricket frog remains in the area until the onset of unfavorable weather.

Range: The northern cricket frog is found from southeast New York and Long Island through the coastal states to the Panhandle of Florida, and west to eastern Texas. In West Virginia it occurs in the Eastern Panhandle (Jefferson, Berkeley, Morgan, Mineral, and Hampshire counties). There are unverified records from Pocahontas and Fayette counties. Wilson and Friddle (1950) do not list it from Hardy County.

34 **Blanchard's Cricket Frog** *Acris crepitans blanchardi* Harper

Named for Frank N. Blanchard, a professor and herpetologist at the University of Michigan.

Description: Blanchard's cricket frog is slightly larger and bulkier than the northern cricket frog (no. 33) and its skin is wartier or rougher.

Habitat and Habits: The habitat of Blanchard's cricket frog is similar to that of the northern cricket frog, although it prefers the more open sandy or muddy edges of streams and ponds. Johnson and Christiansen (1976) made an extensive study of its food habits in relation to its size, reproductive status, and sex. They found that its diet consisted primarily of terrestrial organisms, although the frogs were collected in aquatic situations. They concluded that *Acris* are opportunistic feeders that eat whatever animal of suitable size is available.

Breeding: During the spring and autumn, Blanchard's cricket frogs are active only during the day, but in warmer weather they are active both day and night. Females deposit up to 400 eggs which hatch in a few days. The tadpoles transform five to ten weeks later. Johnson and Christiansen (1976) found that the egg masses were smallest in April and increased to their largest size in June when the size of the fat bodies were smallest. Recently transformed frogs were collected at McCullough's Pond, Mason County, on September 14, 1940 (Green, personal observation).

Remarks: The two subspecies of cricket frogs known to occur in West Virginia are separated from one another geographically, so mere locality should be sufficient for identification. In Blanchard's cricket frog, the stripe along the thigh is not obvious and blends with the dark pigment above it, while in the northern cricket frog the stripe is sharply defined.

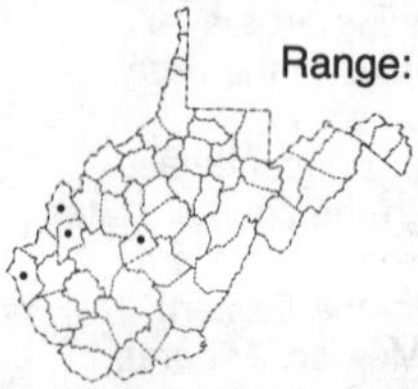

Range: Blanchard's cricket frog ranges from Michigan and Ohio to northern Tennessee westward to eastern Colorado and New Mexico. In West Virginia, it has been collected in Wayne, Putnam, Clay, and Mason counties. It is presumed to occur in Ohio Valley counties as far north as Wood County.

Genus *Hyla* Laurenti • Treefrogs

The genus *Hyla* is one of the largest groups of Anura. Its members have adhesive discs on their toes which, with their long limbs and digits, enhance their climbing ability. The genus contains about 250 species. Thirteen species occur within the United States, and three of these are found in West Virginia.

35 Northern Spring Peeper *Hyla crucifer crucifer* Wied

Gr. *hyle,* belonging to the forest: L. *crux,* cross; L. *fer,* bearing

Description: The spring peeper is a small frog which may attain a snout-vent length of 1.2 to 1.4 inches (3.0–3.5 cm). The tips of its digits are conspicuously expanded, and the webbing is moderately developed. The back usually bears a dark X-shaped mark which may be imperfect in outline. The dorsal color ranges from pinkish through light tan to brown or almost black. The ventral surface is cream colored. The female is slightly larger than the male. Mature males may be identified by the large, heavily pigmented, subgular vocal sac.

Confusing Species: The spring peeper is frequently confused with the mountain chorus frog (no. 37), which is active at the same time throughout most of the peeper's range in West Virginia. Chorus frogs have much less webbing between the hind toes, a longer fourth toe, smaller toe discs, a different dorsal pattern, and a white line along the margin of the upper jaw.

Habitat and Habits: The spring peeper is predominantly terrestrial, inhabiting woods and thickets. It is common to hear the first peeper of spring calling from a hillside above the breeding area. It emerges from hibernation from mid February to late March, depending upon the elevation, and makes its way to swamps or pools from which the chorus originates. Blanchard (1933) collected a large number of peepers early in November and described them "snuggled together in little groups or clumps in small depressions or cavities in the ground under the leaves." Although able to climb, they are seldom found far above the ground except on warm, rainy nights. During the breeding season they congregate in large numbers in pools, swamps, and roadside ditches. They are rarely encountered outside the breeding season except when hopping among the fallen leaves and other vegetation of the forest floor. Recently transformed individuals may be found among the vegetation along the edge of the pond or swamp from which they have recently emerged.

In a study of the eating habits of the spring peeper, Oplinger (1967) concludes that the food was based on availability rather than preference. Spiders, ants, and beetles were the predominant prey throughout the season. Various types of food appeared more frequently in the stomach contents as these food types became seasonally abundant. No aquatic prey was taken; even peepers at breeding ponds took only terrestrial prey.

Breeding: The voice of the peeper, one of the first signs of approaching spring, is a familiar sound from February through April. It can be heard from roadside ditches and swamps, and a large chorus may carry for some distance across the landscape. The call is a shrill, high-pitched trill or monosyllable, described as a "peep." The males emerge from hibernation and reach the breeding pond before the females. Both sexes arrive in staggered numbers, that is, a few appear at a time, and the males outnumber the females at any one time. Clasping pairs have been observed from mid February to early July. The eggs are laid singly and attached to plant stems beneath the surface or dropped to the floor of the pond. Transformation takes place from 90 to 100 days (Wright 1914). Large numbers were found transforming at a pond in Mason County during the last week of June 1940 (Green, personal observation). Oplinger (1966) gives a detailed account of the reproduction cycles of the spring peeper.

The chorus continues through March, but declines in April only to resume when rain fills the pools. By midsummer vocalization ceases, although a few isolated males will call intermittently from wooded areas throughout the fall.

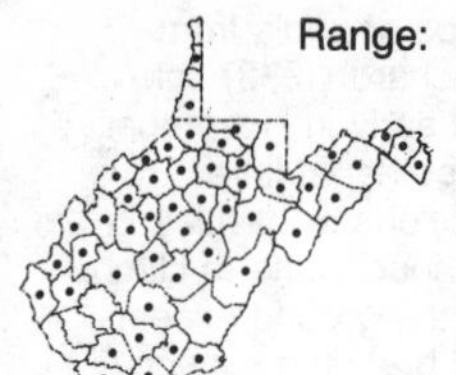

Range: Spring peepers have a wide range, from Ontario, Quebec, and southeastern Manitoba south to northern Florida and eastern Texas. The species is widely distributed in West Virginia and is probably found in every county.

36 **Gray Treefrog** *Hyla versicolor* complex (*Hyla versicolor* LeConte and *Hyla chrysoscelis* Cope)
L. *vers,* turn or change; Gr. *chrys,* golden; Gr. *scelis,* a leg

Description: This well-known treefrog may attain a snout-vent length of 2.3 inches (5.8 cm). The fingers and toes have conspicuous discs, and the hind toes are fully webbed. The front toes are slightly webbed. The concealed surfaces of the hind legs are bright orange mottled with black. It has a white spot below each eye. The color of the upper parts may be white, gray, green, or brown, with a dark, roughly star-shaped blotch on the back. The belly is white and the skin is granular.

Habitat and Habits: Gray treefrogs are commonly found in open woodlands where they frequent thickets and the branches and trunks of trees. They are easily overlooked because their coloration blends so well with the lichen-encrusted bark. They are rarely encountered on the ground except during the breeding season as they migrate to ponds. They announce their emergence from hibernation around mid April with a rattling trill from a thicket. Although breeding activity may extend from mid April to mid July, adults may continue to call from their perches in the trees throughout the summer on hot, humid days and nights.

Breeding: Toward the end of April the males migrate to suitable breeding sites; temporary pools such as woodland pools, flooded meadows, and cattail swamps, and permanent pools including artificial impoundments. In residential areas, they may select a swimming pool. A sizeable chorus is noisy, and pairs in amplexus may be observed on a perch above the surface or floating in the water. A breeding chorus may last for one night, only to resume a few nights later with the onset of rainfall. The eggs are deposited in a thin surface film that slips through the fingers easily. A single female may lay up to 1,800 eggs in small masses of 30 to 40 eggs. The eggs hatch in four to five days. The tadpoles, which may be identified by their reddish tails, transform about 60 days after hatching. On June 6, 1960, large numbers of tadpoles were transforming around many small pools in Huntington. They were bright green with a distinct white spot below the eye (Green, personal observation).

Remarks: The two species within this complex are distinguishable only by sonogram analysis of call characteristics. *Hyla versicolor* has a trill rate of 17–35 pulses per second. The call of *Hyla chrysoscelis* is a high-pitched buzzing trill with 34–69 pulses per second. The rate depends upon the temperature. For proper identification, a tape recording of the call and the treefrog's temperature must be analyzed in the laboratory. The differences between the diploid (*H. chrysoscelis*) and tetraploid species (*H. versicolor*) can be determined by examination of cells from the palpebral membrane, a transparent membrane in the frog eyelid erroneously referred to as the nictitating membrane. The red blood cells of *H. versicolor* are larger than those of *H. chrysoscelis* (Johnson 1977). Johnson (1966) reports that the two gray treefrog species are genetically separate throughout their distribution.

Ralin (1968), in a study of the ecological and reproductive differences in the cryptic species of the *H. versicolor* complex, reported that *H. versicolor* usually issued its mating call from the ground, while *H. chrysoscelis* called from trees and bushes. He also reported that during the breeding season *H. versicolor* fed more on terrestrial insects, while *H. chrysoscelis* fed on arboreal insects. Pauley (personal observation) observed *H. chrysoscelis* calling from the ground at Olson Bog, an elevation of 3,240 feet (987 m). The range of the two species of the *H. versicolor* complex has been determined for much of Wisconsin and Texas and parts of Illinois, Georgia, Louisiana, Virginia, Maryland, and Delaware by sonogram or karyotype.

Within West Virginia, the distributions of the species have been determined by Little (1983), as shown in the range map.

• *Hyla chrysoscelis*
≡ *Hyla versicolor*
|||| Sympatry
(Adapted from M. L. Little 1983)

Genus *Pseudacris* Fitzinger • Chorus Frogs

The genus *Pseudacris* is found only in North America, occurring throughout most of the United States and over most of Canada. The members of the genus are terrestrial hylids with reduced toe discs and a very small amount of webbing between the toes. An extremely elongated fourth toe on the hind foot is a conspicuous feature. Seven species are recognized, of which two occur in West Virginia.

37 **Mountain Chorus Frog** *Pseudacris brachyphona* (Cope)

Gr. *pseudes,* false; Gr. *akris,* a locust; Gr. *brachys,* short; Gr. *phone,* sound

Description: The mountain chorus frog may attain a snout-vent length of 1.5 inches (3.8 cm). Females are slightly larger than males and lack the darkly pigmented subgular vocal sac. The dorsal coloration varies from pinkish cream to deep brown. The dorsal markings consist of a pair of broad stripes which curve inward toward the midline and, in approximately 35 percent of the population, meet to form a cruciform pattern (Green 1969). The ventral surface is clear white with a trace of yellow in the groin. A dark triangle between the eyes is usually present. The hind legs are long, and when they are extended forward along the side of the body, the heel reaches a point anterior to the middle of the eye.

Habitat and Habits: The mountain chorus frog is a woodland species that is often found some distance from water. Throughout the breeding season it frequents pools, roadside ditches, seepages, and the outflow of woodland springs. In late summer and fall, it may be encountered on hillsides with wood frogs (no. 41) and spring peepers (no. 35). It is an excellent leaper, but there is no evidence that it climbs like a *Hyla* (Walker 1932).

Green (1952) examined the stomach contents of 42 individuals and found coleopterons (45 percent), spiders (25 percent), and hemipterons (13 percent). The remaining 17 percent consisted of ants, leaf hoppers, dipterons, centipedes, earthworms, and lepidopteron larvae. All of the animals eaten lived on or near the ground. The presence of small stones and sand grains in 35 percent of the stomachs indicated that prey was picked up from the ground.

Breeding: The temperature of the area over a period of several weeks influences when the frogs will emerge from terrestrial hibernation. Choruses may occur during warm spells in January, but breeding activity usually starts in mid to late February in the Huntington area, later at higher altitudes. Breeding aggregations of many males form in shallow pools along slopes and on valley floors. The number of males builds up rapidly and remains relatively constant for several weeks. They call from exposed stations in shallow water along the edge of a pool or while supporting themselves on vegetation in the deeper parts of the pool. Females visit the pool for only one night (Green 1952) during the breeding season. Once the female makes contact with a male oviposition takes place.

The call of the male is a rapidly repeated, rasping, drawn out monosyllable that seems to repeat "rake . . . rake" (Barbour 1971). The rate of call, as well as the intensity, is influenced by the air and water temperature. Males remain in the vicinity of the pool throughout the breeding season, returning to the water to call and breed after each successive rainfall.

A female may deposit 300 to 900 eggs over a period of several hours. The eggs are laid in loose irregular masses of 10 to 50 eggs attached to leaves, sticks, and other vegetation beneath the surface of the water. Tadpoles 0.18 to 0.20 inch (0.45–0.5 cm) hatch within three or four days. Transformation occurs in 50 to 64 days when the tadpoles attain a length of approximately 1.18 inches (3.0 cm). Recently transformed mountain chorus frogs range from 0.4 to 0.5 inch (1.1–1.3 cm) in snout-vent length (Green 1952).

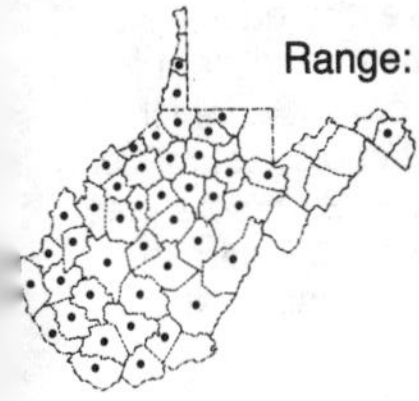

Range: The mountain chorus frog ranges from extreme western Maryland and Virginia, west through southwest Pennsylvania and eastern Ohio, south to eastern Tennessee and northern Alabama. Fowler (1967) reported collecting *Pseudacris brachyphona* in eastern Garrett County, Maryland, in the Potomac drainage. In West Virginia it occurs in all the Allegheny Plateau counties, from the Allegheny Front westward to the Ohio Valley. There is one record from the Eastern Panhandle.

38 **Upland Chorus Frog** *Pseudacris triseriata feriarum* (Barid)

Gr. *treis,* three; L. *seriatus,* in series; L. *feria,* festive

Description: The upland chorus frog may attain a snout-vent length of 1.5 inches (3.8 cm). The dorsal pattern usually consists of three longitudinal stripes, which may be broken into rows of spots, on a light brown background. A dark triangular spot between the eyes and a white line along the upper lip are also present. The underparts are cream colored. The heel of the hind legs, when extended forward along the sides, does not reach the eye.

Habitat and Habits: Upland chorus frogs are found in swampy areas of broad valleys, grassy swales, moist areas of woodlands, and borders of heavily vegetated ponds. Compared with the mountain chorus frog (no. 37) it (1) emerges earlier in the spring, (2) selects more heavily vegetated ponds for breeding, (3) is more secretive and therefore more difficult to locate, (4) may call more frequently during the day, (5) has a breeding activity which is both nocturnal and diurnal and is of greater intensity, and (6) has a shorter breeding season.

Breeding: The reproductive pattern in the upland chorus frog is similar to that of the mountain chorus frog. Hibernating sites include leaf-filled depressions under rotting stumps and logs, and holes under rocks. Males emerge from mid February to early March and attract females by their chorus. The call has a lower pitch than that of the mountain chorus frog, and the pulses are distinctly separate. The call of the mountain chorus frog is uttered more rapidly and with a higher pitch. Each female deposits up to 1,000 eggs, attaching them to vegetation in the water in loose masses of 40 to 60 eggs. The eggs hatch within three to four days and transformation occurs in about 60 days.

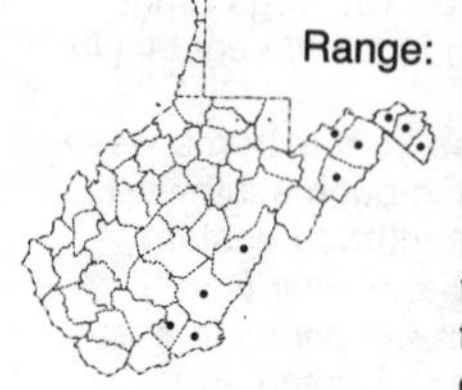

Range: The upland chorus frog ranges from central Pennsylvania to the Florida Panhandle, west to east Texas and southeastern Oklahoma. In West Virginia it is confined to the Ridge and Valley province, which includes most of the Eastern Panhandle, south along the Virginia border into Monroe, and Summers counties. Wilson (1944) records collecting the upland chorus frog in a swamp on Droop Mountain along with the mountain chorus frog.

Family Ranidae • True Frogs

The family Ranidae is the largest and most widespread family of frogs. There are nearly 700 species in 47 genera. It is widely distributed throughout the world, with representatives on every major land mass except Antarctica. The largest genus in the family is *Rana,* with over 250 species. *Rana* is the only genus of this family in the United States.

These are the animals which people usually think of when they speak of frogs. They are typically of medium to large size, have a smooth skin, and long legs with webbing between the toes. The rear margin of the tongue has a pair of lobelike projections. Members of this family frequently have dorsolateral folds (a glandular fold or ridge along each side of the back).

Genus *Rana* Linnaeus • True Frogs

39 Bullfrog Rana *catesbeiana* Shaw
L. *rana,* a frog; named after Mark Catesby, a naturalist of the eighteenth century.

Description: The bullfrog is the largest frog in West Virginia and may attain a snout-vent length of 6.0 to 7.0 inches (15.2–17.9 cm). It is the only member of this genus in West Virginia which lacks dorsolateral folds. A raised fold of skin does, however, extend posteriorly from the eye and encircles the rear edge of the tympanum down to the shoulder. The back may be green, gray, brown, or black, occasionally with dark wormlike markings or blotches. The nose is bright green and the ventral surface is white with gray mottling. The throat of males is yellow, and the diameter of the tympanum is larger than the eye in the males. The toes are fully webbed, the webs reaching to the tips of all but the fourth toe, of which a small tip may be free.

Habitat and Habits: Bullfrogs frequent bodies of permanent water such as rivers, lakes, farm ponds, impoundments, swamps, and marshes. During the winter months they bury themselves in mud on the floor of ponds or rivers. They are voracious feeders and can consume large food items such as birds, mice, snakes, small fish, and crayfish. A detailed list of food items is given by Korschgen and Moyle (1955) and by Stewart and Sandison (1972). On one occasion a bullfrog was observed creeping among a chorus of spring peepers in early April, picking off the calling males. His stomach contained one female and six male peepers when examined (Green, personal observation). On another occasion, two toads in amplexus were found in the stomach of a large bullfrog (Pauley, personal observation).

Breeding: Bullfrogs emerge from hibernation early in March. Calling begins in mid May and may continue throughout the summer. Breeding males establish territories and call from the same location night after night (Emlen 1968; Ryan 1980). The males secure the females in a pectoral amplexus. Spawning occurs from mid May through July. The eggs are small, averaging only about 0.05 inch (.13 cm) in diameter, and are laid in a more or less circular film on the water's surface, usually among brush and aquatic plants. According to Walker (1946), the egg mass may be two feet or more in diameter and often has a frothy appearance due to the presence of air bubbles in the gelatinous matter which surrounds the eggs. A female may deposit from 10,000 to 20,000 eggs. The eggs hatch in three to four days, and the tadpoles usually undergo transformation the following summer. The tadpole has many small, sharply defined black dots on the dorsum which are more numerous on the upper half of the tail. The size at which tadpoles transform, as well as the date of transformation, varies according to temperature. Ordinarily the tadpole stage lasts for 12 to 14 months. A large number of bullfrogs were observed metamorphosing along Twelvepole Creek, Wayne County, on July 20, 1940. Many individuals could be found under stones in the shallow water. One rock about 9.0 inches (23 cm) square sheltered ten juveniles (Green, personal observation). On August 25 of the same year, a large number of tadpoles were observed swimming in the same stream. Their size indicated that they were close to transformation.

Remarks: The males call from selected stations along the bank, whence they seek safety by diving into the water. Bullfrogs are inclined to be sluggish, and although they rarely venture far from the water's edge, there are times when they may be encountered in a meadow some distance from water. In this situation they are easily captured. At night they can be approached more easily with a flashlight or headlamp and captured by hand.

The bullfrog is classified as a game animal by the West Virginia Department of Natural Resources and is protected under the state's fishing regulations. Although the regulations do not specify the species of frog, sportsmen are not interested in any other species because of their smaller sizes. The regulations specify a daily creel limit of 10, with no minimum size and a possession limit of 20. The season runs from 9:00 P.M. on June 14 to midnight on July 31. The decline in bullfrog populations, not only within West Virginia, but in many eastern states, has for some time concerned sportsmen as well as other conservationists. In West Virginia a study is being undertaken to determine the reasons for the decline. Factors cited include habitat destruction, over harvesting, use of pesticides and herbicides, drought, and improper land use.

Landowners with access to suitable habitats have succumbed to the propaganda of get-rich-quick schemes in bullfrog propagation. They are soon discouraged when they discover that bullfrogs require an enormous supply of live food, and that they take several years to reach maturity. Several publications are available which offer valuable information. Leaflet 436, issued by the U.S. Fish and Wildlife Service in 1956, discusses commercial possibilities and limitations in frog raising.

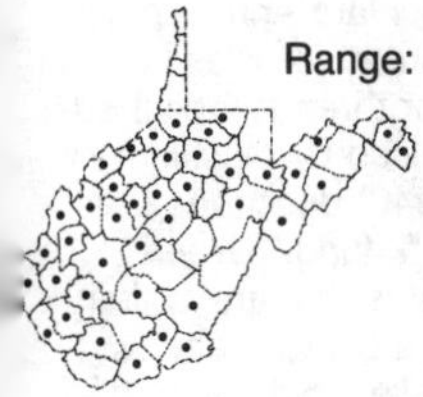

Range: The original range of the bullfrog encompassed most of the eastern United States, but in recent years the species has been introduced in so many of the western states that it is difficult to define the original range. It has also been introduced in Mexico, Cuba, Canada, and the Orient. In West Virginia it probably occurs in every county.

40 Green Frog *Rana clamitans melanota* (Rafinesque)
L. *clamitantis,* loud calling; Gr. *melina,* black; Gr. *nota,* back

Description: The green frog may attain a snout-vent length of 3.5 to 4.0 inches (8.9–10.2 cm). Dorsolateral folds extend down the back approximately two-thirds of the distance to the groin. The dorsal color may be brown, greenish or gray, with or without small irregular spots. The sides of the head below and anterior to the eye are green. In males the throat is yellow, and the diameter of the tympanum is greater than that of the eye. Females usually grow to a larger size than males.

Habitat and Habits: Green frogs are found in open country or forest land in a variety of permanent aquatic situations such as ponds, streams, marshes, brooks, and springs. They are decidedly aquatic and seldom go far from water. The frogs spend most of their time stationed along the shore of a pond or stream within leaping distance of the water, and when disturbed they can reach safety by a single leap, usually accompanied by a scream or a squeal. Male green frogs are territorial during the breeding season (Martof 1953; Wells 1977).

Hamilton (1948), in a study of the food and feeding behavior of the green frog in New York, found that green frogs will normally select a stand and await their prey, thus eating the food that is most readily available; they feed as frequently at night as during the day, relying heavily on sight in the capture of prey; they eat their cast skin; and they capture some of their food beneath the water surface. Stewart and Sandison (1972) report that coleoptera, hemiptera, hymenoptera, and spiders are the most important food items for green frogs. Whitaker (1961) compares the habitat and food of juvenile green frogs and leopard frogs.

Breeding: Green frogs usually hibernate in the muddy bottom of a pond or stream, although there are isolated exceptions (Bohnsack 1951). Adults emerge in early to mid March, but do not begin to call until late April. April 25 is the earliest calling date recorded for West Virginia. The call consists of two or three low-pitched musical notes similar to that produced by plucking a bass string on a banjo. Walker (1946) describes it as an explosive, vibrant, low-pitched "k-tung." Green frogs rarely engage in a large chorus, but are solitary in habit. On a summer evening in a broad meadow, their calling echoes through the valley, but the calling individuals are rarely close together.

Each female deposits several thousand eggs in shallow surface masses. Each egg is black above and white below, with a diameter of 0.06 inch (0.15 cm). The egg mass usually measures less than one foot (30.5 cm) in diameter. Development is rapid, and the eggs hatch within a few days. The larvae resemble those of the bullfrog, but can be distinguished by the presence of large, faintly outlined spots scattered over the entire tail. Most authors claim that the tadpole spends one winter before transforming the following summer, but there is evidence that this is not always the case. Martof (1952) cites an instance of transformation the same summer. Ting (1951) reared larval green frogs which transformed 113 days after insemination in the laboratory. Richmond's observations (1964) also indicate that the green frog is capable of transforming within one season. The recently transformed young measure from 1.1 to 1.3 inches (2.8–3.3 cm). A detailed description of the reproduction in southern Michigan has been published by Martof (1956).

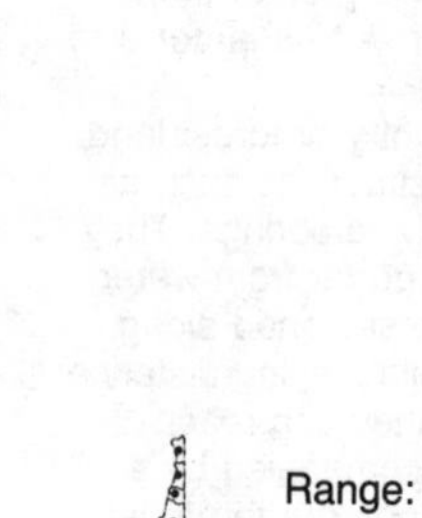

Range: The subspecies *melanota* occurs from Newfoundland and New Brunswick to western Ontario, and south to eastern Oklahoma, southern Illinois, northern Georgia, and eastern North Carolina. Green frogs are found throughout West Virginia.

41 **Wood Frog** *Rana sylvatica* LeConte

L. *sylva,* a wood or forest

Description: The wood frog is a medium-sized frog which may attain a snout-vent length of 3.0 inches (7.6 cm). Its distinguishing mark is a black mask extending from the eye through the tympanum to the shoulder. A prominent white line runs along the upper lip above a narrow black line. Another black line extends from the snout through the nostril to the eye. There is a dark blotch at the base of each forelimb. Dorsolateral folds extend to the groin and are frequently marked with small, dark speckles. The back is unspotted between the dorsolateral folds, and its color varies from pinkish through light tan or salmon to very dark brown. The belly is usually white, and there are dark crossbars on the femur and tibia.

Among breeding adults, males differ from females in having the bases of the thumbs swollen, the forearms stouter, and the webbing of the toes more extensive (the margins of the webs are convex rather than concave). The paired lateral vocal sacs may be seen externally as folds of skin between the angle of the jaw and shoulder.

Habitat and Habits: Except for a brief spawning period in early spring, the wood frog is terrestrial in habit, active in the daytime, and solitary. It occurs most frequently in moist, deciduous woodlands with well-developed leaf litter. It is unusual to find the wood frog in open fields or grassy woodland. It hibernates on land, seeking shelter under leaves, logs, and trash. Its period of activity ranges from mid February to November 9 in West Virginia.

The major food sources for the wood frog include molluscs, spiders, mites, and insects (Moore and Strickland 1955).

Breeding: Wood frogs emerge from hibernation in mid to late February. They can be found swimming in pools that still contain ice. The earliest date on record in West Virginia is February 20, 1939, on Droop Mountain, Pocahontas County (elevation 3,100 feet or 945 m) (Wilson 1944). Males congregate in large numbers at small woodland pools, from which they utter their characteristic short, explosive calls of two or three syllables. Clasping and calling males float at the surface or cling to clumps of debris. The voice has little carrying power, but a large chorus may be heard for some distance on a quiet night; it sounds like a flock of quacking mallards (Walker 1946). During the brief spawning season the males are shy and wary, and when disturbed they escape by diving below the surface. On the evening of March 4, 1970, a large chorus in the pools along Twelvepole Creek, Wayne County, contained so many frogs that one could not walk among them without disturbing their mating activity (Green, personal observation).

The eggs are laid in globular masses measuring 3.0 to 4.0 inches (7.6 to 10.2 cm) in diameter, usually attached to twigs and stems beneath the surface of the pool. They may contain up to 3,000 eggs. Wood frog eggs are found at the same time of the year as those of the spotted salamander (no. 4) and frequently in the same pools. Wood frog eggs retain their spherical shape along the outer surface of the mass; those of the spotted salamander are flattened. Spotted salamander egg masses are usually cottony white; those of the wood frog are somewhat clear.

As many as 300 pairs of wood frogs may deposit eggs at a communal site. The egg masses in the center of the clump are insulated from thermal extremes, and their temperatures may be 7.2 to 12.6° F (4.0–7.0° C) above the ambient water temperature. These central masses have significantly greater hatching success than the peripheral masses because of the warmer temperature (Waldman and Ryan 1983).

The eggs hatch within two or three weeks, and the larval period lasts for six to ten weeks. The tadpole metamorphoses into a froglet when it measures approximately 0.63 inch (1.6 cm). Juvenile wood frogs are common in the fall of the year hopping among the vegetation on hillsides above the breeding area. Females become sexually mature in the third year; the males in the second year (Bellis 1961).

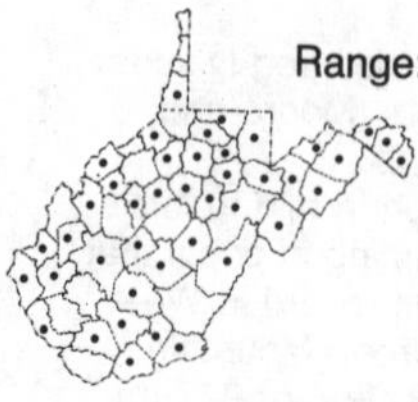

Range: Wood frogs are found from Labrador to Alaska, south in the Appalachians to South Carolina, Georgia, and Alabama, and west through Tennessee, Kentucky, Indiana, Wisconsin, and Minnesota. They are widely distributed throughout West Virginia, from the lowest elevations in the Eastern Panhandle to the top of Spruce Knob in Pendleton County at 4,860 feet (1,481 m).

42 **Northern Leopard Frog** *Rana pipiens* Schreber

L. *pipiens,* peeping, to peep

Description: The leopard frog, also known as the meadow frog or grass frog, is the species most widely used in introductory biology courses. It may attain a head-body length of 2.0 to 4.0 inches (5.1–10.2 cm). The dorsal coloration of its body is brown or green with two to three rows of dark spots. Conspicuous, light-colored, dorsolateral folds extend from the eyes to the groin. Two or three incomplete rows of rounded spots with light-colored borders lie between the dorsolateral folds. There are additional rounded dark spots along the sides below the folds. A snout spot is usually present while the tympanal spot characteristic of the southern leopard frog is usually absent. There is a light stripe along the upper lip, bordered by dark stripes. The belly and undersurfaces of the hind legs are a clear white.

Males differ from females in having the bases of the thumbs swollen, stouter forearms, and internal vocal sacs between the angles of the jaws and the shoulder regions. Males are smaller than females.

Habitat and Habits: The leopard frog utilizes a wide variety of aquatic habitats including swamps, ponds, lakes, marshes, rivers, and creeks. During the summer it may venture far from water into fields, meadows, pastures, and occasionally into wooded areas. When approached it squats close to the ground in preparation for a leap to safety.

Their food, mostly of terrestrial origin, consists of a wide variety of invertebrates, including several types of insects, spiders, snails, and sow bugs (Linzey 1967). Whitaker (1961) compares the habitat and food of young leopard frogs and green frogs (no. 40).

Breeding: Although leopard frogs hibernate under water, they often make extended migrations to the breeding ponds (Walker 1946). The breeding season begins early in March. In West Virginia, March 1 is the earliest date on record for calling to occur; eggs have been collected as early as March 13. Leopard frogs are highly gregarious spawners, and a large chorus is impressive in volume. They breed in a variety of sites such as temporary and permanent ponds, swamps, and sluggish streams. Calling, clasping, and oviposition may extend throughout March and April. The egg mass is an oval shape which is flattened on top (plinth), about 5 or 6 inches (12.7–15.2 cm) in diameter. It may contain 300 to 800 eggs (Zenisek 1963) and may either be attached to grass or other plant material or lie unattached on the bottom of the pond or stream. Hatching occurs within a week, and the tadpoles undergo transformation after reaching a total length of 2.0 to 3.1 inches (5.0–8.0 cm). Recently transformed individuals have been collected in Cabell County as early as May 21. Sexual maturity is attained at three years of age (Force 1933).

No problem in North American herpetology has been the subject of so much discussion and controversy as the taxonomy of leopard frogs. Their extensive distribution in a variety of habitats as well as their morphological variation has challenged naturalists for over 50 years. The early naturalists studied the voices of these frogs and attempted verbal descriptions, but the descriptions were never so precise as to permit comparison with the sounds heard in the field.

The first serious attempt to classify the calls of *Rana pipiens* was made by Nobel and Aronson (1942), using northern *R. pipiens* in the laboratory. The problem of describing nonverbal sounds was ultimately solved through the use of electronic equipment which permitted the reproduction of calls, both in the field and the laboratory. The oscilloscope analyzes calls into pulses so that different individual calls can be compared. Thus, through the medium of spectrographic analysis, it was learned that leopard frogs, unlike many other anurans, produce numerous different vocalizations which can be heard simultaneously from a single chorus.

In the mid 1960s a University of Michigan student with an interest in speciation undertook a study of the biological interactions among individuals of different populations in the field. This led to the comprehensive work on leopard frogs by Ann Pace (1974). According to Pace, the three sounds most often heard in a *Rana pipiens* chorus consist of the long, many pulsed thrill (A) which she refers to as the mating call of the species, or the female attracting call. The second part consists of a short trill with a faster pulse rate (B). This is the short distance direction signal. The third sound most frequently heard in a chorus is aggressive or territorial and is used primarily in male-male interactions (C).

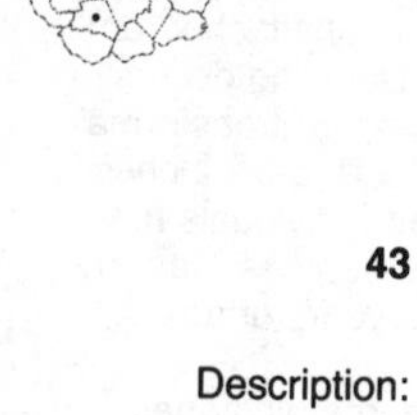

Range: The northern leopard frog ranges from southern Labrador south to Pennsylvania and Kentucky, and west to the Pacific states. It is not a common frog in West Virginia but appears to have a wide distribution. A few records exist from counties in the Allegheny Plateau which have not been verified. There is no evidence that the southern leopard frog, *Rana utricularia* (= *Rana sphenocephala*) enters the state along its eastern or southern borders (Pace 1974).

43 **Pickerel Frog** *Rana palustris* LeConte

L. *paluster,* marshy

Description: The pickerel frog is a medium-sized, spotted frog which may attain a snout-vent length of 3.0 inches (7.6 cm). The concealed surfaces of the hind legs are bright yellow or orange, and this coloration may extend onto the belly. The parallel rows of dark, squarish spots down the back lie between the distinct, light-colored dorsolateral folds. The background coloration of the dorsal surface is brown or tan. Young frogs have a metallic luster which becomes bronzelike in older frogs. Male pickerel frogs have enlarged thumbs, each of which bears a small pad on the inner surface. Paired lateral vocal sacs are present but not evident unless inflated. The females are larger than the males and usually lighter in color.

Habitat and Habits: Pickerel frogs are most frequently encountered in cool, shady ravines along clear, unpolluted streams and springs. In the spring they breed in a variety of aquatic situations, but in the summer they wander away from the water and may be found in meadows, pastures, golf courses, and humid ravines. They are active jumpers and are difficult to capture when surprised in dense undergrowth.

Several authors allude to the presence of these frogs in limestone caves. Barbour (1971) states that he often found them in the twilight zone of caves and that they frequently winter in caves. Johnson (1977) states that large numbers of pickerel frogs crowded together have been observed in Missouri caves during the winter. Two specimens were collected in Schoolhouse Cave on the Higganbotham Farm, Greenbrier County, on June 29, 1949, by Maurice Brooks.

Breeding: Pickerel frogs emerge from hibernation in the mud on the floor of ponds in mid March. The earliest dates at Huntington are March 18 (1945) and March 21 (1952). Breeding may occur in woodland pools, sloughs, creeks, or water-filled ditches. They are often highly gregarious, with many individuals concentrated in a small area.

The voice is a low-pitched snore of two to three seconds duration, rising to a louder pitch at the end. On April 9, 1946, in a Wayne County pond, pickerel frogs were calling from a small area close to the shore. Because none of the frogs could be seen, it was assumed they were calling from under the water (Green, personal observations).

The female deposits her eggs in a globular mass attached to submerged vegetation. The 2,500 to 3,000 eggs laid in each mass are distinctive in having a brown animal pole and a yellowish vegetal pole. Hatching occurs within ten days, and the tadpoles transform around 90 days. At Huntington, froglets have been collected on June 27, 1960. Individuals of subadult size are frequently found in the spring; apparently the young do not reach maturity until the third year.

Remarks: Pickerel frogs superficially resemble leopard frogs (no. 42), but the latter have rounded, light-bordered dorsal spots and lack the orange on the undersides of the hind legs. The skin secretions of pickerel frogs are noxious or distasteful to many animals. Numerous accounts in the literature refer to this character; in fact, they often describe experiments which indicate the vertebrate species which are affected. Dogs, snakes, and other predators avoid or reject pickerel frogs. When closely confined with other amphibians, as in a collecting bag or jar, the result is often fatal to the other specimens.

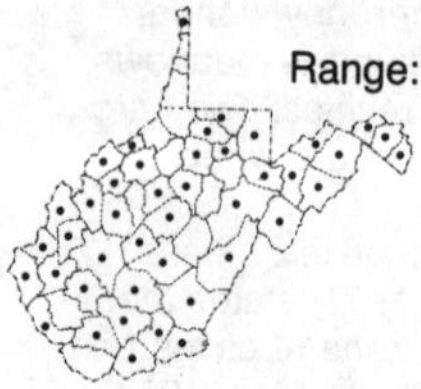

Range: Pickerel frogs range from southern Canada westward through Wisconsin, south to eastern Texas, and east through northern Alabama and Georgia to South Carolina. The species is found throughout the state.

Reptiles

REPTILES arose from primitive amphibians about 300 million years ago in the late Carboniferous period. Their success as the dominant members of the animal kingdom for many millions of years was due to a combination of several characteristics which permitted them to invade land areas that were not accessible to the moisture-bound amphibians. Freed from this constraint, and without the competition later provided by the birds and mammals, they spread rapidly into new environments. Some took to air, others took to water with newly acquired adaptations, many remained on land. During this period of adaptation, which occupied most of the Mesozoic Era of 120 million years, there appeared no less than 16 orders consisting of more than 170 families. Included within these families were many bizarre forms and some of the largest animals ever to walk the earth.

Among those characteristics which enabled reptiles to exploit the terrestrial environment were a dry scaly skin and the development of the *cleidoic* or *amniotic egg*. This innovation provided the developing reptilian embryo with the advantages of the amphibian's pond environment. The egg was protected from the external environment by a porous, leathery (or brittle), calcareous shell. Membranes inside the shell protected the developing embryo. Surrounding the embryo was a sac (the *amnion*), containing a fluid that supported and bathed the embryo. The egg contained a sufficient supply of yolk to nourish the embryo until it was ready to hatch. Another membrane, the *allantois,* developed a circulation which provided oxygen and the release of carbon dioxide through the shell and also collected and stored the wastes of the developing embryo's metabolism.

In addition to the scaled body covering and cleidoic egg, reptiles differ from amphibians in that they do not pass through a gill-bearing larval stage. In addition, they have five toes with claws on each foot (where limbs are present), better developed and more efficient lungs, an incomplete septum within the ventricle of the heart which permits better oxygenation of the blood, and various other internal structures which differentiate them from amphibians.

Among reptiles, fertilization is internal: sperm transfer is accomplished in most by an intromittent organ. Reptiles that lay eggs are designated as *oviparous,* while those which retain the eggs within the body of the female until development is complete and the young are born alive are referred to as *ovoviviparous.*

A third condition is referred to as *viviparous*. In this case, the young develop in the female and obtain some nourishment from maternal tissues. These reproductive characteristics may vary for snakes and lizards, but the turtles and crocodilians all lay eggs.

Of the sixteen orders of reptiles present during the Mesozoic Era, only four remain. The order Rhynchocephalia contains a single living species, the tuatara, found on islands adjacent to New Zealand. Another small order, the Crocodilia, includes the crocodiles and their allies and is mostly tropical in distribution. The two remaining orders are the Testudines (the turtles) and the Squamata, which includes the Suborder Sauria (the lizards), and the Suborder Serpentes (the snakes). These last two orders contain the entire West Virginia reptilian fauna, a total of 38 species.

Color Plates

Boldface numbers correspond to species numbers in text.

1 Eastern Hellbender. *Cryptobranchus alleganiensis alleganiensis*

2 Mudpuppy. *Necturus maculosus maculosus*

3 Jefferson Salamander. *Ambystoma jeffersonianum*

4 Spotted Salamander. *Ambystoma maculatum*

5 Marbled Salamander. *Ambystoma opacum*

6 Smallmouth Salamander. *Ambystoma texanum*

7 Red-spotted Newt, Eft. *Notophthalmus viridescens viridescens*

8 Northern Dusky Salamander. *Desmognathus fuscus fuscus*

9 Mountain Dusky Salamander. *Desmognathus ochrophaeus*

10 Appalachian Seal Salamander. *Desmognathus monticola monticola*

11 Blackbelly Salamander. *Desmognathus quadramaculatus*

12 Redback Salamander. *Plethodon cinereus*

13 Ravine Salamander. *Plethodon richmondi*

14 Valley and Ridge Salamander. *Plethodon hoffmani*

15 Cheat Mountain Salamander. *Plethodon nettingi*

16 Slimy Salamander. *Plethodon glutinosus glutinosus*

18 Wehrle's Salamander. *Plethodon wehrlei*

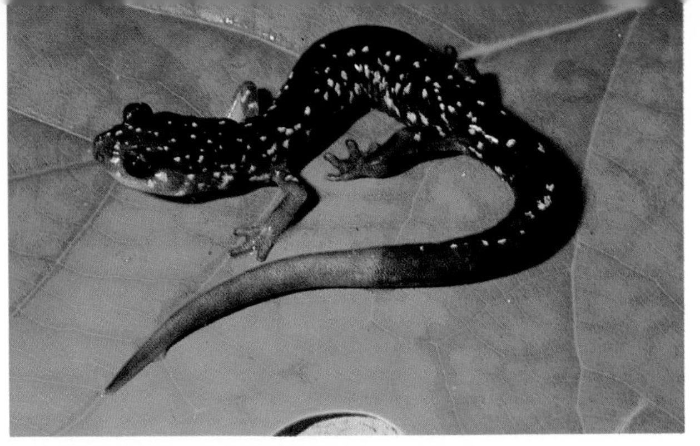

19 White-spotted Salamander. *Plethodon punctatus*

20 Four-toed Salamander. *Hemidactylium scutatum*

21 Northern Spring Salamander. *Gyrinophilus porphyriticus porphyriticus*

22 Kentucky Spring Salamander. *Gyrinophilus porphyriticus duryi*

24 Midland Mud Salamander. *Pseudotriton montanus diastictus*

25 Northern Red Salamander. *Pseudotriton ruber ruber*

26 Green Salamander. *Aneides aeneus*

27 Northern Two-lined Salamander. *Eurycea bislineata bislineata*

28 Longtail Salamander. *Eurycea longicauda longicauda*

29 Cave Salamander. *Eurycea lucifuga*

30 Eastern Spadefoot. *Scaphiopus holbrookii holbrookii*

31 Eastern American Toad. *Bufo americanus americanus*

32 Fowler's Toad. *Bufo woodhouseii fowleri*

34 Blanchard's Cricket Frog. *Acris crepitans blanchardi*

35 Northern Spring Peeper. *Hyla crucifer crucifer*

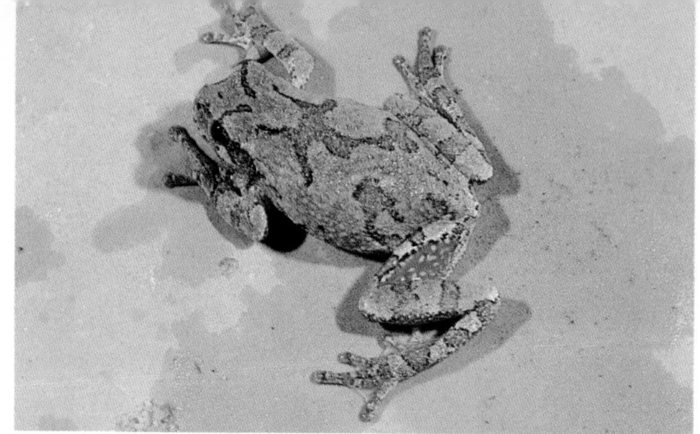

36 Gray Treefrog complex. *Hyla versicolor-Hyla chrysoscelis.*

37 Mountain Chorus Frog. *Pseudacris brachyphona*

38 Upland Chorus Frog. *Pseudacris triseriata feriarum*

39 Bullfrog. *Rana catesbeiana*

40 Green Frog. *Rana clamitans melanota*

41 Wood Frog. *Rana sylvatica*

42 Northern Leopard Frog. *Rana pipiens*

43 Pickerel Frog. *Rana palustris*

44 Common Snapping Turtle. *Chelydra serpentina serpentina*

45 Spotted Turtle. *Clemmys guttata*

46 Wood Turtle. *Clemmys insculpta*

47 Eastern Box Turtle. *Terrapene carolina carolina*

48 Map Turtle. *Graptemys geographica*

49 Ouachita Map Turtle. *Graptemys pseudogeographica ouachitensis*

50 Eastern Painted Turtle. *Chrysemys picta picta*

51 Midland Painted Turtle. *Chrysemys picta marginata*

52 Red-eared Slider. *Trachemys scripta elegans*

53 Eastern River Cooter. *Pseudemys concinna concinna*

55 Redbelly Turtle. *Pseudemys rubriventris rubriventris*

56 Stinkpot. *Sternotherus odoratus*

57 Eastern Spiny Softshell. *Trionyx spiniferus spiniferus*

58 Midland Smooth Softshell. *Trionyx muticus muticus*

59 Northern Fence Lizard. *Sceloporus undulatus hyacinthinus*

60 Ground Skink. *Scincella lateralis*

61 Five-lined Skink. *Eumeces fasciatus*

62 Broadhead Skink. *Eumeces laticeps*

63 Northern Coal Skink. *Eumeces anthracinus anthracinus*

64 Queen Snake. *Regina septemvittata*

65 Northern Water Snake. *Nerodia sipedon sipedon*

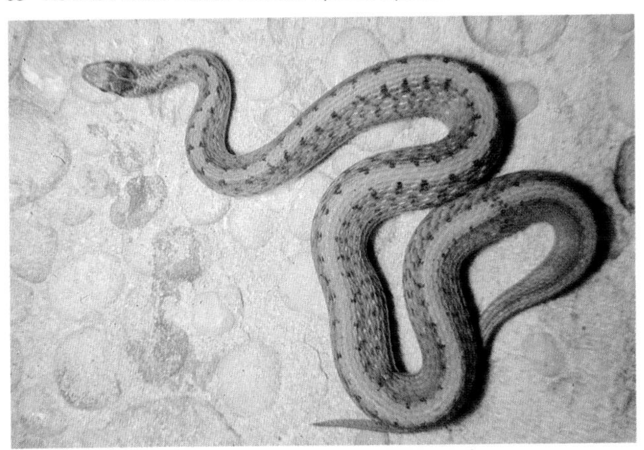

66 Northern Brown Snake. *Storeria dekayi dekayi*

67 Northern Redbelly Snake. *Storeria occipitomaculata occipitomaculata*

68 Eastern Ribbon Snake. *Thamnophis sauritus sauritus*

69 Eastern Garter Snake. *Thamnophis sirtalis sirtalis*

70 Eastern Earth Snake. *Virginia valeriae valeriae*

72 Eastern Hognose Snake. *Heterodon platirhinos*

73 Northern Ringneck Snake. *Diadophis punctatus edwardsii*

74 Eastern Worm Snake. *Carphophis amoenus amoenus*

75 Northern Black Racer. *Coluber constrictor constrictor*

76 Rough Green Snake. *Opheodrys aestivus*

77 Eastern Smooth Green Snake. *Opheodrys vernalis vernalis*

78 Corn Snake. *Elaphe guttata guttata*

79 Black Rat Snake. *Elaphe obsoleta obsoleta*

80 Northern Pine Snake. *Pituophis melanoleucus melanoleucus*

81 Eastern Kingsnake. *Lampropeltis getulus getulus*

82 Black Kingsnake. *Lampropeltis getulus nigra*

83 Eastern Milk Snake. *Lampropeltis triangulum triangulum*

84 Northern Copperhead. *Agkistrodon contortrix mokasen*

85 Timber Rattlesnake. *Crotalus horridus*

ORDER TESTUDINES—TURTLES

Turtles have existed nearly unchanged for almost 175 million years. A fossil turtle from South Dakota known as *Archelon* lived in the Cretaceous seas over 100 million years ago. It attained a length of 12 feet (3.7 m), and probably weighed a ton. The largest North American species, and probably the largest land tortoise known, was *Testudo locrisekressmanni* from the Pliocene period in Florida. The largest living turtle today is the marine leatherback turtle, which attains a weight of 1,500 pounds (680.4 kg) and extends 12 feet (3.7 m) across the flippers. The largest freshwater turtle in the United States is the alligator snapper, which exceeds 200 pounds (90.7 kg).

The terms *turtle, tortoise,* and *terrapin* are often used interchangeably. A tortoise is strictly a land form which usually has stump-shaped hind limbs with toes that lack webbing. Terrapins are fresh or brackish water species. Regardless of the term applied they are all turtles, that is, reptiles which have the distinctive upper shell called a *carapace* with a flattened lower half covering the ventral side, the *plastron*. The two parts of the shell are joined at the sides by a narrow *bridge*. In some species the plastron is hinged, permitting complete closure of the two shells. The ribs are fused to form the carapace, as are the thoracic, lumbar, and sacral vertebrae. Both the plastron and the carapace consist of an inner layer of bony plates and an outer layer of horny epidermal scutes. In softshell turtles, there are fewer bones in the shell, and they are covered with a leathery skin.

Turtles do not have teeth. The jaws are covered with bony ridges which are very sharp in some species. The snapper and softshell have long necks which extend the head with lighteninglike speed and can catch one unaware with a painful bite. Even the docile box turtle may bite when provoked.

The biology of turtles varies in some details, but is uniform in basic respects. Courtship varies in complexity with different species. For example, the male painted turtle strokes the female's face with his long slender nails as he swims backward in front of her, and the giant tortoise utters loud roars as he pounds the female's body. During copulation, a penis is extruded from the male's vent, thus fertilizing the eggs internally. The eggs, which have hard or leathery calcareous shells, are deposited on land regardless of how aquatic the habits of the turtle may be. The female excavates a depression in the soil or a decaying log into which she places her clutch. In some cases, she expels fluid from the bladder during this activity in order to soften the soil and make digging easier. Mating usually occurs once a year, and a single mating may serve to fertilize eggs for two or three years.

The world's turtle fauna consists of more than 200 species divided into two suborders. The suborder Pleurodira or "side-necked turtles" is restricted in distribution to South America, Africa, Madagascar, New Guinea, and Australia. The suborder Cryptodira contains nine families and 56 genera and is the largest suborder, being represented on every continent except Antarctica. West Virginia has 15 species and subspecies of turtles, but it does not have certain habitats which are conducive to large turtle populations, such as glacial lakes, marine shorelines, or large swamps.

Family Chelydridae • Snapping Turtles

The members of this family are large, vicious, freshwater turtles which are distributed throughout the eastern United States and Canada, Central America, northern South America, and southeast Asia. The family has three genera, one of which is found in West Virginia.

Genus *Chelydra* Schweigger • Snapping Turtles

The genus contains four subspecies. One reaches Mexico, one extends into Ecuador, and the remaining two are found within the United States. The nominate subspecies occurs in West Virginia.

44 Common Snapping Turtle *Chelydra serpentina serpentina* (Linnaeus)
Gr. *chelys,* a tortoise; L. *serpens,* a serpent

Description: The snapping turtle attains a carapace length of over 17 inches (43.2 cm) and may weigh over 40 pounds (18.1 kg). It has a bulky head, a small plastron, and an unusually long tail with a saw-toothed dorsal ridge. The carapace, which is brown to black, is usually covered with algae or mud and has a serrated posterior margin. The plastron is cross-shaped and too small to cover the fleshy underparts, thus leaving them exposed. The small beady eyes are dorsolateral in position and can be seen from above.

Habitat and Habits: Snapping turtles are found in a variety of aquatic habitats. They prefer streams and rivers with muddy bottoms and abundant marginal vegetation. Snappers are occasionally found traveling overland to other water courses. They frequently bury themselves in the mud with just the nostrils and eyes exposed. Snapping turtles are pugnacious, and the bite of a large specimen can be dangerous. They should be carried by the tail with the body free of the ground. Unlike many species of turtles, they rarely bask in the sun, perhaps because they are unable to retain body moisture (Collins 1974).

Snappers are omnivorous. Their food consists of aquatic vegetation and almost any animal life which can be captured (Lagler 1943). One morning, while fishing in the Tygart River at Elkins, N. B. Green saw a large snapping turtle capture a cottontail rabbit which had come down to the edge of the water for a drink.

Breeding: Snapping turtles may mate at any time from April through October. Courtship behavior and mating have been reported by Conant (1951) and Collins (1974). The female may remain fertile for at least three years after one insemination. Nesting probably occurs in June in West Virginia (Loncke and Obbard 1977; Petokas and Alexander 1980). The female excavates a nest 5.0 to 7.0 inches (12.7–17.8 cm) deep in sandy or other soft soil and deposits about 30 white eggs the size of golf balls. The length of the incubation period is dependent upon temperature and other factors. The hatchlings are about 1.5 inches (3.8 cm) in carapace length at birth.

Remarks: Snapping turtles, erroneously referred to as "mud turtles," are well known for their food value, and many rural families view a large snapper as a prize catch. They are often fattened on garbage and table scraps until deemed suitable for consumption. Skunks, raccoons, crows, herons, and many species of fish also prey upon the eggs and young of snapping turtles, as well as those of many other species of turtles.

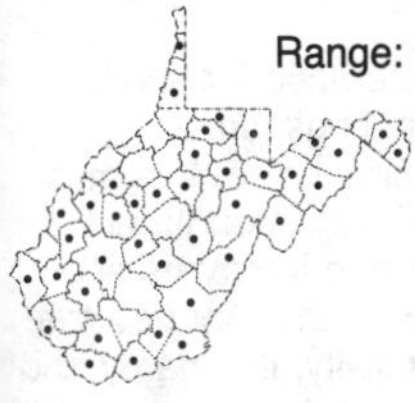

Range: The snapping turtle is found from southern Canada to the Gulf of Mexico and from the Atlantic Coast to the Rocky Mountains. It is widely distributed throughout West Virginia and very common in many localities.

Family Emydidae • Emydid Turtles

The emydids are the most diverse group of modern turtles, as well as the largest family of living turtles. It contains aboout 30 genera with more than 80 species and found throughout the world except in Australia, Antarctica, and central and southern Africa. Most species are aquatic and are referred to as pond turtles, while others are semiaquatic and a few are terrestrial. All have short tails and well-developed shells with the carapace and plastron usually united by a broad, bony bridge. Their diets range from carnivorous to herbivorous. The family includes such well-known species in the eastern United States as the box, spotted, wood, painted, and map turtles. Six genera and nine species occur in West Virginia. For a review of this family and the relationships among the members see McDowell (1964).

Genus *Clemmys* Ritgen • Pond Turtles

These turtles are of medium-size. The shell has a relatively low profile with the plastron firmly united to the carapace. The alveolar surface of the upper jaw is without a median ridge, and the skull has a bony temporal arch. Members of this genus occur in Europe, Asia, North Africa, and North America. Of the four North American species, one is found in the Pacific area and three in the East. Two of these occur in West Virginia.

45 Spotted Turtle *Clemmys guttata* (Schneider)
Gr. *klemmys,* a tortoise; L. *gutta,* a drop, spotted, speckled

Description: The spotted turtle is a small turtle which rarely exceeds 5.0 inches (12.7 cm) in carapace length. The smooth black, or brownish black, and somewhat flattened carapace has from one to several bright yellow or orange circular spots in each scute. The head and neck are black above and marked with a few yellow spots. Ventral surfaces are yellowish with black markings.

Habitat and Habits: The spotted turtles shows a preference for shallow, quiet water and may be found in bogs, small streams, wet meadows, and quarry holes. It is most active during the spring, from March through mid June (Ernst 1976; Ernst 1982) when it may be seen sunning itself on a log, a stump, or the root of a tree projecting from the water. In captivity, it is hardy and omnivorous (i.e., it will accept animal or plant food). In nature, Ernst (1970) found that spotted turtles eat plant matter such as aquatic grasses and filamentous algae, animal matter such as aquatic insect larvae, crustaceans, and snails. Ernst also observed turtles eating *Bufo americanus* tadpoles and carrion.

Breeding: Only scattered observations on the reproductive behavior of this species appeared in the literature until Ernst (1970) reported on a three-year study conducted in southeastern Pennsylvania. He found that in early evening females constructed flask-shaped nests averaging 1.98 inches (5.03 cm) in depth and 1.97 inches (5.01 cm) in diameter. Each nest contained from 3 to 5 white, elliptical, leathery-shelled eggs that averaged 1.3 inches (3.29 cm) in length and 0.7 inch (1.67 cm) in width. Incubation ranged from 70 to 83 days. Nemuras (1967) observes that in the spring young spotted turtles spend much time sunning, but they become very scarce with the onset of hot weather. He theorizes that they hide at this time of the year or may even estivate when it becomes extremely dry.

Range: The spotted turtle occurs from southern Maine south along the Atlantic coastal plain to northern Florida, west into western Georgia, Ohio, Indiana, and Illinois. Only one locality is known for the spotted turtle in West Virginia; a swamp near Charles Town in Jefferson County. Netting (1940) discusses this occurrence along with other factors associated with its capture.

46 **Wood Turtle** *Clemmys insculpta* (LeConte)

L. *insculpo,* to cut in, engrave

Description: The wood turtle is a medium-sized turtle which may attain a carapace length of 9.0 inches (22.9 cm). The shell is very rough; each large scute is composed of a series of grooves and ridges which build up to a point at the center like a pyramid. The plastron is yellow with large, dark brown blotches along the outer margins of the scutes. The skin of the neck and forelegs is often reddish orange. Males have a concave plastron, a longer tail, and a wider head than females.

Habitat and Habits: Wood turtles are both terrestrial and aquatic. In the eastern part of the state they may be found wandering in meadows and woodland, as well as on the highway. They hibernate under water and are often taken from rivers and marshy meadows.

In the early part of the century, the wood turtle was hunted for food but its numbers have declined so that it is no longer commercially profitable. It makes an excellent pet, is not aggressive, and rarely attempts to bite. It eats a variety of animal and vegetable matter (Lagler 1943; Strang 1983).

Breeding: Most observations on reproduction in the wood turtle have been made in captivity. There is a lengthy courtship in which the male and female approach each other with their necks extended and heads held high, then suddenly lowered when they get to within about eight inches (20.3 cm) of each other. They then swing their heads from side to side for several hours without stopping. See Carr (1952) for a more nearly complete description of the mating process. Apparently copulation takes place under water. The female usually lays from 4 to 12 eggs during the afternoon in May or June in a nest excavated on land. Pallas (1960) describes in detail the nesting of a captive specimen. Allen (1955) reports the incubation period as 77 days. The newly hatched young measured 1.6 inches (4.1 cm) in carapace length, with a tail 1.3 inches (3.4 cm) long.

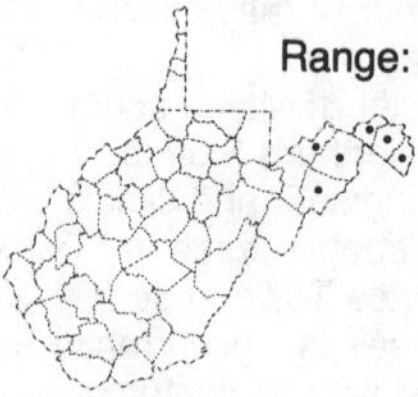

Range: The wood turtle ranges from Nova Scotia south to northern Virginia and west into the Great Lakes region to Minnesota and Iowa. Within West Virginia it is confined to the counties of the Eastern Panhandle with records from Berkeley, Hampshire, Hardy, Jefferson, Mineral, and Morgan counties.

Genus *Terrapene* Merrem • Box Turtles

Box turtles have a high, arched carapace. Their shells can be closed completely because of the hinged lobes of the plastron. There is no temporal arch, and the alveolar surface of the upper jaw is without a ridge. Six species are recognized; two occur in the United States, four in Mexico, and one in West Virginia.

47 Eastern Box Turtle *Terrapene carolina carolina* (Linnaeus)

Terrapene, of Algonquian Indian origin; *carolina,* the locality where first collected

Description: The Eastern box turtle is a medium-sized turtle which may attain a carapace length of 6.0 inches (15.2 cm). The shell is dome-shaped, and the plastron is large, completely filling the opening of the carapace. There is a transverse hinge between the pectoral and abdominal scutes and the underlying bones. This species can withdraw its head, limbs, and tail into the shell and close it tightly. Its carapace color is brown and yellow with variable markings of radiating spots and bars of light colors on a darker background. Concentric growth rings on the scutes are usually evident. Males have a concave plastron, reddish eyes, and the vent opens nearer the tip of the tail than in the female.

Habitat and Habits: Box turtles are more terrestrial than any other species of turtle within the state, and as a result many are killed on the highways. They may be encountered in almost any terrestrial habitat and appear to be more active after summer showers than at any other time. In the autumn they move into valleys where they bury themselves in the mud of a stream bed. They hibernate on land, selecting a shallow depression on a hillside where soil and leaves will provide scanty protection. Box turtles are not aggressive and rarely attempt to bite. They make excellent pets.

Box turles are omnivorous in their diet. They are opportunistic feeders and will vacillate from animal to vegetable matter. They are fond of fruits such as tomatoes and strawberries. Box turtles frequently feed upon mushrooms, but are not affected by those which are poisonous. There are reports of people becoming ill after eating box turtles which had fed upon poisonous fungi.

Breeding: Mating begins shortly before hibernation or after emergence (Ewing 1943). Courtship is rudimentary: the male chases the female with much biting of her head, neck, and the edges of her shell. Evans (1953) provides a detailed description. Nesting occurs from May to July, nearly always in late afternoon and evening. The female selects a nest site in loose or sandy soil. The nest is flask-shaped. She may deposit 2 to 7 (usually 4 or 5) elliptical eggs that usually measure 0.75 by 1.26 inches (1.9 x 3.2 cm). The incubation period is extremely variable and may range from 70 to 90 days. The hatchlings may remain in the nest over winter.

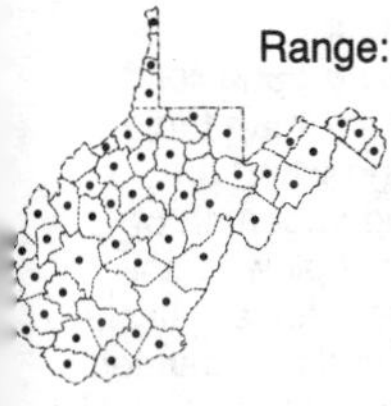

Range: The eastern box turtle ranges from New Hampshire west to Michigan and Illinois and south to Tennessee and Georgia. Within the United States several subspecies of *Terrapene carolina* occur, and wherever two of these races come in contact an intergradation of characters takes place. The species is widely distributed throughout West Virginia.

Genus *Graptemys* Agassiz • Map Turtles and Sawbacks

Members of this genus have a smooth carapace with a dorsal keel. The hind edge of the shell is usually flared and often serrate. The neck and sides of the head have light stripes on a darker background. The genus includes ten species, all of which are confined to the eastern half of the United States and a small portion of Canada. Two species occur in West Virginia.

48 **Map Turtle** *Graptemys geographica* (LeSueur)
Gr. *graptos,* inscribed, painted; *geographica,* the maplike lines on the carapace

Description: The map turtle is a fairly large turtle which may attain a carapace length of nearly 11.0 inches (27.9 cm). The carapace is somewhat flattened, with a distinct dorsal keel and a flared, serrate posterior edge. The shell is covered with an intricate design of yellow lines on a greenish background that resembles the lines on a map. The plastron is yellowish and generally unmarked. The head is greenish and streaked with numerous longitudinal yellow lines. The head pattern nearly always involves a longitudinally elongate spot behind the eye. Both sexes have very broad, smooth jaw surfaces. Males are much smaller, with a relatively smaller head and a much longer and thicker tail.

Habitat and Habits: The map turtle usually prefers large, slow-moving, or quiet bodies of water with aquatic vegetation, a soft bottom, and large logs for basking. Mount (1975) states that it will move up into small brooks. They spend much of their time resting in the sun on the logs. They are gregarious and may congregate in large numbers where conditions are ideal. They are shy and wary and difficult to collect, but may be caught in traps or nets. Their food consists almost exclusively of animal matter in the form of crayfish, snails, mussels, aquatic insects, fish, and some carrion (Lagler 1943). The broad jaws are a special modification for crushing molluscan food.

Breeding: There is little known about the breeding behavior, especially the courtship behavior, of the map turtle. Egg-laying usually takes place in June when the females wander long distances inland in search of suitable nesting places such as freshly plowed soil or clear, dry sand away from water. The nest is a flask-shaped cavity. The eggs are placed in the expanded portion in two layers and usually number from 10 to 16. The average dimensions as listed by Cahn (1937) are 0.83 by 1.26 inches (2.1 x 3.2 cm). Hatching occurs in late August and September.

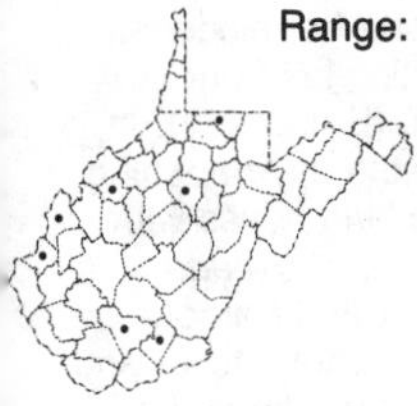

Range: The map turtle occurs from Lake George and Lake Champlain westward through the Great Lakes to Wisconsin and the Mississippi drainage from Minnesota, south to Louisiana and Alabama. The presence of this turtle in West Virginia was first reported by Frum (1947). Since then it has been found in some of the streams of the western part of the state. Many sight records have been made and some of these might be discounted because of the difficulty of distinguishing this species from the Ouachita map turtle (no. 49). There are records from Cabell, Lewis, Mason, Monongalia, Raleigh, Summers, and Wirt counties.

49 **Ouachita Map Turtle** *Graptemys pseudogeographica ouachitensis* Cagle

Named for the Ouachita River which flows through Louisiana

Description: This is a fairly large aquatic turtle which may attain a carapace length of 10.0 inches (25.4 cm) in females. The males are much smaller. The carapace has a median keel which may be accentuated by prominent knobs or blunt spines on at least the second and third vertebrals. The posterior margin of the carapace is serrate. The carapace is grayish brown or greenish with a variable pattern of narrow yellow lines that resembles the map turtle's (no. 48). The plastron is yellowish, with a dark central figure which becomes obscure with age. The undersides of the marginals have concentric dark rings at the seams. The Ouachita map turtle can be further distinguished by the presence of a yellow spot or line behind each eye, one to three light neck lines that reach the eye, and a pair of light spots on the jaws (one below each eye and one on the chin).

Habitat and Habits: The Ouachita map turtle inhabits large impoundments and slow-moving streams. The species is gregarious, especially in its basking habits, and many of these turtles may be observed lined up on stranded logs. It is difficult to capture because of its wariness, but captives are timid and not inclined to bite.

Vogt (1981), in a study of three species of *Graptemys,* concluded that *G. ouachitensis* was an omnivore which specialized in surface feeding. Its diet was composed of about 60 percent vegetation (of which a large amount was the duckweed *Lemna*), transforming mayfly larvae, caddis fly cases, damsel fly larvae, beetles, molluscs, and fish carrion.

Breeding: The male courts the female by biting her hindquarters, forelegs, and head and vibrating his front toenails against her neck and face (Ernst 1974). In addition, Jenkins (1979) observed the male bobbing his head during courtship and touching noses with the female. The nesting habits for *G. p. pseudogeographica* are described by Ernst and Barbour (1972). The egg complement varies from 7 to 13 and is laid in a flask-shaped nest similar to that of the map turtle. The young measure 0.87 to 1.3 inches (2.2–3.4 cm) (Webb 1961).

Range: The Ouachita map turtle range extends from Nebraska, Iowa, Illinois, Indiana, Ohio, and West Virginia, south to the Ouachita River system of northern Louisiana.

The presence of this turtle in West Virginia was first reported by Richmond (1953) on the basis of specimens from the Little Kanawha River near Palestine, Wirt County. To date this is the only locality within the state where it has been collected. Richmond believed that it might have been introduced because the nearest known locality at that time was western Kentucky in the Mississippi Valley and it is one species commonly handled in pet shops. Since Richmond's paper, the species has been found to be abundant in some sections of the Scioto River drainage in Ohio (Conant *et al.* 1964). Apparently West Virginia's is a relict or isolated population. Because of the difficulty in collecting this species and the ease with which it may be confused with the map turtle, it may have a wider range within the state than the record indicates.

Genus *Chrysemys* Gray • Painted Turtles

The painted turtles contain a single species, *Chrysemys picta* (Schneider), whose range includes most of the United States. Four subspecies are recognized, two of which occur in West Virginia. The carapace is smooth, flattened, and unkeeled. It is black to olive in ground color and marked with patterns of red and yellow. The marginals always bear red markings. The plastron is unhinged and yellow, and is joined to the carapace by a bony bridge. The upper jaw is notched in front with tooth-like projections on each side. The feet are moderately webbed. Males have elongated claws on their forefeet and longer tails than females.

50 **Eastern Painted Turtle** *Chrysemys picta picta* (Schneider)

Gr. *chrysos,* gold; Gr. *emys,* a fresh water tortoise; L. *pictus,* painted.

Description: This is a medium-sized turtle which may attain a carapace length of 7.0 inches (17.8 cm). The carapace is smooth, dark brown, and somewhat flattened, with no keels or ridges. The seams of the second and third vertebral scutes are lined up with the seams of the adjacent costals; the front margins of the lateral seams are bordered in tan or yellow, forming lines across the carapace. The plastron is yellow and mostly unmarked. The marginals are conspicuously marked with red. There is a pair of yellow spots behind the eyes. Markings on the legs and other soft parts are red.

Habitat and Habits: Eastern painted turtles are common in areas where creeks, rivers, sloughs, ponds, and swamps provide a habitat with mud or a silty bottom and an abundance of aquatic vegetation. They are fond of basking and are sometimes encountered wandering overland, presumably in search of a new habitat or a nesting site.

Small painted turtles are often kept as pets. They are docile and rarely attempt to bite. They feed on a variety of animal and vegetable food (Knight and Gibbons 1968; Ernst and Barbour 1972). They hibernate in the mud at the bottom of a pond or other quiet body of water, emerging in March or April.

Breeding: Courtship takes place sometime after emergence from hibernation. Ernst (1971) observed courtship from April to mid June and reports that the male swims backward in front of the female and vibrates his elongate front claws while stroking her lores; the female responds by stroking the male's limbs. Copulation follows. Nest-digging and egg-laying take place from mid May to July (Gibbons 1968; Ernst 1971; Mitchell 1985). The female may wander several hundred yards from water in search of a suitable place to dig her nest. The flask-shaped cavity is dug with her hind feet, using first one and then the other. In late afternoon she drops from 4 to 10 eggs into the nest (Cagle 1954; Gibbons 1968), arranging them with one of her hind feet. The eggs are white and elliptical and usually measure 0.55 by 1.3 inches (1.4 x 3.3 cm). After a final watering down of the area with the contents of her urinary bladder, she fills the neck of the nest with a plug of mud and moves back and forth over the nest with her plastron until all evidence of the nest is obliterated. Finneran (1948) reported on four nests in Connecticut and found that the average incubation period was 78 days. Ernst and Barbour (1972) report 76 days to be the average in Pennsylvania. The occurrence of nestlings in early spring, before egg-laying has taken place for that season, leads to the conclusion that hatchlings winter in the nest. Woolverton (1963) studied a nest of hatchlings in Minnesota throughout the winter and observed their emergence the following spring.

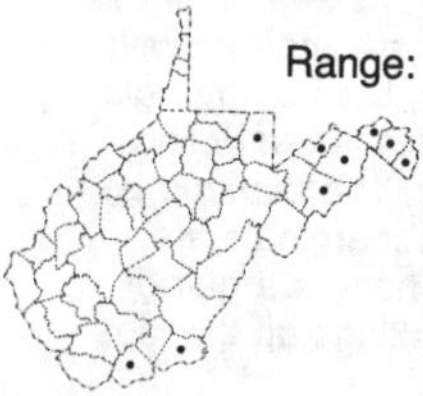

Range: The eastern painted turtle is found from Nova Scotia to Alabama. In West Virginia it intergrades with *Chrysemys picta marginata* (no. 51) in the Eastern Panhandle, as well as in Monroe, Summers, and Mercer counties. Hoffman (1949) lists turtles along the Virginia–West Virginia border in the James River drainage of Monroe County as intergrades between *picta* and *marginata.* Seidel (1982) discusses the influence of the Roanoke and James river drainage systems on the turtle fauna of the upper New River system.

51 Midland Painted Turtle *Chrysemys picta marginata* Agassiz

L. *margo,* edge or border

Description: This turtle is very similar to the eastern painted turtle (no. 50) in size and coloration. It differs in that the seams of the pleurals alternate with those of the vertebrals, and the plastron bears a dark central figure which varies in size and shape.

This turtle occupies habitats similar to those of its eastern relative. Food habits (Raney and Lachner 1942), breeding habits, and a strongly developed basking habit are all similar.

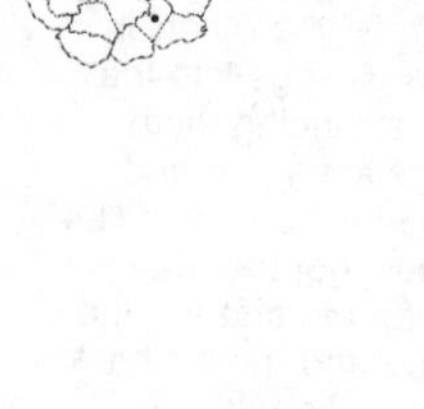

Range: The midland painted turtle ranges from Quebec and southern Ontario to Alabama. In West Virginia the main ridge of the Alleghenies, which divides the eastern Potomac drainage from the western Ohio River drainage, separates the range of the midland painted turtle from that of the eastern painted turtle. This is an area where the ranges overlap and many of the painted turtles are intergrades, having characteristics of both subspecies. Midland painted turtles are widely distributed throughout the section of West Virginia which lies west of the Alleghenies, the Allegheny Plateau.

Genus *Trachemys* Agassiz • Sliders

The genus (or subgenus) *Trachemys* (Agassiz 1857) occupies a taxonomically controversial position along with *Chrysemys* and *Pseudemys* (McDowell 1964). Seidel and Smith (1986) have proposed the substitution of *Trachemys* for *Pseudemys* in the *scripta* group. According to McDowell (1964), *Trachemys* contains forms with a rounded ventral surface of the dentary, no anterior cusp on the middle ridge of the upper triturating surface and three phalanges on the fifth toe. The use of the genus name *Trachemys* in place of *Pseudemys* for the red-eared slider is based on the research and recommendation of Michael Seidel of Marshall University.

52 **Red-eared Slider** *Trachemys scripta elegans* Wied

Gr. *trachy,* false; Gr. *emys,* a fresh water tortoise; L. *scriptus,* written; L. *elegans,* neat, elegant

Description: This is a medium-sized turtle which may attain a carapace length of 10.0 inches (25.4 cm). The short elliptical carapace is evenly convex and rather low and flattened. The posterior margin flares outward and is moderately serrate. The ground color of the carapace is brown or olive brown with yellow and black lines, mostly in a transverse pattern. The plastron is yellow and usually has black eye-like markings or smudges on each of the scutes. The most distinctive feature is a broad red stripe behind each eye.

Males are somewhat smaller than females. The vent opening of the male is on the tail beyond the posterior edge of the shell, while that of the female does not extend beyond the edge. Another sexually dimorphic difference is that older males tend to become darker. This gradual darkening of the shell and soft parts eventually obscures the typical pattern and may become so developed that identification is very difficult (Carr 1952).

Habitat and Habits: The red-eared slider is aquatic and shows a preference for the quiet water of oxbows and sloughs with ample basking sites, mud bottoms, and aquatic vegetation. It is occasionally found in swamps and shallow water, preferably two to three feet (61.0 to 91.4 cm) deep. The adults may be observed floating lazily on the surface.

Adults are generally herbivores but will eat animal food when it is available (Clark and Gibbons 1969). Juveniles eat more animal matter in the form of aquatic insects (Hart 1983). Their flesh is edible, and a large individual may provide enough meat to make cleaning it worthwhile.

Breeding: Jackson and Davis (1972) describe the courtship behavior of the red-eared slider: the male swims behind his mate and may display a short period of cloacal sniffing; he maneuvers into a frontal position facing her and extends his arms in a signaling position; the male titillates the female, moves behind her, and mating occurs. Several males may simultaneously court the same female (Minton 1972). Nesting takes place in May or June. The female selects the nesting site in the morning or late afternoon and begins excavating. If she is disturbed she will abandon the nesting site permanently (Cagle 1937). She deposits from 5 to 22 eggs, the number varying according to the size of the female. Hatchlings may emerge in two to two-and-one-half months, but most overwinter in the nest. Males mature in two to five years (Cagle 1948).

Range: The range of the red-eared slider extends from the United States to Argentina. Relict colonies occur in Michigan, Ohio, Kentucky, and West Virginia. Its presence in West Virginia was discovered by Adler (1968), who collected four specimens from a lagoon along the Kanawha River in Putnam County. Seidel and Green (1981) discuss its status and range in West Virginia.

Genus *Pseudemys* Gray • Cooters and Redbelly Turtles

The members of this genus are medium-sized to large turtles. Their range extends from the northeastern United States to New Mexico. The alveolar surfaces of the upper jaw of the members of this genus always have an elevation parallel with the edge; this may be a continuous ridge or a row of more or less conical tubercles. The carapace of the adult may or may not be keeled; in either case, it is usually somewhat wrinkled and has a serrate hind margin. Two species are found in West Virginia: *Pseudemys concinna* LeConte, represented by two subspecies, and *P. rubriventris.*

On numerous occasions herpetologists have proposed the splitting of *Pseudemys* or combining it with other genera. Such was the case when McDowell (1964) placed *Pseudemys* in the genus *Chrysemys* on the basis of skull characters. Recently, Vogt and McCoy (1980), on the basis of new biochemical data and other morphological evidence, concluded that *Chrysemys* and *Pseudemys* were distinct lineages. Most recently, Seidel and Smith (1986) have separated *Trachemys* (*scripta*) from the genus *Pseudemys.*

53 Eastern River Cooter *Pseudemys concinna concinna* (LeConte)
Gr. *pseud,* false; Gr. *emyd,* a freshwater tortoise; L. *concinnus,* neat, skillfully joined

Description: Females may attain a carapace length of 12.0 inches (30.5 cm); the males are somewhat smaller. The carapace is flattened (i.e., it lacks a keel) and serrated on the rear edge, and it is usually pinched inward in front of the hind legs. The river cooter is dark in color with numerous concentric markings and usually has a light C-shaped mark on the second costal scute. The plastron is yellow, usually with a dark pattern that is especially apparent along the margins of the scutes. The smooth upper jaw may be notched at the tip. The legs, neck, and head are brown or dark olive with yellow stripes. Almost all the marginals have dark, doughnut-shaped markings. The alveolar surface of the lower jaws is relatively narrow, without high, isolated conical "teeth" on the median ridge. Males have long claws on the forefeet, and the vent is close to the tip of the tail.

Habitat and Habits: The river cooter's preferred habitat is a quiet backwater associated with a large, open body of water. It is fond of basking. Because of its wariness, it is very difficult to capture; in fact, it is difficult to approach closely enough to identify. According to Brimley (1939–1943) and Seidel (1982), the adults are entirely herbivorous since all efforts to get captives to feed on animal food failed.

Breeding: The literature contains few references to the breeding behavior of this particular subspecies, but it is probably the same as or similar to other subspecies of *Pseudemys concinna.* In courtship the male approaches the female from above and vibrates his long claws against her head. After mating, nesting takes place in late May or early June in sandy soil on elevated ground near the water. Nests may occur 100 yards or more from water (Robert Mount, personal communication). The female deposits up to 19 pinkish white eggs which are about 0.98 by 1.5 inches (2.5 x 3.8 cm). Hatching occurs in August or September, and most hatchlings remain through the winter in the nest.

On July 14, 1983, Michael Seidel (Marshall University) observed nesting behavior of *P.c. concinna* at the Bluestone Reservoir, Summers County. At 11:45 A.M., air temperature 87.8° F (31° C) in direct sunlight, a large female (12.0 inches or 30.5 cm carapace length) was digging a flask-shaped nest in an open area (camp site) 26 feet (7.9 m) from the water's edge. The hole, which she excavated with her hind claws and moistened with bladder contents, was 5.0 inches (12.7 cm) deep with an opening 2.7 inches (6.8 cm) in diameter. The turtle abandoned the site before depositing eggs.

Range: The river cooter ranges from the coastal plain of southeastern Virginia south to eastern Alabama. In West Virginia this species has been found in Fayette and Summers counties. A population of cooters in Bluestone Reservoir and adjacent portions of the New River, formerly identified as *Chrysemys floridana* (Bayless 1972) has been reidentified as *Pseudemys c. concinna* (Seidel 1982). In his report Seidel comments on the probable origin and relationship of this disjunct population.

54 **Hieroglyphic Turtle** *Pseudemys concinna hieroglyphica* (Holbrook)

Gr. *hieros,* sacred; Gr. *glyphe,* a carving (mysterious markings)

Description: Adult females may attain a carapace length of 13.8 inches (35.0 cm). The carapace is dark brown to olive with an intricate pattern of yellow lines and a C-shaped mark on the second costal. The carapace is relatively long and narrow and oftentimes constricted in front of the hind legs with the marginals flaring posterior to the constriction. The plastron is yellow with dark pigment along the plastral seams. The cutting edge of the upper jaw is smooth; the alveolar surfaces of the lower jaw are relatively broad with a few high, isolated conical "teeth" on the median ridge.

Males are somewhat smaller than females. The digits of the front toes of the males bear long curved claws and the tail is thicker and longer with the vent located beyond the edge of the carapace.

Habitat and Habits: These turtles are usually found in large, shallow oxbow ponds which communicate with a larger stream or river. This is especially true during flood stage. They avoid swift water and are occasionally found in isolated lakes. Their diet may contain both animal and vegetable matter, depending upon the time of the year, the age of the turtle, and the availability of the food.

Breeding: While little data are available on this subspecies, the breeding behavior is most likely similar to that of the river cooter (no. 53).

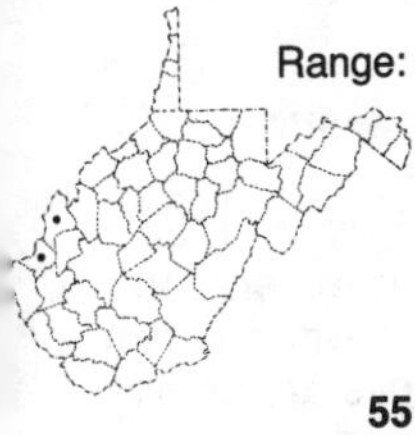

Range: The hieroglyphic turtle ranges from southern Illinois and southeastern Kansas south to eastern Texas, central Alabama, and northern Louisiana. Specimens are known from the Ohio River drainage from Cabell and Mason counties (Seidel and Green 1982).

55 Redbelly Turtle *Pseudemys rubriventris rubriventris* (LeConte)
L. *rubeo,* to be red; L. *venter,* the belly

Description: This turtle may reach a carapace length of 15.0 inches (38.1 cm). There is a notch in the upper jaw with a cusp on each side, and both jaws are strongly serrate on the cutting edges. The color above is dark brown or nearly black, with a transverse, laterally branching reddish bar on each of the first three costals. The plastron is usually pinkish or reddish with some large gray smudges. Older males are likely to be melanistic.

Habitat and Habits: The redbelly turtle occurs in deep ponds, lakes, streams, and rivers. It has been collected in swift water as well as slow-moving water. It selects basking sites near deep water for escape routes. Although it is mostly herbivorous, food items also include such animal matter as snails, crayfish, and tadpoles.

Breeding: After courtship and mating, nesting takes place in June and July. The number of eggs deposited is related to the size of the turtle; a large redbelly may deposit up to 35 eggs. Graham (1971) observed a female depositing 17 eggs on June 30 in his laboratory. These eggs averaged 1.3 inches (3.4 cm) in length and 0.94 inch (2.4 cm) in width. They hatched on September 11. The hatchlings may remain within the nest until the following spring.

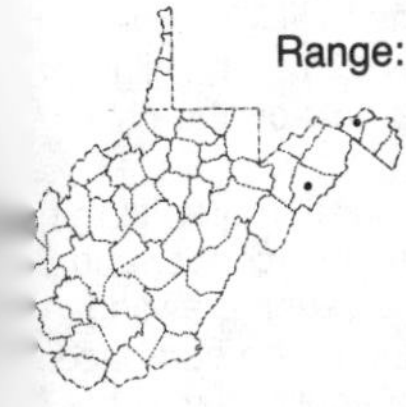

Range: The redbelly occurs on the mid-Atlantic coastal plain from New Jersey south to North Carolina and west to West Virginia. Wilson and Friddle (1949) report on three places in eastern West Virginia, where this species has been collected, all within the Potomac drainage. On May 23, 1981, Michael Seidel of Marshall University obtained a specimen of the redbelly turtle about a mile south of Fisher, Hardy County. The turtle had been recently shot and was lying on the bank. Rodney Bartgis of the West Virginia chapter of the Nature Conservancy has reported on sightings in Back Creek near Hedgesville in Berkeley County and in the Shenandoah River near Millville in Jefferson County.

Family Kinosternidae • Musk and Mud Turtles

The kinosternids (from the Greek *kineo,* to move, movement, and *sternon,* breast or chest) include four genera of New World turtles commonly referred to as musk and mud turtles. These are small turtles with dome-shaped carapaces, chin barbels, and ten or eleven marginal scutes on the plastron. Much of their time is spent walking on the bottom of a stream or pond or basking in shallow water with the upper part of the carapace exposed. All members of the family have two pairs of odor-producing musk glands beneath the border of the carapace. They are largely carnivorous. One genus (*Sternotherus*) occurs in West Virginia.

Genus *Sternotherus* Gray • Musk Turtles

In this genus the plastron is cruciform and is smaller than the carapace opening. The common name derives from its ability to produce a musklike odor from the marginal glands. There are four species in North America; one of these occurs in West Virginia.

56 Stinkpot *Sternotherus odoratus* (Latrielle)
Gr. *sternon,* breast; Gr. *thairos,* hinge; L. *odorus,* odorous

Description: The stinkpot may attain a carapace length of 5.0 inches (12.7 cm). The carapace is smooth, olive brown to black, highly domed, and frequently covered with algae. The plastron is small with 11 scutes and a single hinge. The tail in the male (and occasionally the female) ends in a horny "nail." The head, which is large for the size of the turtle, has two light yellow stripes on each side and barbels on the chin and throat.

Habitat and Habits: The stinkpot is seldom found on land. It frequents the shallow water of creeks, rivers, swamps, ponds, and lakes. In deep water it will usually be seen crawling leisurely over the bottom. The shape of the carapace and the algal covering provide a camouflage which enables the turtle to escape detection by predators.

Stinkpots are usually bad-tempered. One should be careful when handling them since the neck is sufficiently long and the jaws are sharp enough to inflict a wound. When first captured the musk turtle may release a musky odor from the secretions of two pairs of glands lying beneath the border of the carapace.

Stinkpots emerge from hibernation around the middle of April. There is evidence that they hibernate in large groups in the mud at the bottom of streams (McCauley 1945). On warm sunny days following emergence, stinkpots, fond of climbing, may be seen in small saplings up to 3 feet (91.4 cm) above the ground overhanging the water. When disturbed, they drop into the water and swim to safety.

These turtles eat both animal and vegetable matter (Lagler 1943; Mahmoud 1968). Smaller items are swallowed whole, but larger items are torn apart by their strong jaws. They will devour almost any small aquatic creature they can catch. Occasionally they feed upon carrion.

Breeding: Mating in the stinkpot occurs in the spring shortly after emergence from hibernation and occasionally in the fall. Egg-laying extends from May through June (Tinkle 1961). The eggs are deposited in a variety of places such as decaying stumps and logs, sand, and abandoned muskrat houses, all of which are located close to the shore of the stream or lake. From 2 to 5 eggs are usually deposited in the nest, although there may be as many as 9. The eggs (usually 0.59 x 1.0 in. or 1.5 x 2.6 cm) are white and elliptical with a brittle shell. Barbour (1971) states that the eggs may be deposited on the surface and not covered at all. From 60 to 90 days are required for incubation.

Range: The stinkpot occurs from New England and southern Ontario to southern Florida, west to Wisconsin and Texas. It is widely distributed throughout West Virginia.

Family Trionychidae • Softshell Turtle

Trionychid turtles are characterized by an incomplete or reduced plastron. The carapace is flattened like a pancake with the peripheral bones lost. Each forefoot bears three claws. Softshells are excellent swimmers. All species are carnivorous. They may be short-tempered and quick to bite. The snout is long and thin and serves as a snorkel as the turtle lies buried in the mud or sand. The largest is *Chitra indica* which usually attains a carapace length of over 3 feet (91.4 cm).

The softshelled turtles of the genus *Trionyx* are an ancient and widespread group. They are known to exist as far back as the Jurassic period (Webb 1962). The family includes 26 or so species in 7 genera with 3 of these in North America, 6 in Africa and about 17 in Asia.

Genus *Trionyx* Geoffroy • Softshell Turtles

The genus occurs in North America, northern Africa, southern Asia, and Indonesia and contains about 15 species. Two species are found in West Virginia.

57 Eastern Spiny Softshell *Trionyx spiniferus spiniferus* (LeSueur)
Gr. *treis,* three; Gr. *onyx,* nail or talon; L. *spini,* a spine, thorn; L. *fer,* to bear

Description: Adult females may attain a carapace length of 18.0 inches (45.7 cm). Adult males are about half that size. These are very distinctive turtles with flat, pancakelike shells with flexible margins. The carapace is gray or olive with many dark eyespots along the front area; these markings are fewer toward the rear. The anterior area of the carapace has numerous small spines which impart a rough, sandpapery surface to the shell. The plastron is small, cruciform, and leaves much of the soft underpart exposed. The feet are strongly streaked and spotted. The head is long with a pointed snout, and the nostrils have a lateral ridge extending from the septum. There is a dark-bordered light stripe on each side of the head.

Habitat and Habits: Softshells are strictly aquatic and are found on land only when depositing eggs. They are equally at home in shallow or deep water and their excellent swimming ability makes them difficult to catch. They may occasionally be found basking on logs, but they prefer to float on the surface in large bodies of water. Visitors to Jackson's Mill, Lewis County, will not forget the experience of standing on the swinging bridge over the backwater of the West Fork River and counting the large spiny softshells as they float lazily underneath the bridge.

Although they are strong, fast swimmers, they are frequently observed floating on the surface of quiet water or buried in the sand or mud of shallow water with just the proboscis above the surface. They are difficult animals to hold because of their short tails and long claws which can produce deep scratches. Their long necks can be extended suddenly and their sharp jaws can inflict a painful wound.

Spiny softshells are mostly carnivorous, eating insect adults and larvae, crayfish, worms, snails, fish, and so forth. Food studies by Lagler (1943), Williams and Christiansen (1981), and Cochran and McConville (1983) showed that food is mainly animal but a fair amount of plant material is consumed. It is not known whether plant matter is consumed intentionally or incidentally. Their flesh is highly esteemed, and a turtle hunter will catch them by "noodling"—creeping along the bank and running his hand and arm up into the burrow, hoping to grasp one from behind.

Breeding: Adults emerge from hibernation in mud or sand at the bottom of a pond or stream in April or May. Mating occurs shortly after emergence, and egg-laying follows in late June. A few eggs are deposited in the bottom of the hole and covered with soil, and the process is repeated until the clutch is complete and the cavity filled. The female packs the soil down and reenters the water. The clutch may contain from 10 to 25 spherical, white, and thick-shelled eggs. Hatchlings usually emerge from August to October, but may remain in the nest until the following spring. For a detailed review of the natural history of the spiny and smooth softshell turtles see Webb (1962).

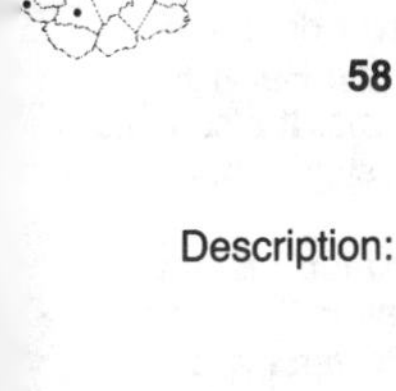

Range: The eastern spiny softshell ranges from western New York to Wisconsin and south to the Tennessee River. In West Virginia it occurs west of the Allegheny Mountains to the Ohio Valley.

58 Midland Smooth Softshell *Trionyx muticus muticus* LeSueur
L. *muticus,* curtailed, unarmed

Description: Females may attain a carapace length of 14.0 inches (35.6 cm); males are somewhat smaller. This species is very similar to the spiny softshell (no. 57), but lacks spines or tubercles along the anterior edge of the carapace, the sandpapery surface of the shell, and the dark streaks or spots (for the most part) on the feet, and the ridges in the nostrils. The carapace is dark olive to light yellowish brown.

Habitat and Habits: The smooth softshell generally occurs in the same habitats as the spiny softshell. However, Fitch and

Plummer (1975) found that they prefer streams with sand and a swift current. Plummer (1977a) states that males prefer areas near sandbars and females prefer steep mud banks near deep water. Smooth softshell turtles spend much of their time in water but may emerge to bask or feed at the water's edge. Food is similar to that of *T. spiniferus,* that is, primarily animal material. However, Plummer and Farrar (1981) found that fruits and cottonwood seed were consumed when available.

Breeding: Courtship occurs generally in the spring; it involves rapid surface swimming and some nudging with the snout on the banks. Mating occurs in deep water (Plummer 1977b). Nesting takes place chiefly in June and July, usually on sandbars free of vegetation. Small, permanent islands high enough to be relatively safe from flooding are especially favored. While nests are sometimes near cottonwood saplings or weeds, they are always on bare sand in places free of roots. Eggs are laid in one or two layers, in sand that is slightly damp—not saturated. They are spherical in shape and have white, calcareous hard, fragile shells. Plummer (1977b) reports the average clutch size to be 11 eggs, and two or more clutches may be deposited per season. The number of eggs per clutch apparently varies according to latitude. Webb (1962) suggests that in northern populations the eggs are smaller, there are more per clutch, and only one clutch per season, whereas in southern populations the eggs are larger and fewer per clutch. Webb found the clutch difference between the northern and southern populations to occur in the spiny softshell turtles (no. 57) as well. This trend has been observed in other North American freshwater turtles.

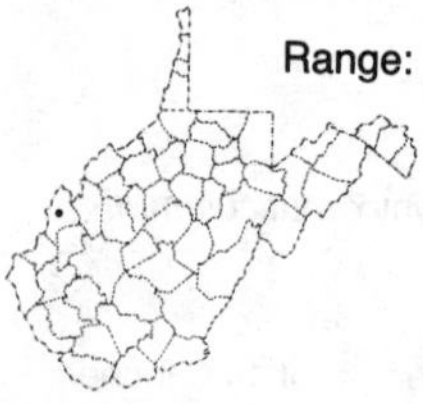

Range: *Trionyx muticus* occurs in the Mississippi Basin, including the entire Ohio River drainage of the eastern United States, the Missouri River drainage (except its northwestern part) and the Red River drainage of the southern Great Plains. It also occurs in several adjacent smaller river systems that empty into the Gulf of Mexico.

The only well-documented record for this turtle in West Virginia (WVBS 3760) was taken by Richard Workman, a student at Marshall University, on July 2, 1968, in Ten Mile Creek, Mason County. The specimen was a female with a carapace length of 8.3 inches (21.0 cm).

ORDER SQUAMATA—LIZARDS AND SNAKES
Suborder Sauria—Lizards

Lizards are elongated reptiles which are sometimes confused with salamanders, whose body form is somewhat similar. The lizard body is covered with scales, eyelids are present, and most have external ear openings. The cloacal opening is a transverse slit, and in the male the pair of saclike hemipenes are everted from the basal portion of the tail during copulation. Most lizards have four limbs, each of which bears five toes with claws. Some burrowing forms have lost their toes and in some cases even the limbs.

Lizards have a worldwide distribution. They are found in greatest abundance in warm, dry regions, but their habitats may be subterranean, arboreal, or even aquatic. The approximately 3,000 species are grouped into 18 families, of which two are represented by five species in West Virginia's lizard fauna.

None of our local species is venomous, although specimens may attempt to bite when handled. Their food consists mainly of insects and other small invertebrates. All local species lay eggs, which are usually deposited in soil, sawdust piles, under rocks, or in a decayed stump or log. Lizards are agile and swift-footed and masters of escape. A collector must resort to many devices to assure capture and handle the prize very cautiously to avoid losing its tail.

Family Iguanidae • Iguanas

The iguanids (from the Spanish *iguana,* the name of a large lizard) comprise the largest family of lizards in the New World. In tropical Central and South America some species of iguanids may attain a length of 6 feet (1.8 m), and are used as food by the natives. The members of this family differ from those of the only other lizard family in West Virginia, the Scincidae, by the presence of rough scales (keeled) and femoral pores. Our only representative is a common species found around abandoned farm buildings and rock piles. It can be recognized by the head-bobbing antics which are characteristic of members of the family.

Genus *Sceloporus* Wiegmann • Spiny Lizards

These are small- to moderate-sized lizards with strongly keeled scales which are sometimes sharply pointed and bristling. It is the largest genus of lizards in the United States, with 17 species. *Sceloporus* extends from Washington east to southern Pennsylvania and southeastern New York, south to Central America. The genus name refers to the femoral pores.

59 **Northern Fence Lizard** *Sceloporus undulatus hyacinthinus* (Green)
Gr. *scelo,* leg; Gr. *poros,* pore; L. *undulatus,* to rise in waves; *hyacinth,* a mythological character

Description: This is a medium-sized lizard which may attain a total length of 7.0 inches (17.8 cm). The overlapping scales are keeled, each with a terminating spine. The color varies with age and sex. Females and young are gray to brown or tan with a series of dark, wavy crossbands on the back and a cream or light tan venter with some small dark flecks. Adult males are dark gray or brown with the dorsal bands less distinct and often obscure in older specimens. The belly and throat of the male have conspicuous patches of iridescent blue, bordered with black. If the tail is intact, it is slender and tapering, longer than the rest of the animal. In those with regenerated tails, the new growth is easily distinguished from the original portion. Occasionally the broken segment is not completely discarded so that the new section, along with the original section, forms a forked tail.

Habitat and Habits: Fence lizards are found in dry, open, wooded areas around abandoned farm buildings, old fences, slab piles, and stone outcrops. When approached they escape by climbing the nearest tree and keeping the trunk between themselves and their enemy. On sunny days they may be found basking on a fence rail or rock.

Their food consists of a large variety of insects and other small invertebrates. The lizard will eat any moving prey which it can catch and subdue. It can see small objects at a distance of a few feet and quickly react to anything in motion.

Breeding: Mating activities begin shortly after the lizards emerge from hibernation in late March or early April. The males set up small territories and defend them vigorously against other males. Courting males indicate their territory by head bobbing and "push-ups." If a female enters a male's territory, courtship and mating may occur. Egg-laying usually takes place during May and June. (These mating and egg-deposition dates agree with those established by Marion [1970, 1982] in Missouri, which is approximately the same latitude as West Virginia.) The elliptical eggs are deposited in a nest dug by the female in soil or under or within a decayed log or stump. The eggs average 0.29 inch by 0.46 inch or 0.74 by 1.16 cm (Trautwein 1983) and usually number 6.3 per clutch (Tinkle and Ballinger 1972). The incubation period is approximately 45 days (Trautwein 1983). Older females may deposit more than one clutch a season.

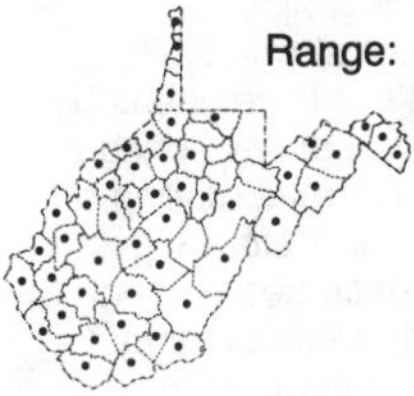

Range: The northern fence lizard ranges from southeastern New York to southern South Carolina, west to eastern Kansas and central Texas. In the deep southeast, it is replaced by the southern fence lizard with which it interbreeds along a zone of contact. Records throughout West Virginia indicate its widespread distribution. It probably occurs within every county in the state.

Family Scincidae • Skinks

This large family contains about 50 genera with over 600 species, only a small number of which live in the New World. Three genera are represented in the United States, and two of these occur in West Virginia. The family is characterized by smooth, flat, overlapping scales, the presence of osteoderms, and the absence of femoral pores. Its members are alert and agile; they may be terrestrial, fossorial, or arboreal.

Genus *Scincella* Mittleman • Window-eyed Skinks

The genus contains more than 40 species, with 7 species in North and Central America. One species occurs in West Virginia. The genus has, at times, been included in *Leiolopisma* and at other times in *Lygosoma*.

60 Ground Skink *Scincella lateralis* (Say)

L. *scincela,* little skink; L. *lateris,* the side, flank

Description: The ground skink is a slender, elusive, secretive lizard which rarely exceeds a total length of 4.0 inches (10.2 cm). Its scales are smooth and overlapping. The lower eyelid has a transparent "window." The dorsal color is a rich bronze-brown, flecked with black. A distinct dark stripe extends down each side from behind the eye onto the tail. The skink bears a superficial resemblance to the two-lined salamander (no. 27) from which it can be distinguished by its scales and claws. The ventral surface is yellowish to grayish white.

Habitat and Habits: The ground skink inhabits dry, open woodland where it is more often heard than seen as it scurries among the dry leaves for concealment. It is truly a ground skink; it rarely climbs. It is often overlooked except for those who know how to find it. According to Barbour (1971) "there is a simple technique by which one can see a ground skink almost at will. Walk silently and slowly (at a rate of 30 or fewer steps per minute) along a woodland path on a sunny spring or summer day. Listen carefully for the faint rustling of the leaves as the skinks scurry over them. By going slowly and silently, one can approach near enough to hear the animals and often see them before they disappear under the leaf mold. It is not uncommon for a particularly alert person to see a dozen or so within a space of a few hundred yards in some areas."

Ground skinks eat small insects, millipedes, centipedes, spiders, isopods, and other invertebrates (Brooks 1963). They spend the winter in rock crevices and in tunnels left by rotting roots below the frost line. They make their appearance with the first warm days of spring, but do not become active until sometime in April.

Breeding: Mating occurs soon after emergence from hibernation. The eggs are deposited under a rock or in rotting wood or soil. On June 24, 1963, a female which had been collected the day before in Wayne County deposited 3 eggs in the laboratory. Each egg was approximately 0.24 by 0.39 inch (0.6 x 1.0 cm). This species of lizard may produce several clutches in a season, each clutch containing 1 to 5 eggs. For additional information on the ecology of the ground skink, see Brooks (1967).

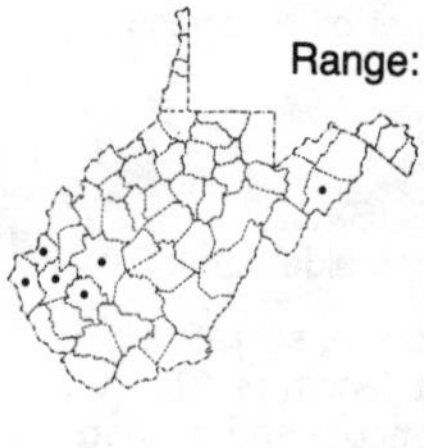

Range: The ground skink ranges from southern New Jersey to the Florida Keys, west to eastern Kansas and central Texas. It was first reported in West Virginia by Wilson (1941) on the basis of two specimens from Hardy County. In 1950 Wilson and Friddle reported an additional three specimens from the same county. In both Cabell and Wayne counties, numerous specimens have been collected within a small area, thus suggesting the presence of well-defined colonies. Because of its secretive habits, it is possible the species is not always observed and it therefore may have a much broader distribution than the records indicate.

Genus *Eumeces* Wiegmann • Striped Skinks

The members of this genus are elongate, smooth, shiny-scaled lizards that may have longitudinal stripes along the body. The genus occurs in North and Central America, Africa, and Asia and contains about 40 species. Three species are known from West Virginia.

61 Five-lined Skink *Eumeces fasciatus* (Linnaeus)

L. *fasciatus,* to envelop with bands

Description: This is a medium-sized, smooth, shiny-scaled lizard that may attain a total length of 8.0 inches (20.3 cm). The juveniles have bright blue tails which become brown as the lizard grows older. Adults have five longitudinal yellow or white stripes on a black background, but these also become less distinct as the lizards grow older. The females may retain some traces of the stripes, but old males lose them completely, becoming uniform olive or brown on the trunk and tail. Older males develop rusty-red coloration on the head and often have entirely red heads. The belly color varies from pale cream to pale olive.

Confusing Species: The five-lined skink is known locally as the blue-tailed scorpion or just as a scorpion. Because of the similarity in coloration it is easily confused with the broadhead skink (no. 62), known locally as the red-headed scorpion, but the two can be distinguished on the basis of scale characteristics. Five-lined skinks have 26 to 30 scale rows at midbody; the broadhead has 30 to 32 rows. The five-lined has four labials anterior to the subocular, and the broadhead usually has five (check the diagram in the key). The five-lined has two enlarged postlabials, and the broadhead has at most one enlarged postlabial. These differences notwithstanding, confusion may still exist in identification and it may be necessary to secure an expert's opinion on the matter.

Habitat and Habits: The five-lined skink is our most common smooth-scaled lizard. It occurs in a wide variety of habitats such as around abandoned barns and houses or in cut-over woods where there are stumps, sawdust piles, and rock piles. They may also be found by peeling the dead bark from standing or fallen trees. These skinks are essentially terrestrial and rarely climb trees for any distance. Fitch (1954) found their moisture requirements higher than those of other species. They usually seek a slightly damp environment and occasionally may be found around pond margins and along streams. Five-lined skinks are also found in dry areas as reported by Wilson and Friddle (1950): "We have a few records from dry, sandy soil and one individual from the shale barrens of Hardy County."

Five-lined skinks winter in burrows in the earth and in rock crevices below the frost line. They emerge with the first warm days in March to bask in the sun, but do not become active until early April. Their food consists of spiders as well as a large assortment of insects (Fitch 1970; Groves 1982) and other invertebrates. They have been known to feed on their own eggs as well as their hatchlings.

Breeding: Courtship and mating occur in May. The males are aggressive, but not territorial. Violent encounters for mates may ensue between males, especially the older ones with red heads. During early June the female deposits her clutch of eggs under a rotten log or beneath a sizeable stone. The number of eggs deposited varies from 4 to 16 (Fitch 1954). A female with a nest containing 13 eggs was found on June 29, 1949, in Wayne County. The eggs were brought into the laboratory, and they hatched on July 15, measuring 0.39 by 0.51 inches (1.0 x 1.3 cm) (Green, personal observation). It has been found that more than one female may share a communal nesting area but the nests are separate (Fitch 1954). The female stays with her eggs and protects them against intruders. After hatching, the young may remain in the nest for a day or so before leaving.

Range: The five-lined skink ranges from New England to northern Florida, west to Wisconsin and eastern Kansas, Oklahoma, and Texas. It is distributed throughout West Virginia.

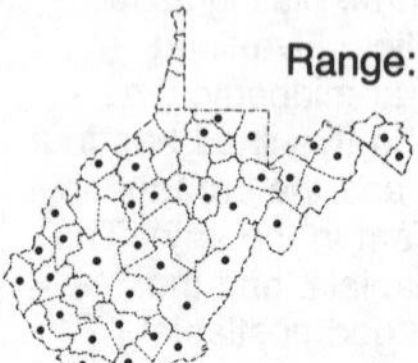

62 Broadhead Skink *Eumeces laticeps* (Schneider)

L. *latos,* broad; NL. *ceps,* head

Description: The broadhead is our largest skink and may attain a total length of 12.0 inches (30.5 cm). The juveniles are similar in appearance to the five-lined skink (no. 61) except for scale arrangement. Older specimens lose their longitudinal stripes and blue tails at a larger size than the five-lined. Big olive-brown males with rusty heads broadened in the temporal region are feared by many people throughout Appalachia. Its bite may be painful but is not poisonous. The chin scale is composed of two postmentals, and the underside of the tail has a middle row of scales noticeably wider than the adjacent row of scales; the upper labials usually number eight; the enlarged postlabials are absent or, if present, there is usually just one on each side.

Habitat and Habits: In West Virginia the broadhead skink is much less abundant than the five-lined skink. It is the most arboreal of our skinks, and it readily takes to a nearby tree when encountered. It is rare to find one any distance from a tree. They make use of hollow trees and holes in trees and occasionally hide under loosened bark. They occupy wooded areas or woodland borders where they may be found among scattered debris, trash, and brush piles. Moehn (1980) found the broadhead skink in Illinois to be mostly a ground-dweller with a woodland edge habitat.

Their food includes spiders, insects, and other arthropods. Carr (1940) observed them feeding on wood-boring insects and their larvae. Minton (1972) states that a broadhead skink ate a specimen of *Scincella* and badly mauled a five-lined skink in his collecting bag.

Breeding: Little is known about their mating behavior in the northeastern United States although Carr (1940) observed broadhead skinks mating on May 2 in Florida. A nest containing 20 eggs, along with an adult female 8.8 inches (22.3 cm) long, was opened in the loose soil of a flower bed in Spring Valley, Wayne County, on August 4, 1952. The eggs, which hatched in the laboratory, produced brightly striped young with bright blue tails. They ranged from 2.7 to 2.9 inches (7.0–7.4 cm) total length (Green, personal observation). Fitch (1970) discusses the various studies of the reproductive cycle of this species of skink.

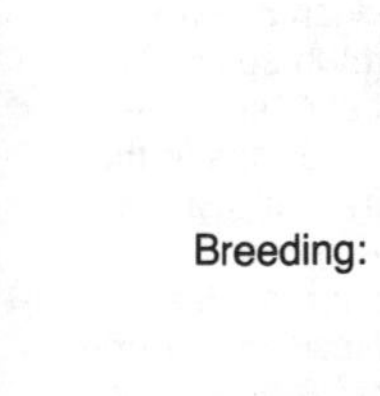

Range: The broadhead skink ranges from southeastern Pennsylvania to central Florida and west to eastern Kansas and east central Texas. It has been collected in Cabell, Calhoun, Jefferson, Kanawha, and Wayne counties in West Virginia.

63 **Northern Coal Skink** *Eumeces anthracinus anthracinus* (Baird)

Gr. *anthrakon,* coal

Description: The coal skink is a medium-sized, smooth-scaled, glossy lizard which may attain a total length of 7.0 inches (17.8 cm). Its dorsal color may be brown or greenish-brown. A lateral coal-black stripe of several scales wide, flanked above and below by a narrow yellow or white stripe, extends from the neck onto the tail on each side. West Virginia coal skinks also have a light yellow line running through the posterior upper labials. There is a single postmental scale and no postnasal scales. The other two species of "lined" skinks known to occur in West Virginia (see no. 61 and no. 62) have a middorsal stripe and two postmentals. In the northern coal skink, the sides of the head may be reddish in older males in the spring. The young have violet-blue tails.

Habitat and Habits: The northern coal skink is found on damp, wooded hillsides which have an abundance of leaf litter and loose stones. Rotten logs, brush piles, and stacks of lumber are also good habitats. According to the literature, it prefers a moist habitat, but in West Virginia it favors the dry shale barrens in the eastern and southern parts of the state. "Coal skinks (*E. anthracinus*) are locally common on shale slopes. These stout bodied lizards have blackish-brown bodies and dull blue tails. They sun themselves in the hottest weather and on the most exposed outcrops. When disturbed they dart into crevices in the shale, their movements extraordinarily fast" (Brooks 1965).

Breeding: There are no data on breeding behavior in West Virginia, Smith (1946) states that in New York courtship and mating occur in May and that 8 or 9 eggs ranging from 0.24 to 0.67 inches (0.6–1.7 cm) are deposited in late June. Eggs hatch in four to five weeks.

Range: The Northern coal skink ranges from New York to Virginia and Kentucky in a pattern of disjunct populations. Within West Virginia specimens are known from Greenbrier, Hampshire, Hardy, Kanawha, Logan, Pocahontas, Pendleton, and Putnam counties.

ORDER SQUAMATA—LIZARDS AND SNAKES
Suborder Serpentes—Snakes

Snakes are specialized reptiles which are easily recognized by their elongate scaled bodies and the absence of limbs, external ear openings, and eyelids. Other characteristics include a lower jaw separated into two halves connected by an elastic ligament, and an elongate, deeply forked, retractile tongue. The belly of a snake from chin to the vent is covered by a series of overlapping, transverse plates. The vent, which is the exterior opening from the cloaca, receives the products of the large intestine, the kidneys, and the gonads, and separates the trunk from the tail. In the male, the paired hemipenes are retracted through the cloacal vent into sacs in the base of the tail. During copulation one of the hemipenes is everted and inserted into the cloaca of the female to effect the transfer of seminal fluid. The hemipenes of a snake are unique for each species and are important in establishing taxonomic relationships and identification.

The earliest known snakes date from the late Cretaceous period, about 80 million years ago. Although they undoubtedly evolved from lizards, the relationship has never been established satisfactorily, partly because the bones of a snake's skull are fragile and loosely connected and are soon scattered and lost after death, resulting in a poor fossil record.

There are approximately 2,700 species of snakes in the world. These are contained within 10 to 11 families and approximately 396 genera. Snakes occur on all the continents except Antarctica. They are absent from Ireland, Iceland, and New Zealand. Five of the families are represented in the United States and Canada, two of them in West Virginia. Twenty-two species and subspecies of snakes occur within West Virginia; two of the species are venomous.

The habits of snakes are extremely diversified; some are terrestrial, others spend most of their time underground, some are arboreal, and others are aquatic (one group is entirely marine). Some species are diurnal, and others are nocturnal. All of them are predaceous carnivores and swallow their food whole.

Many snakes prey upon small animals which are easy to capture. A few snakes overcome large prey by the sheer strength of their jaws, while others kill their prey by winding about it and thus suffocating it. The ultimate in the evolution of snake feeding devices is the attainment of a salivary toxin which can be injected into prey.

Snakes probably grow throughout their lives, but the growth rate slows with age. They shed their outer skin periodically, usually in one piece from head to tail. Although it is not known for certain what factor(s) regulate the frequency of shedding, it is known that weather conditions, feeding frequency, and endocrine secretions are important.

Many of our species of snakes may be readily identified by color or pattern, size, and in some cases, habits. However, a careful student will want to confirm the identification by counting the scale rows, determining whether the scales are keeled or smooth, whether the anal plate is single or divided, and whether the scales on the underside of the tail are in one or two rows (consult the glossary for definitions). All this must be done with the snake in hand and preferably in an immobile condition. Of course, great care must be taken in the handling of poisonous snakes (cf. section on poisonous snakes, p. 181).

Family Colubridae • Colubrid Snakes

This is the largest of the snake families, the members of which represent more than three-fourths of the world's 2,700 known snake species. They range throughout the world and are the predominant snakes on all continents except Australia.

Members of the family have teeth on the maxillary, palatine, pterygoid, and dentary bones but never on the premaxillary. Although the teeth of most species are solid, without grooves, there are a few, such as the African boomslang, with grooves in the rear teeth which are connected to poison glands.

There is great variation in size, habitats, and food among the members of the family. Some feed on warm-blooded prey while others devour amphibians, reptiles, and fishes. Some are opportunistic feeders and take whatever they encounter, and others have very specialized diets such as the egg-eating and snail-eating snakes.

The family is divided into about six subfamilies which include (1) the Colubrinae, the largest and most diverse of the colubrids; (2) the Natricinae, the water snakes, garter snakes, earth snakes, and brown snakes of North America; and (3) the Xenodontinae, the majority of neotropical snakes such as *Heterodon.*

Genus *Regina* Baird and Girard • Crayfish Snakes

Crayfish snakes are slender, striped snakes with keeled scales, divided anal plate, and 19 midbody scale rows. The young are born alive (ovoviviparous). Four species of snakes are assigned to this genus at the present time. The generic name was resurrected from synonymy by Smith and

Huheey (1960), but herpetologists disagree as to its status. The four members of this genus are found from the midsection of the United States to the southeastern coast. One species occurs in West Virginia.

64 Queen Snake *Regina septemvittata* (Say)
L. *regina,* royal; L. *septem,* seven; L. *vitta,* band or stripe

Description: The queen snake is a medium-sized, slender snake which may attain a length of 30.0 inches (76.2 cm). The dorsal coloration is olive brown to gray. The belly is dirty white or yellowish. The sides have a yellow stripe on the first and second row of scales. The venter has four longitudinal dark stripes which converge near the throat; these may be obscure in adults. The scales are keeled, in 19 rows, and the anal plate is divided. Three indistinct dark stripes may be visible on the back.

Habitat and Habits: Queen snakes frequent streams with rocky bottoms where they may be found under rocks along the shore or basking in a bush over the water. When approached they drop down and escape into vegetation or water. If captured, they thrash about vigorously, discharging liberal quantities of musk. They may attempt to bite, but the small head and mouth pose no danger.

Their food consists almost exclusively of soft-bodied crayfish (those which have recently moulted), although they are reported to eat small fish and tadpoles (Branson and Baker 1974).

Breeding: Branson and Baker (1974) report the following from their ecological study of the queen snake in Kentucky. Mating probably occurs in both spring and fall. The females give birth to up to 17 young (12.8 average) in late summer or early fall. The total length of the young range from 5.3 to 8.3 inches (13.5–21.0 cm). Females become sexually mature during their third year and males in their second year. Ford (1982) describes the courtship behavior of the queen snake.

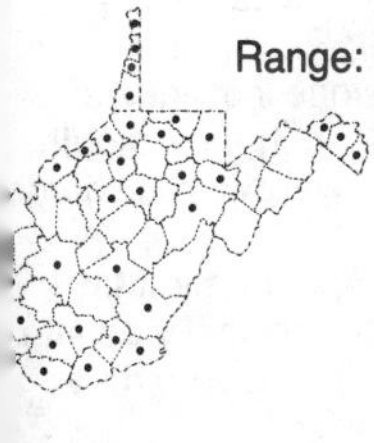

Range: The queen snake ranges from the southern Great Lakes through Pennsylvania south to the Gulf Coast and westward to the Mississippi Valley. A small population occurs in southern Missouri and northern Arkansas. The species is found throughout West Virginia, although records are lacking from several of the central counties and Eastern Panhandle and the lower Ohio Valley.

Genus *Nerodia* Baird and Girard • Water Snakes

This genus consists of stout, somewhat large-bodied, semiaquatic snakes. They have heavily keeled scales, divided anal plates, and from 21 to 33 mid-body scale rows. They all give birth to their young (ovoviviparous). With one exception, members of this genus are confined to the eastern half of North America. Seven species have been described, of which one is found in West Virginia.

65 Northern Water Snake *Nerodia sipedon sipedon* (Linnaeus)

Gr. *neros,* a swimmer; Gr. *ode,* a thing like; L. *siren,* a siren

Description: The northern water snake is a heavy-bodied snake which may reach 40.0 inches (101.6 cm) or more in length. In large or older specimens, the dorsal color may be an unpatterned dark gray. In smaller specimens, the dorsal pattern is a series of dark blotches on a lighter background. The blotches, which are broader on the back than on the sides, may be reddish brown or gray. The ventral side is usually yellow or cream with numerous orange or reddish crescent blotches. The scales are strongly keeled, and the row count is 21 to 25. The anal plate is divided.

Habitat and Habits: The northern water snake is one of our most abundant snakes, and it may be found almost everywhere that a reasonable amount of water exists. Throughout Appalachia it is referred to as a water moccasin and is too frequently killed on sight. It will escape if given the chance, but if cornered it flattens its body and strikes viciously. If captured, it bites and voids an ill-smelling musk. Water snakes are both nocturnal and diurnal and may be found feeding at any time of the day or night. They are fond of basking, and large numbers may be observed on exposed boulders along rivers.

The water snake's diet consists of fish, frogs, salamanders, insects, crayfish, and occasionally small mammals (Uhler *et al.* 1939; Raney and Roecher 1947). On several occasions individuals have been observed with fish lodged in their mouths which they were unable to either swallow or disgorge (Green, personal observation).

Breeding: Mating usually occurs from early April to mid May (Conant 1938; Minton 1944) and occasionally as late as early June (Mushinsky 1979). They give birth to their young in late summer or early fall. The number of young varies from 16 to 30 (Fitch 1970) and their length from 6.5 to 9.5 inches or 16.5 to 24.1 cm (Wright and Wright 1957).

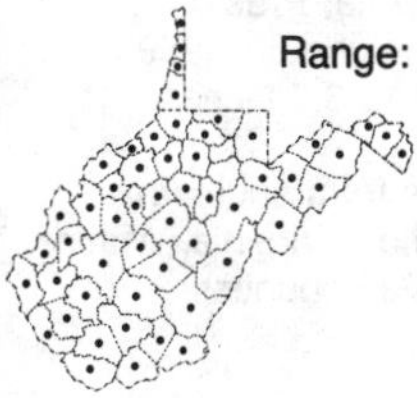

Range: The northern water snake ranges from Maine to Quebec, south to North Carolina and Tennessee, and westward to Nebraska and Kansas. Within West Virginia it is widely distributed throughout the state, with records from almost every county.

Genus *Storeria* Baird and Girard • Brown Snakes and Redbelly Snakes

These are small, slender, secretive, terrestrial snakes with shortened heads, keeled scales, and a divided anal plate. They are ovoviviparous. They have no loreal head scales. They are found from the eastern United States to Guatemala and Honduras. The genus, named for David Humphreys Storer, contains two species, both of which occur in West Virginia.

66 Northern Brown Snake *Storeria dekayi dekayi* (Holbrook)

Named for D. H. Storer and J. E. DeKay

Description: The northern brown snake is a small snake which measures from 10.0 to 15.0 inches (25.4–38.1 cm). The dorsal color is brown or gray with a yellowish midline stripe that is bordered by two parallel rows of dark spots. The belly is cream or pinkish color, and there may be a series of small black dots on the edges of the ventrals. The scale row count is 17–17–17. The scales are keeled and the anal plate is divided. The newly born snakes have a conspicuous yellow band two to two-and-one-half scales wide across the neck.

Habitat and Habits: The northern brown snake is a secretive species frequently overlooked by collectors. The few records from West Virginia are located where extensive collecting has been done. The brown snake is more commonly found in urban areas and usually exists in large numbers in "colonies." For example, near the old tannery at Elkins, Randolph County, one can almost always find a sizeable number on a collecting trip. Favorite cover objects include old bark slabs, strips of linoleum, and tar paper. Brown snakes eat slugs, snails, insects, and earthworms (Judd 1954).

Breeding: Mating takes place in late March and early April; the number of young born ranges from 9 to 20 (Clausen 1936). A female collected at the West Virginia University Biological Station at Terra Alta, Preston County, gave birth to 11 young on June 30, 1969. Their total length ranged from 3.4 to 3.7 inches (8.7–9.3 cm).

Range: The northern brown snake ranges from southern Canada and Maine south to southern Virginia. Within West Virginia it is known from seven counties.

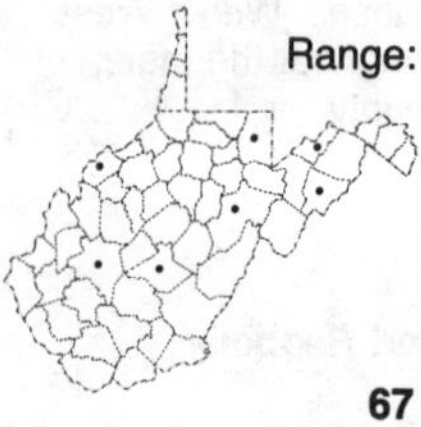

67 Northern Redbelly Snake *Storeria occipitomaculata occipitomaculata* (Storer)
L. *occipito,* back part of head; L. *macula,* spot

Description: The redbelly snake may attain a length of 16.0 inches (40.6 cm), although most individuals are smaller. The female is larger than the male (Blanchard 1937a). Its dorsal color is gray, black, or brown. A light stripe may run down the back, and if so, is bordered by indistinct black lines. There are numerous white flecks on the sides and back. Three yellow spots appear at the base of the head, and these sometimes fuse to form an indistinct ring. The belly is red, gray, yellow, or orange, and occasionally, in specimens from higher altitudes, blue-black. The scales are keeled and in 15 rows. The anal plate is divided.

Habitat and Habits: The redbelly snake frequents open forest land and woodland borders among a variety of habitats which may include wet, sedgy meadows and borders of swamps. It is one of the few species that may be collected in the higher elevations of the Alleghenies; records indicate that it seems to prefer mountainous terrain. The snake has been noted to climb in bushes, and numerous specimens have been taken from anthills. However, most specimens have been collected under stones, debris, bark, and logs.

When captured it is entirely defenseless except for the discharge of musk from its anal glands. Some specimens curl back their upper lips by turning the maxillary bones outward. The result is a sneer which may be used for intimidation. Redbelly snakes rarely, if ever, bite.

The species feeds almost exclusively on slugs, although there are records of earthworms being eaten (Hamilton and Pollack 1956). Conant (1951) found seven redbelly snakes in the stomach of a red-tailed hawk killed in Portage County, Ohio.

Breeding: Matings have been reported in both spring and fall; the young are born alive, the number in a litter ranging from 1 to 13 (Trapido 1944). Blanchard (1937a) reported that birth occurred from late July through early September (in upper Michigan). He found that the young measured a little more than 3.0 inches (7.6 cm).

Range: The northern redbelly snake ranges from Nova Scotia to southern Georgia, west to Saskatchewan, the Dakotas, and the eastern parts of Kansas, Oklahoma, and Texas. It probably occurs throughout West Virginia.

Genus *Thamnophis* Fitzinger • Garter Snakes

The genus consists of small to medium-sized, slender snakes with three longitudinal lighter stripes (these are found on most species). *Thamnophis* and *Pituophis* (pine snake) are the only genera in West Virginia in which the anal plate is single and the scales are keeled. They are viviparous. The garter snakes are close relatives of the water snakes but are more terrestrial. The range of the genus extends between both coasts across southern Canada and south to Costa Rica. A total of 22 species of garter snakes are recognized; 14 are in North America, and 2 of these occur in West Virginia. These are the most abundant snakes in North America.

68 Eastern Ribbon Snake *Thamnophis sauritus sauritus* (Linnaeus)

Gr. *thamnos,* a bush; Gr. *ophis,* a snake; Gr. *saaros,* lizard

Description: The eastern ribbon snake is a medium-sized, slender snake which may attain a total length of 36.0 inches (91.4 cm). The tail is slender and may comprise up to 36 percent of the total length. The dorsal color is rich brown with three longitudinal yellow stripes, one of which extends down the midline and the other two on the third and fourth lateral scale rows above the ventrals on each side. The belly is unmarked bluish green or yellowish. The upper and lower lip plates are unmarked, and a vertical light bar is present on the preocular. There are 19 scale rows at the midbody. The scales are keeled, and the anal plate is single.

Habitat and Habits: The ribbon snake is semiaquatic and therefore is not found far from water. It frequents swamps, margins of oxbow ponds, grassy stream borders, hatchery ponds, and weedy lake shores. It is quick and alert and when alarmed disappears rapidly through the undergrowth. When taking to the water it swims over the surface with the head slightly elevated, in contrast to water snakes which swim underwater. There are observations in the literature of the species basking in low bushes and also on the broad leaves of spatterdock or cow lily. When captured, it thrashes around and exudes quantities of musk through the cloaca. It eats chiefly tadpoles, small frogs, a variety of small salamanders, small fish, earthworms, and insects (Uhler *et al.* 1939).

Breeding: These snakes mate in the spring and bear live young in July and August. Wilson and Friddle (1950) reported on three specimens collected on May 13, 1946, in Hardy County, West Virginia, which contained 14, 16, and 16 embryos, respectively. McCauley (1945) reported on seven broods which ranged from 8 to 15, with an average of 10. The number of young may be as low as 3 or as high as 26.

Range: The eastern ribbon snake ranges from southern Maine to South Carolina, southwest to southeastern Illinois, eastern Louisiana, and the Florida panhandle. It is an uncommon snake in West Virginia, with records from Greenbrier, Hardy, Mason, Monroe, and Randolph counties. There is an unverified record from Preston County.

69 **Eastern Garter Snake** *Thamnophis sirtalis sirtalis* (Linnaeus)

NL. *sirtalis,* like a garter

Description: The eastern garter snake is a medium-sized, stout species which may attain a length of 36.0 to 48.0 inches (91.4–121.9 cm). Large specimens are closer to 36.0 inches (91.4 cm). The background coloration may be brown or green with occasional speckles of white, blue, or green. The juvenile specimens are more brightly colored than the adults. Often there is a conspicuous pale middorsal stripe and a less prominent light stripe involving the second and third scale rows along each side. Scale rows are 19 at midbody, and they are strongly keeled. The anal plate is single.

Habitat and Habits: The eastern garter snake is found in a variety of habitats such as grassy areas; damp, open woodlands; and marshes and bogs. It will try to escape when encountered, and if cornered, will flatten the body, which makes it appear larger. If captured, it may bite as it writhes and squirms and smears the vile-smelling musk from its anal glands.

Its food consists of "cold-blooded" prey such as frogs, toads, salamanders, and small fish, as well as earthworms and some insects. There are also records of small birds being eaten. (Studies on the food of garter snakes include Uhler *et al.* 1939; Hamilton 1951; Hamilton and Pollack 1956.) Captive garter snakes will feed on chopped fish, sardines (canned in oil, but not mustard), small frogs, and earthworms.

Breeding: It has been known for some time that snakes depend upon their olfactory sense to detect the opposite sex. Male garter snakes have been observed trailing a female prior to courtship and copulation. Devine (1976) cites experimental evidence for the role of pheromones in mate selection in garter snakes. Ford (1978, 1981) shows that pheromones are important in the trailing process as well as for species specificity between two sympatric species of *Thamnophis.*

Blanchard and Blanchard (1942) describe the courtship and copulation of the eastern garter snake in detail (also see List 1950). Birth occurs three to four months after mating in late April, the date of birth depending upon the summer temperature (Blanchard and Blanchard 1942; Zehr 1962).

The number of young in a litter varies considerably. There is perhaps no other snake in North America with so high a breeding potential. Many references in the literature cite unusually large litters: Schmidt and Davis (1941) report 73 to 78 young; Behler and King (1979) list 7 to 85; Martof *et al.* (1980) list 7 to 101. The average litter size is 14 to 15 (Fitch 1965). A gravid female collected near the Tucker County line in Randolph County on August 20, 1937, gave birth to 66 young ranging in length from 2.4 to 2.5 inches (6.0–6.5 cm). The female measured 30.3 inches (77.0 cm) (N. B. Green, personal observation).

Mating may occur in fall or spring but most frequently after spring emergence (Fitch 1960b, 1970). N. B. Green observed mating activities of several garter snakes on March 15, 1942, in the southeastern edge of Huntington, West Virginia, in an area referred to at that time as the "brickyard swamp," but now the location of the Cabell Huntington Hospital. "It was a warm Sunday morning and observations were being made on bird activity with 7x35 binoculars in a cattail swamp when my attention was attracted to a rustling in a mass of Japanese honeysuckle at the foot of a steep shale bank. I was able, through the aid of binoculars, to observe the movement of a large mass of snakes which were easily identified as *Thamnophis s. sirtalis.* Several dozen individuals were involved in a loosely formed ball about two feet in diameter. I observed the mass at a distance of 30 feet with the glasses as I didn't want to disturb them. Snakes were moving in and out of the mass, heads appeared, then disappeared, tongues flicked actively while the position of the mass remained relatively unchanged. I interpreted the observation as an emergence from hibernation with preliminary mating activities. No actual copulation was observed."

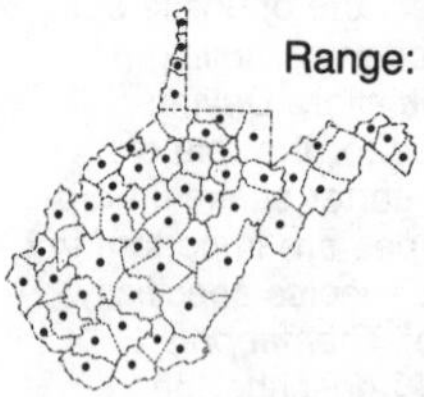

Range: The eastern garter snake ranges from Canada to the Gulf of Mexico and west to Minnesota and eastern Texas. It is one of the most frequently encountered snakes within West Virginia with records from almost all 55 counties. Pauley (1980a) found it to be the most common snake at elevations above 3,500 feet (1,067 m) in West Virginia.

Genus *Virginia* Baird and Girard • Earth Snakes

The earth snakes are small, secretive, uniformly colored snakes confined to the eastern United States. They have 15 or 17 rows of smooth or keeled scales and a divided anal plate. They are ovoviviparous. The generic name *Haldea* was applied to this genus until recently. Members of the genus are found from New Jersey west to southern Iowa, south to eastern Texas and east to northern Florida. Two species are known, and one of them, *Virginia valerae,* is found in West Virginia.

70 Eastern Earth Snake *Virginia valeriae valeriae* Baird and Girard

After Virginia, and after Valeria Blaney

Description: The eastern earth snake is one of two subspecies occurring in West Virginia. It is a small snake with a moderately stout body, small pointed head, and no perceptible neck. It may attain a length of 13.0 inches (33.0 cm). The dorsal color is brown or gray. Often there are tiny black spots on the back, more or less scattered or arranged in four rows. The belly is uniformly white. There are 15 rows of scales. Except for a few scales on the posterior part of the body that may be weakly keeled, the scales are smooth. There are six upper labials; a loreal is present, and the anal plate is divided.

Habitat and Habits: The earth snake frequents grassy areas near or in forests where it may lie buried in the leaf mold of the forest floor or hidden under logs or stones. It is nowhere common in West Virginia, but its scarcity may be more apparent than real because of its highly secretive nature, its small size, and the collector's unfamiliarity with its ecology. It is most often found under stones after prolonged rains which interrupt a long dry period. Dates of activity range from April 1 through November 16. Its food consists of earthworms, slugs, and other small invertebrates.

Breeding: Little has been published on its breeding behavior. McCauley (1945) listed 4 to 8 young in five specimens; Behler and King (1979) listed 2 to 14. The young are born alive in late summer or early fall.

Remarks: Several specimens were collected on a hillside near Wayne (Wayne County) from under stones and trash following a rain after a dry period.

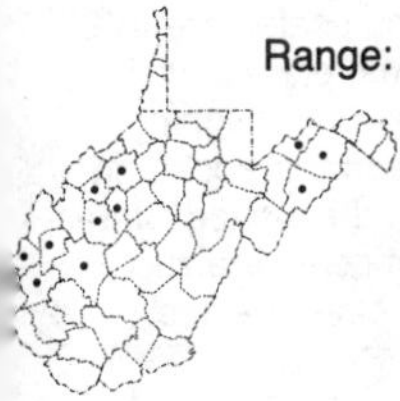

Range: The eastern earth snake ranges from New Jersey to northern Florida, west to Ohio, Tennessee, and Alabama. In West Virginia it has been found in the Eastern Panhandle (Hampshire, Hardy, and Mineral counties) and in several counties within the Ohio drainage: Wayne, Cabell, Lincoln, Putnam, Kanawha, Calhoun, Roane, Wirt, and Ritchie.

71 **Mountain Earth Snake** *Virginia valeriae pulchra* (Richmond)

L. *pulcher,* beautiful

Description: The mountain earth snake differs from the eastern earth snake (no. 70) in having weakly keeled scales in 15–17–17 rows. The dorsal surface is reddish brown to dark gray.

Habitat and Habits: Thomas Cervone (1983) found that the mountain earth snake is most frequently found on short, grassy slopes with flat sandstone rocks, especially in areas associated with deciduous forests near a stream. Richmond (1954) reports that optimum collecting follows periods of heavy rainfall. The food consists entirely of earthworms (Cervone 1983).

Breeding: Cervone (1983) reported that in New York mating occurs in spring or fall, parturition from August 16 to September 20, and the litter sizes ranged from 2 to

11. Richmond (1954) comments on four litters composed of 5, 5, 7, and 8 individuals born in the laboratory between August 19 and September 14, 1953. The newly born young ranged from 3.7 to 4.8 inches (9.5–12.3 cm), with an average total length of 4.2 inches (10.7 cm). The average total length of the four female parents was 11.5 inches (29.2 cm). Pisani (1971) reports on a litter of 14 young born to a female 12.5 inches (31.9 cm) long, collected in July 1970 near Tidioute, Pennsylvania.

Range: The range of the mountain earth snake, as defined by Richmond (1954), is the unglaciated Allegheny high plateaus and Allegheny Mountain section of the Appalachian Plateau province from New York to West Virginia. In West Virginia it has been reported from Preston (McCoy 1965), Pendleton, and Randolph counties (Pauley 1984), and Pocahontas County (Pauley, personal observation).

Genus *Heterodon* Latreille • Hognose Snakes

These are stout-bodied, moderate-sized snakes with an upturned, shovel-like snout. The scales are in 23 to 25 rows and keeled, and the anal plate is divided. They are oviparous. When alarmed and feigning death, members of this genus flatten the neck and head. The range includes much of the United States and Canada and Mexico. Three species are recognized, one with three subspecies. One species occurs in West Virginia.

72 Eastern Hognose Snake *Heterodon platirhinos* Latrielle

Gr. *heteros,* different; Gr. *odous,* tooth; Gr. *platy,* broad; Gr. *rhynchos,* snout

Description: The eastern hognose snake is a medium-sized, moderately stout snake which may attain a length of 45.0 inches (114.3 cm). Its color and pattern usually consist of dark brown or black squarish blotches on a yellow, orange, reddish, or tan ground color, but some specimens are plain black or dark gray. The rostral plate at the tip of the snout is pointed and upturned, which is a unique characteristic of this species among West Virginia snakes. The belly is mottled with gray or greenish on yellow. The tail, which is usually held in a tight coil, is lighter on the underside.

Habitat and Habits: The hognose frequents dry, open sites such as sandy areas, cultivated or abandoned fields, and woodland borders. Davis (1946) describes how this species can use its snout to burrow in dry soil.

The most distinctive feature of this reptile is its behavior. When encountered in the open, it inflates its body with air and flattens its head and neck, hissing audibly as it expels air and strikes blindly with its mouth closed in the direction of the intruder. If further provoked, it may writhe and twist, rubbing its mouth against the ground, and finally roll over on its back as though dead, with its mouth open and its tongue hanging limply. If the snake is returned to its normal position, it promptly rolls over on its back again. Should the intruder depart, the reptile lifts its head, turns over, and slithers away.

The defensive actions of this harmless reptile have earned it a prominent place in folklore. The people of Appalachia call it spreadhead, puff adder, or blowing viper, and many still regard it as poisonous, as well as capable of spitting or blowing its poison. Others are amused by its comical behavior. In captivity it becomes quite tame and cannot be induced to perform. The hognose is unpleasant to handle because it squirms and twists and discharges large amounts of ill-smelling musk.

Despite its threatening behavior, the hognose usually does not bite. There are accounts in the literature, however, which indicate that the saliva of *Heterodon* is mildly toxic: Bragg (1960) and Grogan (1974) report on the effects of bites which were accidentlly inflicted; McCallister (1963) reports on tests which showed the saliva to be lethal for small frogs and salamanders. Smith and White (1955) correlated bufophagy in *Heterodon* with an enlarged adrenal. Other toad-eating reptiles are those of the genera *Thamnophis* and *Nerodia,* both of which have enlarged adrenals. The adrenal secretions are intended to counteract the large doses of digitaloid compounds, found in the skin secretions of toads. Other adaptations to bufophagy cited by Smith and White are the enlarged rear maxillary teeth used by the snake to puncture the inflated toad, the broad head, the expansive gape, its relatively thick body, and the characteristic upturned snout used in burrowing for nocturnal toads.

While more than 75 percent of its diet consists of toads (Surface 1906), the eastern hognose snake consumes a variety of food items. Edgren (1955) ranked them in order of occurrence as toads, frogs, salamanders, insects, small mammals, and birds; Hamilton and Pollack (1956) ranked the items as insects, toads, frogs, salamanders, molluscs, lizards, crustaceans, turtles, centipedes, earthworms, and spiders. Uhler *et al.* (1939) reported on the stomach contents of ten specimens from the George Washington National Forest in Virginia. They found toads and frogs were the favored fare although other vertebrates consumed included a chipmunk, a mouse, and salamanders, including a red-spotted newt.

Breeding: Courtship and copulation of this species are described by Platt (1969) and Nichols (1982). There are numerous references to egg-laying, size of clutch, and other details of reproduction. Edgren (1955) and Fitch (1970) review the available information on number and size of eggs and time of deposition.

Mating takes place in April and May and possibly the fall. Eggs are deposited in loose or sandy soil during June and early July, hatching in late August or early September. Clutch size may range up to more than 60, although the mean number is closer to 20 (Platt 1969). Adults are frequently melanistic, but numerous authors report that the condition is absent in the juvenile and newborn. At 2 to 3 years they are gray in color; melanism appears at 3 to 4 years of age (Robert Mount, personal communication).

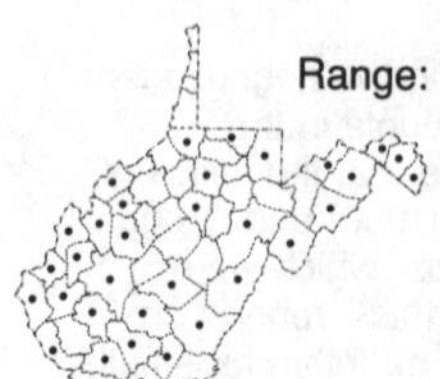

Range: The eastern hognose snake is found from southern New Hampshire to southern Florida, west to Minnesota, southeast South Dakota, Kansas, and Texas. In West Virginia it is believed to occur throughout the state although some areas are not represented in the collections.

Genus *Diadophis* Baird and Girard • Ringneck Snakes

These are small snakes with a yellow or orange continuous or interrupted ring around the neck. The ring may be obscure or occasionally absent. The anal plate is divided, the scales are smooth, and the scale count is 15 to 17 rows at midbody. They are oviparous.

The genus was formerly composed of three species which were divided into twelve subspecies, but now all are placed under the single species *Diadophis punctatus* (Collins *et al.* 1982). The ringneck snakes range from coast to coast except for large areas in the west where it is very dry; they are also found in Canada and Mexico. One subspecies is found in West Virginia.

73 Northern Ringneck Snake *Diadophis punctatus edwardsii* (Merrem)
Gr. *dia,* divided throughout; Gr. *ophi,* snake;
L. *punctus,* spotted; after G. Edwards

Description: The northern ringneck snake is a small, slender snake which may attain a length of 20.0 inches (50.8 cm). Its dorsal color is a glossy black or slightly iridescent slate gray with a bright yellow or orange neck ring and a yellow or orange belly which sometimes has a row of imperfectly formed black dots along the ventral midline. Occurrence of these black dots shows no apparent correlation with either locality or altitude.

Habitat and Habits: Northern ringneck snakes are usually found in or near moist woodlands under the cover of rocks, bark, logs, leaves, or other debris. They are secretive, but not burrowing. They are nocturnal in habit and are frequently encountered at night.

The ringneck snake is docile and rarely attempts to bite. Its defense is to secrete an ill-smelling musk from the cloacal glands. It soon becomes tame and will take food when offered. Dates of collection range from April 1 through November 3. This snake feeds upon small salamanders of the brook and woodland groups, particularly the redback salamander (no. 12; Blanchard *et al.* 1979), and other vertebrates such as small snakes, lizards, and frogs. Earthworms constitute its principal invertebrate food.

Breeding: Little is known of its reproductive behavior in West Virginia, although clutches of 3 to 6 eggs have been found in late May and early June throughout the state. Blanchard (1926, 1930a, and 1937b) and Blanchard *et al.* (1979) made extensive studies of the northern ringneck in Michigan: Eggs are laid in late June and early July in damp, well-rotted logs with a hard outer surface. A single female may lay from 1 to 7 eggs, and a dozen or more females may use the same nest. The eggs are white and elongate, averaging 0.98 inch (2.5 cm) in length and 0.24 inch (0.6 cm) in diameter. Hatching occurs in late August through September, with the hatchlings averaging 3.9 to 5.9 inches (10.0–15.0 cm). Maturity occurs within two to three years. (For the reproductive biology of the ringneck snake in northeastern Kansas, see Fitch 1975.)

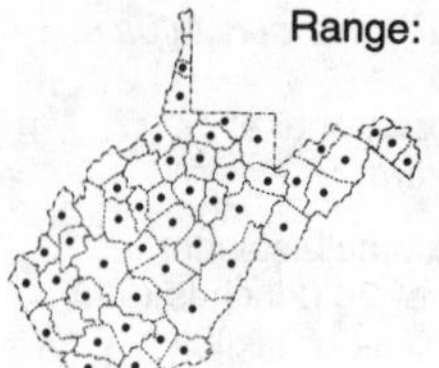

Range: The northern ringneck ranges from Nova Scotia and New Brunswick west to Sault Ste. Marie, and south in the Atlantic coastal plain to central New Jersey. It is found in the mountains of northern Georgia and northeastern Alabama, and in southeastern Illinois. It is widely distributed throughout West Virginia. Pauley (1980a) reports a specimen from Spruce Knob, Pendleton County, at 4,360 feet (1,329 m).

Genus *Carphophis* Gervais • Worm Snakes

These are small, slender snakes which superficially resemble earthworms in habitat, behavior, and appearance. The scales are smooth, usually in 13 rows, and the anal plate is divided. They are oviparous.

The genus ranges throughout a large part of the eastern and central United States. One species, which is divided into three subspecies, makes up the genus.

74 Eastern Worm Snake *Carphophis amoenus amoenus* (Say)

Gr. *carph,* a twig; L. *amoenus,* pleasing, lovely

Description: The eastern worm snake may attain a length of 12.0 inches (30.5 cm). It is uniformly brown above with a pinkish ventral surface. The head is small and rounded with no distinct neck. The tail is short and terminates in a sharp spine. This snake has two separate prefrontals which lie anterior to two internasals. Occasionally a prefrontal will be fused to its internasal, but rarely will those on both sides be fused.

Habitat and Habits: Worm snakes spend most of the day beneath stones, logs, or other cover. They are well adapted for burrowing with their small, pointed heads and tiny eyes. They may be found exploring the soft contents of a decayed log or burrowing underground for some distance. Barbour *et al.* (1969) found that they are most active after 3:00 P.M. They are forest animals preferring a moist rocky soil with partially wooded or grassy hillsides.

Worm snakes are inoffensive creatures unknown to attempt to bite. When handled they try to force themselves between the fingers while using the sharp spine of the tail to surprise the captor into letting go. It is a strong snake for its size and can escape if not kept in a secure container. Collection dates range from March 30 through October 18. It feeds principally upon soft-bodied insects and earthworms.

Breeding: Mating occurs during April and May. There are accounts in the literature of autumn matings, but this has not been confirmed in West Virginia. The eggs are deposited under rocks or in loose dirt or rotted logs in late June or early July. McCauley (1945) found that the number of eggs per clutch ranged from 2 to 5 and measured up to 0.90 inch (2.3 cm) long and 0.39 inch (1.0 cm) in diameter. The incubation period is approximately two months, and the newly hatched young range from 3.5 to 4.1 inches (8.8–10.4 cm) in length.

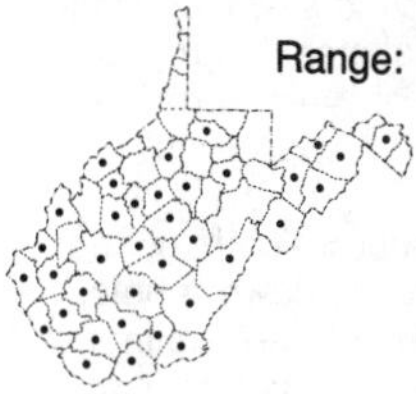

Range: The eastern worm snake ranges from southern New England to South Carolina, central Georgia, and central Alabama. Pauley (1966) studied worm snakes from West Virginia and Ohio in an effort to determine the zone of intergradation between the two subspecies *C. a. amoenus* and *C. a. helenae.* Criteria which he selected were the number of ventral scutes and the fusion or separation of the internasals and prefrontals. He concluded that the entire population of *Carphophis* in West Virginia should be assigned to *C. a. amoenus,* while intergradation with *C. a. helenae* in Ohio occurred west of Lawrence County in the southeastern part of the state. The eastern worm snake is found throughout West Virginia.

Genus *Coluber* Linnaeus • Racers

These are large, slender-bodied, long-tailed, nonvenomous, terrestrial snakes with smooth scales and a divided anal plate. The scale row count at midbody is 17. They are diurnal and occasionally arboreal. Their dorsal coloration varies from glossy black through shades of blue, brown, gray, or black with white flecks. Juveniles differ in color and pattern from the adults in that they are grayish with many dark blotches. They are oviparous. There are seven species of *Coluber;* one of these is found in West Virginia.

75 Northern Black Racer *Coluber constrictor constrictor* Linnaeus

L. *coluber,* a serpent; L. *con,* with; L. *strictus,* draw tight

Description: The northern black racer is a slender snake with smooth, satiny black scales. It may attain a length of 6 feet (1.8 m) or more. The belly is uniformly bluish black; the throat and chin are white, usually with some gray blotches. Juveniles have a pattern of about 60 brown or reddish brown dorsal saddles on a gray background, except on the tail which is uniformly brown; adult coloration replaces this pattern by the time the snake attains a length of 24.0 inches (61.0 cm).

Habitat and Habits: The black racer is an ubiquitous snake which may be encountered in almost any habitat: grassland and woodland borders, swamp and marshland, around old farm buildings, and lurking around sawdust piles. They may be found hiding under stones, boards, a sheet of tin, or tarpaper. It is one of West Virginia's commonest snakes. Many of them are killed on highways throughout the state.

The black racer is an alert serpent which may seek cover when surprised by disappearing down a hole, vanishing in the vegetation, or taking to an available body of water and swimming away. When foraging for food, racers are exhaustive in searching every possible site. They move with their heads raised in an attitude of alertness. When cornered, they fight fiercely, vibrating the tail vigorously and striking at the intruder. Their numerous teeth are sharp but incapable of inflicting more than mere scratches. When captured, they retain their nervous and pugnacious attitude and rarely make good pets. Occasionally one will accept food and become tame.

Appalachian superstition holds that these snakes chase people. Walking along a country road, an individual may be startled to see a black racer dashing full speed toward him. If he steps to one side, he will be relieved to see the racer continue past him into the vegetation below the road. The racer's speed as it heads for cover seems like an attack. Minton (1972) interprets this behavior as indicative that racers have home ranges that they occupy long enough to learn well.

The black racer is one of our speediest snakes, although its elusiveness cannot be attributed solely to its speed. Its alertness, dodging ability, and quickness in finding cover all contribute to its ability to escape. Mosauer (1935) in a study of snake speeds found the coachwhip, *Masticophis flagellum,* the fastest of those tested. Its maximum rate was 3.6 miles (5.8 km) per hour, far less than the speed of the average person. Oliver (1955) reports on a series of tests on the Florida racer, *Coluber constrictor priapus.* The fastest speed he recorded was also 3.6 miles per hour. During these tests several observers estimated the speed to be about three times what it was.

Black racers hibernate in rock crevices, abandoned woodchuck holes, as well as other available sites. These sites are used as communal hibernacula by other snake species such as black rat snakes (no. 79), copperheads (no. 84), timber rattlers (no. 85), and garter snakes (no. 69). Collection dates range from April 9 through October 10.

The black racer is an indiscriminate feeder, and its food is limited only by what is available. Although most of the food items found in stomach analysis are vertebrate remains, the presence of insects and other arthropods raises the question whether their consumption was accidental or intentional. The vertebrates most commonly found are a variety of snakes, lizards, birds and their eggs, small mammals (mostly insectivores and rodents), and small frogs. (See Surface 1906; Uhler *et al.* 1939; Hamilton and Pollack 1956; and Fitch 1963a.) Despite its Latin name, the black racer does not kill by constriction, but by pressing the prey to the ground with the weight of its body and causing death through suffocation. Black racers often swallow prey alive (Robert Mount, personal communication).

Breeding: Black racers mate shortly after emerging from hibernation. The eggs are deposited in sawdust piles, soil, or decaying vegetable matter. A clutch may range up to 25 eggs and occasionally more. The average clutch size is 10.61 (Fitch 1963a). Fitch (1970) determined that egg deposition occurs in late May or June in Kansas. On June 6, 1965, a resident of Huntington, Cabell County, discovered a clutch of 20 eggs in her garden. The granular, oblong eggs measured 1.0 to 1.2 inches (2.7—3.1 cm) long by 0.75 to 0.98 inch (1.9–2.5 cm) wide. Hatching began on July 20 and by July 27 all had hatched (N. B. Green, personal observation). The newly hatched young range from 7.9 to 13.0 inches (20.0–33.0 cm) and mature in two to three years.

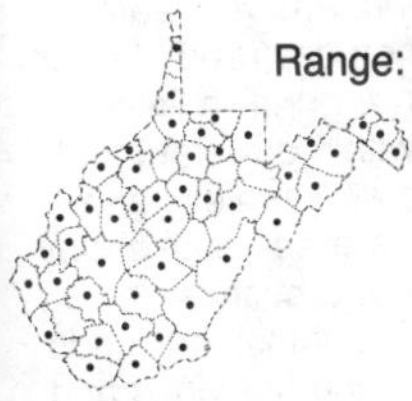

Range: The range of the northern black racer extends from Maine southwest to eastern Ohio and western Kentucky, and south to northern South Carolina, Georgia, and Alabama. It ranges throughout West Virginia.

Genus *Opheodrys* Fitzinger • Green Snakes

These are small, slender-bodied, uniformly green snakes that are arboreal and terrestrial. The scales are either keeled, as in *Opheodrys aestivus,* or smooth as in *O. vernalis*. The scale count at midbody is 15 to 17, and the anal plate is divided. They are oviparous. In America, the genus (represented by two species) ranges in the east from southern Canada south to Florida and west to northeastern Mexico, and in the west from the Maritime Provinces to the Rocky Mountains. Both species are found in West Virginia. The genus also occurs in Asia.

76 **Rough Green Snake** *Opheodrys aestivus* (Linnaeus)

Gr. *ophis,* a serpent; L. *dryas,* an oak; L. *aestas,* summer

Description: The rough green snake is an extremely slender, long-tailed snake which may exceed 40.0 inches (101.6 cm). The tail accounts for more than one-third of its total length. The dorsal color is uniformly pea-green above, becoming bluish after death. The belly is pale green, white, or yellowish. The scales are keeled, in 17 rows at midbody, and the anal plate is divided.

Habitat and Habits: The narrow head with large eyes and distinct neck, and the slender, elongate body and tail, indicate this snake's adaptation to an arboreal habitat. These features facilitate its creeping motion among vines and bushes. It is primarily an inhabitant of open sunny areas and roadside vegetation, such as greenbrier thickets and berry patches. In central Oklahoma the rough green snake prefers a habitat of dense brush in various types of edges, i.e., where two habitats meet (Goldsmith 1984). In Arkansas the rough green snake prefers perches in bushes less than 3 meters in height and within 3 meters of a shoreline (Plummer 1981). It is unusual to find them under rocks, logs, or other cover.

The rough green snake is an inoffensive creature which rarely attempts to bite. When captured, it often opens its mouth widely, revealing a purplish lining. This is probably the only snake within our state that is accepted by the general public as harmless and beneficial. On warm, sunny days a green snake may be seen lying quietly in low trees and bushes. It rarely ascends the trunk of a tree, but instead winds its way slowly and deliberately among the vines and leaves. It frequently lies extended among the branches with half of its body swaying slowly back and forth and its tongue extended.

Green snakes eat insects, chiefly grasshoppers and crickets, insect larvae, and spiders (Hamilton and Pollack 1956; Plummer 1981).

Breeding: Rough green snakes emerge from hibernation and become active later than our other species. The earliest date of appearance on record in West Virginia is May 4. No observations are available on mating, but the earliest date of egg-laying in West Virginia is June 30. On this date a female in captivity deposited 7 capsule-shaped eggs which averaged 0.71–0.83 x 0.31–0.39 inch (1.8–2.1 x 0.8–1.0 cm) (N. B. Green, personal observation). The eggs are usually deposited in loose soil or rotted wood. The young hatch in 6 to 12 weeks and are 7.09 to 7.9 inches (18.0–20.1 cm) long. They mature in one to two years. The snakes become more active and appear to be more numerous in late summer. The latest date known for capture in West Virginia is October 15. For additional information regarding the natural history of the rough green snake see Fitch (1970) and Goldsmith (1984).

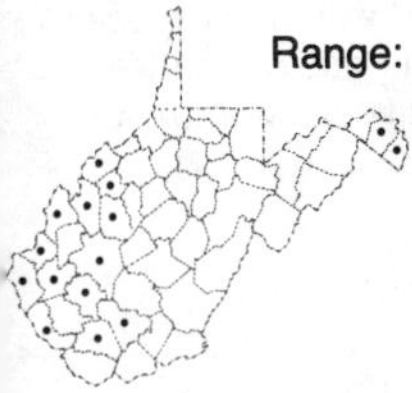

Range: The rough snake ranges from southern New Jersey to the Florida Keys, west to Kansas and Texas, and south into Mexico. Within West Virginia it is characteristically a snake of lower elevations. It has been collected in Jefferson County where Harpers Ferry, the lowest point in the state, is located. West of the Alleghenies it has been taken in the southwestern counties as far north as Wood County.

77 Eastern Smooth Green Snake *Opheodrys vernalis vernalis* (Harlan)

L. *verno,* spring

Description: The smooth green snake may attain a length of 20.0 to 22.0 inches (50.8–55.9 cm). It is bright green on the back, and the belly is yellowish white. The scales are smooth and in 15 rows at midbody. There is little chance that this snake could be confused with the rough green snake (no. 76) even if the observer were to overlook the keels on the scales or the slender, elongate body of the rough green snake, since these two species rarely inhabit the same area.

Habitat and Habits: The smooth green snake is most frequently found in meadows, lawns, and weedy thickets. It may climb into low bushes although it is not as arboreal as the rough green snake. It is frequently found under loose boards and stones, a habitat rarely utilized by the rough green snake.

The smooth green snake is gentle and usually does not bite. When captured it squirms vigorously but soon resigns itself to curling around the fingers. Shortly after death these snakes, like the rough green snake, turn blue or bluish gray due to the breakdown of the unstable yellow pigment that is combined with the more stable blue pigment.

The diet of this snake is almost entirely insectivorous. Stomach analysis indicates grasshoppers, crickets, caterpillars, and spiders to be the main items of food.

Breeding: A limited number of observations are available within West Virginia on this species. Mating has been observed in mid to late August (Wright and Wright 1957). Five to 11 eggs are deposited in late June to early July. Nests have been found under stones exposed along roadside banks. Hatching probably occurs some time in August.

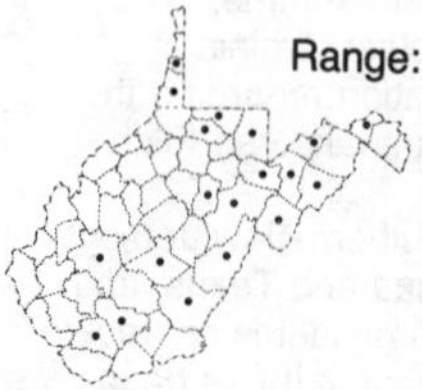

Range: Smooth green snakes range from Canada, south to North Carolina, and west through Wisconsin and Minnesota. Within West Virginia it is more common in the mountains where it is found with such species as the redbelly snake (no. 67), the eastern garter snake (no. 69), and the timber rattlesnake (no. 85; Pauley 1980a).

Genus *Elaphe Fitzinger* • Rat Snakes

These are large, elongated, terrestrial, and arboreal snakes. The adults have several of the dorsal scale rows weakly keeled; the anal plate is divided. They are oviparous and kill their food by constriction. The genus, which is circumglobal, contains six species in North America. Two species occur within West Virginia.

78 Corn Snake *Elaphe guttata guttata* (Linnaeus)

Gr. *elaphos,* a deer; L. *gutta,* spotted, speckled

Description: The corn snake is a distinctly attractive snake which attains an average length of 4 feet (1.2 m) although specimens of 6 feet (1.8 m) are known. The dorsal pattern consists of a series of red blotches, outlined in black, on a tan or orange background. The belly is boldly checkered with black on white. A prominent spear-shaped blotch, lighter in the center, extends from the neck forward between the eyes. The dorsal scales are lightly keeled, and the anal plate is divided.

Habitat and Habits: The corn snake inhabits dry fields and thickets. Although it is able to climb with fair agility, it is usually found on the ground, hiding beneath some surface cover. When cornered it assumes a defensive attitude, vibrating its tail and stiking viciously with a sharp hiss. It is primarily nocturnal and feeds on small mammals, lizards, snakes, and insects (Hamilton and Pollack 1956).

Breeding: Mating takes place from March to May. Clutches of up to 27 (but usually 5 to 10) eggs are deposited from May to July and hatch up to September. The hatchlings range from 10.0 to 15.0 inches (25.4–38.1 cm) in length and mature within three years. Bechtel and Bechtel (1958) reports that eggs hatched in captivity had an incubation period of 73 days and the young ranged in size from 10.0 to 12.0 inches (25.4–30.5 cm). MacMahon (1957) found the incubation period to be 56 to 57 days.

Range: The corn snake ranges from southern New Jersey to southern Florida and southern Louisiana. There are some isolated records from Kentucky. It was first reported from West Virginia on the basis of a single specimen from Morgan County (Grogan 1971). Since then one additional specimen has been collected in the same area. The corn snake was formerly thought to be a snake of the coastal plain. Specimens were known only from the eastern division of the Piedmont province until Norden (1971) collected a specimen in Washington County, Maryland. Additional records from adjacent counties in Virginia left a narrow gap in the Eastern Panhandle of West Virginia which was subsequently spanned by Grogan's record.

79 Black Rat Snake *Elaphe obsoleta obsoleta* (Say)

L. *obsoletus,* indistinct

Description: The black rat snake is a moderately proportioned snake which may attain a length in excess of 7 feet (2.1 m). The dorsal color is nearly uniformly black or dark brown with traces of white and orange between the scales. The belly is mottled with gray and white.

Juveniles have a dorsal pattern of 29 to 38 brownish blotches on a gray background. The juvenile pattern often persists well into adults of 4 feet (1.2 m) or longer as a pattern of indistinct dark blotches. As with other members of this genus, the dorsal scales are weakly keeled, and the anal plate is divided.

Habitat and Habits: Although the black rat snake is essentially a forest animal, it may wander into a variety of habitats such as swamp borders, river flood plains, abandoned sawdust piles, rocky hillsides, mountain ledges, farm buildings, and abandoned dwellings. It frequently basks in bushes along dusty country roads or on highways, where many of them are killed. Although not a truly arboreal snake, the black rat snake is at home in trees, climbing in search of bird eggs or nestlings. On one occasion a rat snake was observed 30 feet (9.1 m) from the ground on a dead snag robbing a woodpecker's nest (N. B. Green, personal observation).

When captured, the response of this snake is quite unpredictable. Some specimens fight viciously, striking repeatedly at the intruder and vibrating their tails vigorously; others remain calm and may be picked up without a show of resistance.

They have been found in association with copperheads (no. 84) and timber rattlers (no. 85), particularly during hibernation, and have been taken as early in the season as April 15. They appear more frequently during the summer months but become rare toward the end of October when the colder nights apparently drive them into hibernation.

Fitch (1963b) conducted an extensive study of this species over a 15-year period in eastern Kansas. He found the home ranges varied from 23 to 29 acres, with males being the more mobile. Sexual maturity is reached in the fourth year at a snout-vent length of a little less than 35.4 inches (90 cm) in males and slightly more in females. The red-tailed hawk is one of the snake's greatest enemies; Fitch found that 46 percent of the bulk of its food consisted of remains of the black rat snake. He also found that the black rat snake is especially subject to parasitism by chiggers. (See also Stickel *et al.* 1980.)

A prevailing myth among the people of the Mountain State is that copperheads (no. 84) interbreed with the rat snake and produce a poisonous black snake. This delusion results from the retention of the juvenile pattern in the rat snake, which remotely resembles the copperhead's pattern. These two species of reptiles are so distantly related that hybridization is impossible.

Earlier vernacular names included pilot blacksnake and mountain blacksnake. However, these names were discarded in favor of black rat snake, because they feed primarily on warm-blooded prey such as mammals, birds, and bird eggs (Uhler *et al.* 1939;

Stickel *et al.* 1980). Larger animals are killed by constriction, and smaller prey may be seized and swallowed. Frogs and lizards have been eaten in captivity and were found by Uhler *et al.* (1939) to comprise about 4 percent of the diet.

Breeding: Fitch (1963b) recorded the following data from northeast Kansas: Mating occurs in late April and May; egg-laying in late June or July; and hatching from late August into early October. The eggs are deposited in loose soil (many of them have been dug up in gardens) and sawdust piles. The number of eggs in a clutch ranges from 4 to 25. The eggs are elongate and oval and range from 1.5 to 1.9 inches (3.7–5.0 cm) in length and 0.83 to 1.1 inches (2.1–2.8 cm) in width. The shell is leathery and may become wrinkled as development progresses. The eggs may stick together forming a clump. The newly hatched young are from 11.0 to 16.0 inches (27.9–40.6 cm) long.

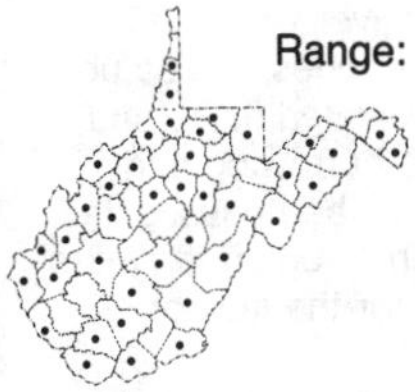

Range: The black rat snake ranges from southwestern New England and eastern Ontario to Georgia, west to Wisconsin, south through Iowa and Kansas to Oklahoma, and east to northern Louisiana. It is found throughout West Virginia where it has been collected up to 3,760 feet (1,146 m) in elevation (Pauley, personal observation).

Genus *Pituophis* Holbrook • Bullsnakes, Pine Snakes, and Gopher Snakes

The members of this genus are large, harmless, belligerent snakes with keeled scales and a single anal plate. They are best known for the audible hiss produced by forcing exhaled air over a flexible epiglottis. Dorsal patterns consist of a series of brownish squares on a white or tan background. The rostral plate at the anterior tip of the head is enlarged, elongated, and modified for burrowing. They are oviparous.

The genus ranges from Canada southward to Guatemala. Some herpetologists recognize three species, while others believe the genus to be composed of a complex of one species. One subspecies has been collected in West Virginia.

80 Northern Pine Snake *Pituophis melanoleucus melanoleucus* (Daudin)
Gr. *pitys,* the pine; Gr. *ophis,* a snake; Gr. *melas,* black; Gr. *leukos,* white

Description: The northern pine snake is known to attain a length of over 6 feet (1.8 m), although most adult specimens average between 4 and 5 feet (1.2–1.5 m). Its dorsal pattern is a series of irregular squarish blotches of black or dark brown on a ground color of white or dirty yellow. The blotches are poorly defined anteriorly, becoming more sharply defined toward the tail. The belly is glistening white with a row of black spots down each side. The head is small in proportion to the rest of the snake. The rostral plate is enlarged, curving backward between the internasals. There are four prefrontals rather than the two of our other colubrids.

Habitat and Habits: The pine snake has apparently invaded Virginia and West Virginia through the James River valley. It is found in sandy soil associated with pines and scrub oaks, as well as in brushy and cultivated fields and dry upland forests. Because it is a burrowing and secretive creature, its presence may be unsuspected even by persons who have lived in a region for years (Conant 1975). This may account for the lack of records in many localities.

The distinctly audible hiss, the rapid vibration of the tail, and the disposition to bite when first encountered are all characteristics of this species. Although diurnal, it spends much of its time underground and forages for food in the early morning or late afternoon hours. It is a powerful constrictor and feeds chiefly on small mammals, but it will also eat birds and their eggs (Fitch 1949). Juveniles may feed on small snakes and lizards.

Breeding: Little is known about its breeding behavior in nature. The eggs, which may number to 12 or more, are deposited from late June to the middle of July and hatch around the middle of September (Conant and Downs 1940; New 1953). The eggs measure 2.2 by 1.2 inches (5.6 x 3.1 cm) (New 1953) and are deposited in a sandy burrow several inches below the surface. New states that eggs hatch in 78 days.

Range: The northern pine snake ranges from southern New Jersey to the coastal plain and piedmont of the Carolinas, west into Kentucky, Tennessee, and Alabama. It was first reported in West Virginia by Llewellyn (1943) on the basis of a specimen found dead on a road in Monroe County, two miles southwest of Waiteville in June 1940 (CM 21265). Records indicate that this species is distributed along the Virginia side of the Virginia–West Virginia boundary, but this is apparently the only authentic record to date from West Virginia.

Genus *Lampropeltis* Fitzinger • Kingsnakes and Milk Snakes

The members of this genus are oviparous, non-venomous, and terrestrial. They are the only snakes in West Virginia that have both smooth scales and a single anal plate. All are strong constrictors and feed largely on other snakes, mammals, and birds. The genus occurs throughout the United States as well as southeastern Canada, Central America, and northern South America. Six species are recognized in North America, two of which occur in West Virginia: *Lampropeltis getulus* (Linnaeus), with eight currently recognized subspecies (two in West Virginia); and *Lampropeltis triangulum,* with nine subspecies (one in West Virginia).

81 **Eastern Kingsnake** *Lampropeltis getulus getulus* (Linnaeus)

Gr. *lampros,* shining; Gr. *pelte,* shield; *getulus,* after Getulia, Morocco

Description: The eastern kingsnake may attain a length of 6 feet (1.8 m), although 3 or 4 feet (0.9 or 1.2 m) is average. It is a shiny black serpent with about 40 narrow white or yellow crossbands which fork on the sides to connect with adjacent bars to form a chainlike pattern. The belly is checkered with black or yellow. The head is small and slightly distinct from the neck. The scales are in 21 or 23 rows at midbody.

Habitat and Habits: The eastern kingsnake is an ubiquitous snake which may be found in a variety of habitats. It frequents river valleys, dry upland pine woods, old sawdust piles, and abandoned dwellings. Wilson and Friddle (1946, 1950) note that many of their specimens have been collected in hay fields at harvest time (presumably searching for meadow voles). Others report them near bodies of water.

Kingsnakes are diurnal and secretive, taking cover under boards, bark, and logs. A freshly-captured specimen can be expected to expel a copious quantity of musk from its cloacal glands, but soon becomes docile when handled. When aroused they vibrate the tail vigorously and may occasionally bite or chew on the hand that holds them.

Kingsnakes feed upon other snakes, both venomous and nonvenomous, but they will take prey such as small mammals, birds, lizards, and frogs. Snakes and lizards are the major food items (Hamilton and Pollack 1956). They are strong constrictors and are capable of subduing a larger adversary. Although they capture and kill poisonous snakes, they apparently do not differentiate between the harmless and the venomous species. They are immune to the poison.

Breeding: Mating occurs shortly after emergence from hibernation in the spring, and egg-laying takes place in mid July. A clutch may contain up to 25 eggs, usually stuck together. They normally are deposited in sawdust or soil. Incubation may take up to 11 weeks, depending upon the ambient temperature. The hatchlings range from 9.0 to 11.0 inches (22.9–27.9 cm) in length.

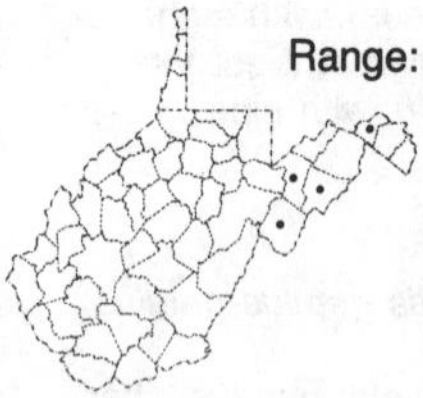

Range: The eastern kingsnake is found from southern New Jersey to northern Florida, and west along the eastern border of the Appalachians. In West Virginia it is known from the South Branch Valley of the Potomac including Hardy, Grant, Pendleton, and Morgan counties. The first recorded specimen from West Virginia was found dead on the highway two miles north of Petersburg, Grant County, on September 14, 1935 (Netting 1936b). Since this first record several specimens have been collected (Wilson and Friddle 1946).

82 Black Kingsnake *Lampropeltis getulus nigra* (Yarrow)

L. *niger,* black

Description: The black kingsnake may attain a length of nearly 5 feet (1.5 m) although most specimens are 3.5 to 4.0 feet (1.0–1.2 m). It is predominantly black above with white or yellow flecks which may form an indistinct chain pattern. The juveniles resemble the eastern kingsnake (no. 81) in that their dorsal pattern is much more distinct. The belly is black and yellow checkered.

Habitat and Habits: The black kingsnake frequents a variety of habitats such as roadside brush and forest borders as well as overgrown fields and golf courses. They are often seen crossing highways and many are killed in this manner. Like many other snakes, they spend much of their time under flat rocks, boards, or trash. They are diurnal and are frequently encountered wandering through vegetation. When surprised their reactions are similar to other kingsnakes: the tail vibrates rapidly, the forepart of the body is raised in a series of menacing loops accompanied by strikes and lunges. After being handled, they usually become tame.

The food of this subspecies is similar to that of the eastern kingsnake. Large snakes, mammals, and birds are seized by the head and encircled by one or more coils of the body which are pulled tightly until the victim is suffocated. Captive black kingsnakes were observed stalking other snakes and refraining from grasping them until an opportunity was afforded to strike at the head (Conant 1951). Snakes of all species are usually seized in this manner by kingsnakes, in spite of repeated bites from the prey.

Breeding: Kingsnakes have been found to mate early in May, with egg-laying in the latter part of July. Conant (1934) indicates an incubation period of 78 to 81 days. The hatchlings measure 9.2 to 10.7 inches (23.4–27.2 cm) in length.

Range: The black kingsnake ranges from southeastern West Virginia and southern Ohio to central Illinois, and south to western Tennessee, northeastern Mississippi, central Alabama, and northeastern Georgia. In West Virginia it has been reported from only the southwesternmost counties: Cabell, Kanawha, Lincoln, Mason, Putnam, and Wayne. A Harrison County record is questionable.

83 Eastern Milk Snake *Lampropeltis triangulum triangulum* (Lacépède)
L. *triangulum,* like a triangle

Description: The eastern milk snake may attain a length of 36.0 inches (91.4 cm). The head is small and slightly distinct from the neck. Like the other members of this genus the scales are smooth, and the anal plate is single. The scale row count is usually 21 at midbody. The dorsal pattern consists of about 35 chocolate brown to reddish brown, black-bordered blotches or saddles down the back alternating with smaller ones along the sides. The ground color is gray or tan. The belly has a checkered pattern of black and white squares. Juveniles are more brightly colored, with a series of red blotches on a light gray background.

Habitat and Habits: The milk snake appears to have no easily defined habitat preferences. It has been collected in grassy fields, woodlands, rocky hillsides, and around deserted dwellings and spring houses. During the day it may be found hiding under boards, logs, tarpaper, trash, and around sawdust piles. It is more active at night and is frequently observed during nocturnal studies of frogs.

Milk snakes are sluggish and cautious in foraging for food. When surprised in the field, they attempt to move away. They are, however, easy to capture. If molested they may assume a defensive pose, vibrate the tail, and attempt to bite. Instead of resorting to repeated strikes, they may seize a hand or finger and continue to chew as if attempting to swallow prey.

Milk snakes are more difficult to find during hotter days of the summer, even beneath suitable cover. Presumably most of this time is spent underground. Collection dates are from March 14 to October 11. The highest elevation at which this species has been collected in West Virginia is 4,433 feet (1,351 m) on Barton Knob in Randolph County.

The milk snake is not as ophiophagous (feeding on other snakes) as the kingsnakes, although it will prey upon other snakes. Small rodents comprise the bulk of its diet, according to several studies (Surface 1906; Uhler *et al.* 1939).

Breeding: The milk snake mates shortly after emergence from hibernation. Egg-laying occurs in June and July. The eggs, up to 18 in a clutch, adhere to one another. A female dug out of a sawdust pile in Wetzel County on June 18, 1961, laid 10 eggs which averaged 1.2 by 0.5 inches (3.1 x 1.4 cm) (N. B. Green, personal observation). The adherence of the eggs to one another is apparently not an accidental result of the egg-laying process, for in one instance the female was observed to contain the entire egg mass within her coils and to maneuver her body so as to press the eggs together in a compact mass. The reason for this behavior is not known, but it may be to conserve the heat necessary to incubate the eggs. Hatching occurs in August and September, from six to nine weeks after the eggs are laid.

Remarks: This snake is known by many names, such as house snake and checkered adder. The vernacular name, milk snake, is based on the belief that this snake sucks milk from cows. The myth presumably originated when the snake was seen searching for mice around barns and cow shelters. The milk snake is frequently killed by those who confuse it with the copperhead (no. 84) because of its superficial resemblance in color and pattern.

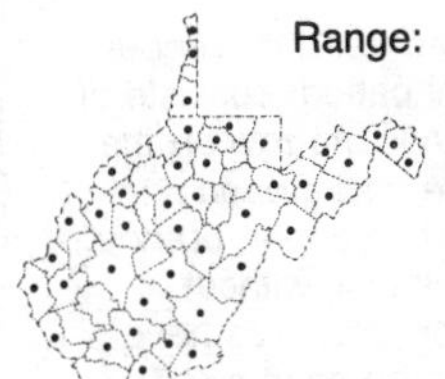

Range: Nine subspecies of *Lampropeltis triangulum* are recognized. These range throughout the eastern, central United States, and westward into New Mexico, Arizona, Utah, and Montana. The eastern milk snake ranges from Maine to Minnesota, south to northern Alabama and Georgia. It is widely distributed throughout West Virginia.

Family Viperidae • Vipers

This large family is found throughout the world except for Antarctica, Australia, and extreme high altitudes of the other continents. Approximately 200 species of the most dangerously poisonous snakes in the world are included. The family is divided into three subfamilies, the largest of which, the Crotalinae, contains all the New World members, in addition to representatives from eastern Europe through Asia to Japan and the East Indies. They are characterized by the presence of heat-sensitive facial pits (hence the name pit vipers), which detect changes in infrared wave lengths and are used to locate and accurately strike warm-blooded prey. Teeth are present in both jaws, with the front pair in the upper jaw bones modified into recurved, retractable hollow fangs. The fangs are folded back along the jaw, move forward as the mouth is opened to strike. In addition to facial pits, the crotalines may be separated from nonvenomous species by the single row of subcaudals except for a few at the tip of the tail. Their eyes have vertical pupils.

Genus *Agkistrodon* Beauvois • Copperheads and Cottonmouths

These are heavy-bodied snakes with strongly keeled scales and short tails. The genus has representatives in Asia, Europe, North America, and Central America. There are two species in North America, and one of these is represented in West Virginia.

84 **Northern Copperhead** *Agkistrodon contortrix mokasen* (Daudin)
Gr. *agkistron,* a fish hook; Gr. *odous,* tooth; L. *contortus,* twisted; *mokasen,* a word of Algonquian Indian origin

Description: The northern copperhead is a medium-sized snake which usually attains a length of 36.0 inches (91.4 cm), although larger specimens are occasionally encountered. It is richly colored, heavy-bodied snake with a large, flat, triangular-shaped head, a slender neck, and a stout body. Its dorsal pattern consists of 15 to 25 chestnut-brown crossbands, narrow on the back and broad on the sides. The background between the dorsal saddles may be copper, orange, or lighter brown. The top of the head is without markings and coppery red in color. Juveniles have a sulphur yellow tail. A facial pit lies on each side between the eye and the nostril. The belly is pale yellowish or cream-colored and marked laterally by dark, irregular blotches. The scales are keeled and the anal plate is single. Scales at midbody are in 23 to 25 rows. There is a single row of subcaudals from the vent to near the tip of the tail.

Habitat and Habits: The northern copperhead is found in a variety of situations which range from the most remote wilderness areas to the borders of the most populous cities. Its preferred habitat seems to be rocky hillsides or wooded slopes with rocky outcrops, although it is often found in valleys along streams and in and around old sawdust piles.

Copperheads are active throughout the day from early April to mid October. During hot weather they are mainly nocturnal and forage for food in the late evening and early morning hours. During daylight hours they remain hidden under stones, boards, leaves, and bark slabs. They remain in the area of hibernation for some time after emergence.

The copperhead is inoffensive, even lethargic, and reluctant to strike unless provoked. The bites are not as severe as those of the rattler (no. 85), partly because the copperhead is smaller and delivers less venom, and partly because the venom is less virulent. Serious effects seldom arise when reasonable treatment is performed.

Copperheads are not discriminating feeders. Their diet consists chiefly of mice and other small mammals, frogs, lizards, small snakes, and insects (Uhler *et al.* 1939; Savage 1967). During the periodical cicada emergence, there are frequent reports of copperheads feeding on the abundant insect.

Breeding: Mating takes place in April or May, shortly after emergence from hibernation. There are accounts of copperheads mating in the fall. Collins (1974) indicates that many female copperheads bear young only every other year. The number of young vary from 1 to 14 and range from 7.0 to 10.0 inches (17.8–25.4 cm) in length. Females attain sexual maturity at three years of age; males at two years (Fitch 1960a). A female copperhead collected at Fort Gay, Wayne County, on August 6 gave birth to 10 young the next day. Another specimen found dead on the highway on July 5 contained 6 embryos (N. B. Green, personal observation). Reese (1926) reported a female giving birth to 3 young on September 4 in West Virginia. For a comprehensive study of the reproductive cycle of the copperhead, see Fitch (1960a).

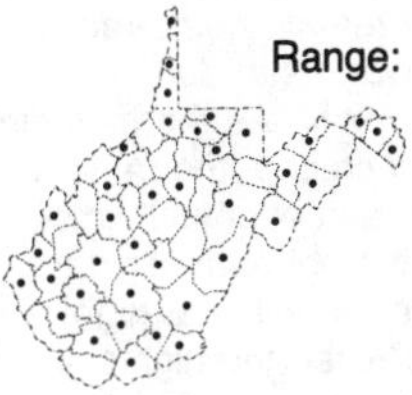

Range: The northern copperhead ranges from Massachusetts west to southern Illinois and western Tennessee, south to Alabama and Georgia. The records from throughout West Virginia indicate that it is the most widely distributed of the two species of venomous snakes within the state.

Genus *Crotalus* Linnaeus • Rattlesnakes

The genus *Crotalus* contains 25 species and subspecies of rattlesnakes within the borders of the United States. Eight additional species occur in Central and South America.

Members of the genus are heavy-bodied with a broad triangular head, a narrow neck, and undivided anal plate and subcaudals. The horny rattle, the structure for which the genus is named, is formed of interlocking segments, one of which is added with each shedding. One species occurs in West Virginia.

85 Timber Rattlesnake *Crotalus horridus* Linnaeus

Gr. *Krotalon,* a rattle; L. *horrens,* creating horror

Description: The timber rattler is a large, thick-bodied snake which may attain a total length of 5 feet (1.5 m), with an occasional specimen reaching 6 feet (1.8 m). The dorsal background color varies from bright sulphur yellow to dark brown, gray, or black with a series of 18 to 25 dark chevron-shaped crossbands extending down the back. The head is unmarked and the tail is velvet black. Specimens which are all black appear to occur more frequently at high elevations in the Alleghenies. Despite popular opinion, these color differences bear no relation to the sex of the individual. The scales are strongly keeled and range from 23 to 25 rows.

Habitat and Habits: The timber rattler is most frequently found in rough, mountainous terrain where brushy ridges and rocky hillsides with ledges abound. It is common in wooded areas, but may occur in valleys, along streams, and among slab piles around old sawmill sites. At one time the timber rattler was widely distributed throughout the state but deforestation, opening of recreation areas, forest fires, and highway development have reduced its numbers, and its occurrence in many areas is uncommon.

Rattlesnakes emerge from their dens during the first warm days of spring. They remain nearby for several weeks, basking in the warm sun during the day and returning to the den at night. As the daytime temperatures of early summer increase, the rattlers move farther from the den area and eventually disperse into the countryside. As the hot summer days continue, the rattlers become more active at night and less active during the day. When the nights become cooler, the snakes return to the den site and repeat the basking cycle as in the spring. They hibernate in deep fissures within the rock ledges below the frost line. Their dens are frequently shared by copperheads (no. 84) and black rat snakes (no. 79).

The timber rattler is not an aggressive snake. When surprised in the open, it will coil and strike, as well as make an attempt to escape. During the day it may be encountered in a torpid, sluggish condition in the shade of a bush. Most bites occur when the victim disregards caution and safety rules (see the following section on snake bite).

Rattlers eat primarily small mammals, mostly rodents such as small mice, voles, chipmunks, and squirrels (Uhler *et al.* 1939; Savage 1967; Keenlyne 1972). The rest of their diet consists of birds and eggs. They feed as the opportunity presents itself, and they may go for extended periods without food.

Breeding: Mating usually occurs in the spring following emergence from hibernation while the sexes are concentrated in the den area. The young are usually born in late summer. The number of young ranges up to 17, with 8 to 10 being the average. Newborn young range in size from 10.0 to 13.0 inches (25.4–33.0 cm) and have a prebutton at birth. Maturity is attained within three to four years. Timber rattlesnakes bear young in alternate years.

The Rattle: It is well known that each time a rattlesnake sheds its skin, it adds a new segment to the rattles. What is not understood is the phenomenon of shedding. Many studies have been undertaken to clarify this process, but contradictions have appeared at almost every step. It is thought that shedding is related to growth, and while this is probably true, newts, eastern garter snakes (no. 69), and red-eared sliders (no. 52) have been observed to shed when starved or not growing. Observations of healthy, growing timber rattlers have revealed four or five sheddings each season. Young, faster growing snakes shed more often.

The rattle is one of the strangest structures in nature. Nothing remotely resembling it occurs anywhere else in the animal kingdom. The buzzing sound produced as the snake shakes it from side to side cannot be heard by the snake, because it is thought that snakes cannot perceive airborne sounds. Many snakes shake the tail vigorously when annoyed or alarmed (rat snakes, kingsnakes, and copperheads). Terminal segments of the rattle are frequently broken, along with the button, as the snake moves over rocks. If an old snake retained all the segments, it would be carrying around an enormous string. This is never seen in nature; in fact, a very long string does not rattle properly.

Range: The timber rattlesnake ranges from southern New Hampshire, south to northern South Carolina, and west into southeastern Minnesota and northeastern Texas. In West Virginia its range extends from the Eastern Panhandle across the Alleghenies south into Mercer and Mingo counties. There are no records for the Northern Panhandle.

POISONOUS SNAKES AND SNAKEBITE

Snakes are easily confused with one another, and the question of whether a certain one is poisonous or harmless arises again and again. Of the 22 different kinds of snakes found in West Virginia, only two are considered dangerous to man. The chance of a person being bitten by one of these poisonous snakes is considerably less than that of being struck by lightning.

Both of the poisonous snakes in West Virginia are pit vipers; that is, they have a small pit or opening between the eye and the nostril on each side of the head. They also have an elliptical or vertical pupil and a pair of long, curved, hollow fangs in the roof of the mouth. These are enclosed in a fleshy sheath and are erected only when the mouth is open and the snake strikes. In addition, our two poisonous snakes have broad, flattened, arrow-shaped heads. This head shape is a result of a narrow neck and the position of the poison glands, which are located along the rear margins of the head. The most distinctive difference between the poisonous and the nonpoisonous snakes in West Virginia can be found on the underside of the tail, posterior to the vent. In the copperhead and the timber rattler there is a single row of scales, while in the nonpoisonous species there is a double row of scales from the vent to the tip of the tail.

For a more detailed description of each of these species, the reader is referred to the species account. Anyone who plans to spend any length of time in terrain where poisonous snakes are known to occur should become familiar with the appearance of the poisonous forms.

Species of Special Concern

WEST VIRGINIA has identified species of special concern that include not only those protected by federal legislation but those with limited ranges or occurrence within the borders of the state. These species are protected in that no one may take or collect these animals without first obtaining a permit from the Wildlife Resources Division of the West Virginia Department of Natural Resources.

The authors are indebted to the Wildlife Resources Division and the Natural Heritage Data Base of the Wildlife Resources Division for the following list of amphibians and reptiles.

Amphibians

Smallmouth Salamander (*Ambystoma texanum*)
Jefferson Salamander (*Ambystoma jeffersonianum*)
Blackbelly Salamander (*Desmognathus quadra-maculatus*)
Cheat Mountain Salamander (*Plethodon nettingi*)
White-spotted Salamander (*Plethodon punctatus*)
West Virginia Spring Salamander (*Gyrinophilus sub-terraneus*)
Green Salamander (*Aneides aeneus*)
Cave Salamander (*Eurycea lucifuga*)
Eastern Spadefoot Toad (*Scaphiopus holbrookii holbrookii*)
Northern Cricket Frog (*Acris crepitans crepitans*)
Blanchard's Cricket Frog (*Acris crepitans blanchardi*)
Upland Chorus Frog (*Pseudacris triseriata feriarum*)
Northern Leopard Frog (*Rana pipiens*)

Reptiles

Wood Turtle (*Clemmys insculpta*)
Map Turtle (*Graptemys geographica*)
Red-eared Slider (*Trachemys scripta elegans*)
Eastern River Cooter (*Pseudemys concinna concinna*)
Hieroglyphic Turtle (*Pseudemys concinna heiro-glyphica*)
Redbelly Turtle (*Pseudemys rubriventris rubriventris*)

Spotted Turtle (*Clemmys guttata*)
Ouachita Map Turtle (*Graptemys pseudogeographica ouachitensis*)
Midland Smooth Softshell (*Trionyx muticus muticus*)
Broadhead Skink (*Eumeces laticeps*)
Northern Coal Skink (*Eumeces anthracinus anthracinus*)
Ground Skink (*Scincella lateralis*)
Eastern Ribbon Snake (*Thamnophis sauritus sauritus*)
Eastern Kingsnake (*Lampropeltis getulus getulus*)
Mountain Earth Snake (*Virginia valeriae pulchra*)
Corn Snake (*Elaphe guttata guttata*)
Northern Pine Snake (*Pituophis melanoleucus melanoleucus*)

Species and Subspecies Which May Occur in West Virginia

THE FOLLOWING species have not been recorded from West Virginia, but because they have been collected close to the boundaries of the state may eventually be added to its herpetofauna. We hope that by listing them here we may alert local collectors to search for them and report any specimens collected to the authors.

This list is by no means complete; there may be species we have overlooked or others which are already present in some remote area of our state and have yet to be discovered. From 1965 to 1985 eight species were added to the West Virginia checklist of amphibians and reptiles. These included newly described species as well as species not previously recorded for West Virginia.

Eastern Tiger Salamander *Ambystoma tigrinum tigrinum* (Green)

This is a stout, heavy-bodied, broad-headed salamander which may attain a length of 13.0 inches (33.0 cm). Its background is dark brown with light spots, bars or blotches of yellowish, olive, or brownish. It has been confused with the spotted salamander (no. 4), but the dorsal markings of the tiger salamander extend onto the belly.

Eastern tiger salamanders could enter the state through the Eastern Panhandle from Maryland or through the Ohio Valley from Kentucky. MacGregor lists a record for Lewis County, Kentucky, which would place it about 50 miles (80.5 km) from Huntington.

Black Mountain Salamander *Desmognathus welteri* Barbour

This salamander is probably the most likely candidate for the next addition to the herpetofauna of West Virginia. It occurs in northeastern Kentucky up to Rowan and Elliott counties and from there south to the Tennessee border and east into western Virginia.

It shows a preference for mountain brooks, streams, and seepage areas where it lurks under stones. It has been collected at elevations of 2,000 to 4,000 feet (609.5–1,219.2 m). In areas where it has been collected nearly every wet spot supported a population (Barbour 1953).

The black mountain salamander is heavy-bodied and brownish in color. It may be confused with the dusky or seal salamander (no. 8, no. 10). It attains a total length of 6.0 inches (15.2 cm). The belly is mottled or stippled with dark pigment with no sharp separation at the sides between dorsal and ventral surfaces. The toe tips are usually dark and the tail terminates in a sharp keel. For a comparison of the larval and adult characteristics of *D. welteri, D. fuscus,* and *D. monticola,* see Juterbock (1978, 1984). Pike County is the only county in Kentucky that borders on West Virginia with a record for the salamander. It should be looked for anywhere in Wayne or Mingo counties.

Appalachian Woodland Salamander *Plethodon jordani* Blatchley

This salamander is a member of a species complex which, at one time, was composed of several distinct forms. It is now known that hybridization has caused the blending of their many characters. Look for a black salamander up to 7.0 inches (17.8 cm) in length. The belly and chin may be dark black or pale gray. Scattered over the back, legs, cheeks, and tail may be small spots or flecks of red, white, silver, or bronze. There are 16 costal grooves. They may be confused with slimy salamanders (no. 16) or Wehrle's salamander (no. 18). They are found at high altitudes throughout much of the humid forested southern Appalachians under logs, leaf litter, trash, moss, and rock slabs.

Highton (1972) discusses interactions between *P. jordani* and *P. glutinosus* and identifies areas in Virginia close to the southern West Virginia border where he has collected this species. These areas include Flat Top Mountain in western Giles County and Buckhorn Mountain in Tazwell and Bland counties.

Virginia Seal Salamander *Desmognathus monticola jeffersoni* Hoffman

This subspecies is likely to occur in the eastern panhandle. Its range is in the Blue Ridge Mountains of western Virginia and toward the West Virginia border at the eastern edge of the Eastern Panhandle. Its habitat is the same as the Appalachian seal salamander (no. 10), that is, shady mountain streams; but it differs in having smaller, dark dorsal markings (about the size of the salamander's eye) that are round and scattered.

Eastern Mud Turtle *Kinosternon subrubrum subrubrum* (Lacépède)

Tobey (1985) shows records for this species in the Potomac River along the Virginia (Loudoun County) and West Virginia (Jefferson County) border. The eastern mud turtle is a small turtle (less than 5.0 inches or 12.7 cm) that resembles the stinkpot. It lacks distinctive neck stripes (there may be yellowish spots or streaks on the head) or other field marks. The carapace is smooth and varies from greenish to blackish in color.

The species frequently leaves water and is found wandering on land. Its preferred habitat is shallow water such as small ponds and marshes.

Six-lined Racerunner *Cnemidophorus sexlineatus sexlineatus* (Linnaeus)

This is a slender, long-tailed lizard with six or seven yellowish stripes on a dark brown or black back. It may attain a length of 10.0 inches (25.4 cm) with two-thirds of the length being tail. The body is covered with tiny, granulelike scales. The belly of the males is bluish and juveniles have bluish tails.

Hoffman (1945) collected this species in Alleghany County, Virginia, just over the border from Greenbrier County. He reported seeing as many as a dozen in one season. The preferred habitat is open, well-drained areas with sand or loose soil. They are also found in open woods and thicket margins.

Northern Scarlet Snake *Cemophora coccinea copei* Jan

This is a small, brightly colored, harmless snake with a pattern of red saddles bordered with black and separated by yellow or white on its back. It may attain a length of 20.0 inches (50.8 cm) or more. The anal plate is single. The belly is plain white or yellow, and the pointed snout is red.

Hoffman (1977) collected a specimen, which had been mashed, along U.S. 60 one mile west of Covington, Alleghany County. Its identification was confirmed by Conant and Grobman, and it was deposited in the United States National Museum. The northern scarlet snake inhabits mixed hardwood or pine forests with sandy or loamy well-drained soils. It is burrowing and nocturnal. Barbour (1971) notes a questionable record from Rowan County, Kentucky.

Kirtland's Snake *Clonophis kirtlandi* (Kennicott)

The least aquatic of the water snakes, Kirtland's snake is usually encountered under flat rocks in wet, marshy meadows. Flattening of the body when surprised, a trait shared by the other water snakes, is developed to a remarkable degree in this species. Although an unlikely species to find within the state, we are listing it here because of the recent accumulation of distribution data throughout its range. Its secretive nature and its preference for a prairie or prairielike habitat make it difficult to find.

Kirtland's is a small snake, less than 2 feet (61.0 cm) long, with a small head and an indistinct neck. Its back is brown or grayish with two rows of dark spots on either side of the midline and a line of black spots along each side of a red belly. Jackson, Hocking, Fairfield, and Perry counties in Ohio, and Allegheny and Westmoreland counties in Pennsylvania lie within its range.

Rossman and Powell (1985) accompany their account of this species with a map of its distribution showing a small portion of the Northern Panhandle of West Virginia.

Excluded or Doubtfully Recorded Species

Eastern Tiger Salamander *Ambystoma tigrinum tigrinum* (Green)

Bond's record (1931) for Monongalia County and Strader's record for Hampshire County (1936) are unsubstantiated. Netting (1938) discusses these two records.

Redbelly Water Snake *Nerodia erythrogaster erythrogaster* (Forster)

Two specimens collected in Pocahontas County near Marlinton in 1933 were catalogued as CM S6920-56921 and originally identified as the redbelly water snake. A preliminary list of amphibians and reptiles of West Virginia issued by M. Graham Netting on December 1, 1931, included *Natrix sipedon erythrogaster.* According to C. J. McCoy, in correspondence dated December 22, 1982, the specimens listed as *N. erythrogaster* are actually patternless *N. sipedon.*

Brown Water Snake *Nerodia taxispilota* (Holbrook)

Bond (1931) includes this species in his Monongalia County list. Wright and Wright (1952) list it as "problematic." There are no valid records for the brown water snake in West Virginia.

Eastern Massasauga *Sistrurus catenatus catenatus* (Rafinesque)

Wright and Wright (1952) list the eastern Massasauga as "problematic." Shaver (1931) refers to it as the "little gray rattler inhabiting the western slope of the Alleghenies to the Ohio River, never plentiful and very scarce now." Although no specimen from West Virginia exists, the possibility of its being a member of the herpetofauna at one time still lingers.

Eastern Cottonmouth *Agkistrodon piscivorus piscivorus* (Lacépède)

Hickman (1922) lists a sight record for the cottonmouth at Bristol, Harrison County, about 300 miles northwest of the nearest verified localities in southeastern Virginia. This species, which is confined to the coastal plain and interior lowlands, is not apt to occur in the Appalachian Plateau, and it cannot be added to the fauna of West Virginia on such fragile testimony. It is also listed in the account of reptiles and amphibians in the *West Virginia Encyclopedia* (Reese 1929). These two accounts have contributed to the prevailing myth that cottonmouths are to be found in West Virginia.

American Alligator *Alligator mississippiensis* (Daudin)

The alligator is cited in *West Virginia Wildlife* (1928) by a man claiming to have caught a 54-inch alligator in a pool in Raleigh County. More recently Michael Seidel has received reports of alligators from Wayne and Lincoln counties. These instances are used here to illustrate the numerous accounts which appear from time to time in the news media of such exotics as horned toads, Carolina anoles, and various species of snakes which have either escaped from captivity or have been released by their thoughtless owners. It is unlikely that any of these displaced creatures can long survive outside their native habitat.

Glossary

Bibliography

Index

Glossary

Adpression of limbs: In some salamanders and lizards, identification involves the number of costal grooves or scale rows between digits of an extended forelimb and hind limb. A forelimb and hind limb on one side of the body are extended full length toward the middle of the trunk, pressed against the body, and held in place while the count is made.

Alveolar surface: Part of jawbone with teeth. In turtles, the crushing surface of the jaw.

Amplexus: In amphibians, the sexual clasp of a female by the male.

Anal plate: In snakes, the large scale immediately in front of and covering the vent. May be single or divided by a diagonal suture.

Balancer: Slender, lateral head appendage in some salamander larvae.

Barbel: In some turtles, a flaplike or conelike fleshy protuberance usually on the chin.

Bridge: In turtles, the narrow connection between the carapace and plastron on each side.

Button: In rattlesnakes, the first permanent rattle acquired, i.e., the final segment of any complete and unbroken string of rattles.

Carapace: In turtles, the dorsal portion of the shell.

Chromatophore: A cell which bears pigment.

Cirrus: In some salamanders, e.g., male *Eurycea,* one of a pair of slender appendages protruding from the anterior edge of the upper lip.

Cloaca: The common chamber into which the intestinal, urinary, and reproductive ducts discharge their contents.

Compressed: Pressed together, flattened from side to side (laterally), as opposed to depressed, i.e., flattened from top to bottom.

Costal fold: In salamanders, the area between two adjacent costal grooves.

Costal groove: In salamanders, one of several vertical depressions on the sides of the trunk.

Cranial crest: In toads, one of the paired raised ridges on the head; crests may be interorbital (between the eyes) or postorbital (behind the eyes).

Cranial ridge: In certain salamanders, e.g., *Notophthalmus,* one of two parallel bony ridges along the top of the skull.

Cusp: A toothlike projection in turtles.

Dentary: One of the bones of the lower jaw.

Diploid: Having chromosomes in homologous pairs.

Dorsal: Pertaining to the upper surface; opposed to ventral.

Dorsolateral fold: In frogs of the genus *Rana,* one of the ridges extending from an eye along the lateral surface of the trunk.
Eft: A transformed, but sexually immature, newt; the terrestrial stage.
Fat bodies: In amphibians, a mass of fatty tissue associated with the gonads.
Femoral pore: A hole in the center of a single enlarged scale on the ventral surface of the thigh in some lizards.
Fossorial: Adapted for digging or burrowing.
Frontal: In snakes and most lizards, a large central plate on top of the head between the eyes.
Gill slit: One of the paired openings from the pharynx to the outside. Gill slits are located just in front of the insertion of the forelimbs.
Groin: The angle formed by the anterior margin of the hind limb and body.
Gular: A transverse fold of skin in the throat region.
Hemipenis: In lizards and snakes, one of the paired copulatory organs.
Hinge: In turtles, a broad articulation between anterior and posterior parts of the plastron.
Holotype: A single specimen designated to represent a particular species.
Intercalary cartilage: A cartilaginous element inserted between the ultimate and penultimate phalanges of members of the *Hylidae,* e.g., *Hyla, Acris,* and *Pseudacris.*
Internasals: In snakes, a pair of scales on top of the head between the nasal openings.
Karyotype: Drawing or photograph that describes the chromosome makeup.
Labial: In some reptiles, one of the scales bordering the lips, i.e., superior and inferior labials.
Lore: Sides of head between eyes and nostrils.
Loreal: In snakes, the scale on each side of the head in front of the eyes.
Marginals: In turtles, the scutes on the outer edge of the carapace.
Maxilla or **maxillary:** One of the two bones of the upper jaw.
Melanistic: More than normal amount of the brown to black pigment *melanin.*
Melanophore: A pigment cell containing the brown to black pigment *melanin.*
Mental gland: In salamanders, a hedonic gland (or cluster of glands) beneath the chin in some males. The secretion of hedonic glands is a sexual stimulant to females.
Naris: One of the paried openings of the nasal cavities; nares may be internal (choanae) or external.
Nasolabial groove: In salamanders of the family Plethodontidae, a groove extending from an external naris to the upper lip.
Nuchal: The bone lying on the anterior margin of the turtle carapace, on the midline. May also be applied to nuchal scute.
Oral disc: The highly complex structures surrounding the mouth opening in larval anurans. Composed of papillae, labial tooth rows, and upper and lower mandibles (beak).
Osteoderm: A bony deposit in the scales of certain lizards.
Palatine: One of two bones in the roof of the mouth.
Papilla: A fleshy projection.

Parasphenoid tooth: In amphibians, one of several teeth borne on the parasphenoid bone.
Parotoid gland: In various toads, a glandular swelling behind each eye.
Pectoral gland: In spadefoot toads, a small gland on the chest of some species.
Phalanges: The finger bones.
Pheromone: A substance secreted by an individual that influences a physiological or behavioral response from another individual of the same species.
Pit: In pit vipers, a deep cavity between an eye and external naris which serves as an infrared detector in locating warm-blooded prey.
Plastron: In turtles, the ventral portion of the shell.
Plica: In certain salamanders, e.g., the Ambystomatidae, one of several ridges of tissue on the tongue.
Plinth: In amphibians, e.g., some frogs, an egg mass that is flattened and somewhat rectangular rather than spherical.
Posteriorad: Toward the posterior axis.
Postlabial: In lizards, any of one of several plates lying behind and in line with the labials.
Postmental: In lizards and snakes, paired or unpaired scale on the underside of the head posterior to the mental scale (a scale at the anterior tip of the lower jaw).
Prebutton: In rattlesnakes, the rattle that is present at birth and lost when the skin is shed the first time.
Prefrontals: In snakes, a pair of scales on top of the head anterior to the eyes.
Premaxillary: The most anterior pair of bones of the upper jaw.
Pterygoid: Pair of bones in the roof of the mouth.
Rostral: In reptiles, the scale at the tip of the snout which separates the superior labial rows.
Scale: In reptiles, one of the many horny epidermal outgrowths which cover the body. A keeled scale has a ridgelike process; a smooth scale lacks the process.
Scale count: In snakes and some lizards, the number of scales in a row is important in classification. A scale row extends diagonally across the body from the ventral (belly) scutes on one side to the ventrals on the opposite side. Scales are usually counted on three regions of the body: back of the head; about the middle of the body; and just in front of the vent. Figures obtained (e.g., 17-15-15) constitute the scale count formula.
Scute: In reptiles, a modified (usually enlarged) scale.
Septum: A partition.
Sonogram: A graphic analysis of sounds used to study frog calls.
Spiracle: In tadpoles, a small opening to the outside from the gill chamber.
Subcaudal: In snakes, a scale on the ventral surface of the tail. Some snakes, such as copperheads and rattlesnakes, have a single row of subcaudals, and others possess a double row.

Subarticular tubercle: In hylid frogs, a small rounded hump or bump located at the joint between two of the bony phalanges.

Subgular: Below the throat.

Supranasal: In reptiles, the scale or scales lying just above the nasal scale and lateral to the internasals.

Symphysis: Junction between two bones that are located in the middle plane of the body.

Synonymy: The various scientific names that have been used in different publications to designate a species.

Tetraploid: Having chromosomes in two homologous pairs.

Triturating surface: In turtles, a grinding surface of the jaws.

Tibia: The bone on the great toe side of the shank of a hind leg.

Tuberculate: With small, discrete, rounded humps or bumps in the skin, e.g., the belly of many hylid frogs.

Twilight zone: The area of a cave illuminated by natural light.

Tympanum: The membrane at the external margin of the middle ear chamber. These membranes do not occur in salamanders and snakes.

Urostyle: In toads and frogs, a rodlike bone formed by several fused vertebrae that makes up the lower part of the vertebral column.

Venter: The belly.

Ventral: Pertaining to the lower surface; opposed to *dorsal*. Also, in snakes, one of the broad scales on the belly (neck to vent).

Vitellus: In amphibians, the egg proper (excluding gelatinous materials).

Vocal sac: In male frogs and toads, the inflatable pouch in the throat or one of the inflatable pouches in the sides of the neck.

Vomerine tooth: In amphibians, one of several teeth borne on the vomer bone (between and near internal nares).

Wart: A hard cornified prominence on the skin.

Bibliography

This bibliography is divided into three sections. The first, General References, contains titles for the general reader who wishes to learn more about herpetology; some books may be out of print but should be available in libraries. Part Two gives full bibliographic information for works cited in the text. The final section lists works consulted by the authors but not directly quoted.

GENERAL REFERENCES

Barbour, Roger W. 1971. *Amphibians and reptiles of Kentucky.* Lexington: The University Press of Kentucky. 344 pp.

Behler, John L., and F. Wayne King. 1979. *The Audubon Society field guide to North American reptiles and amphibians.* New York: Knopf. 719 pp.

Bishop, Sherman C. 1941. *The salamanders of New York.* New York State Museum Bulletin 324. 365 pp.

_____. 1943. *Handbook of salamanders.* Ithaca, N.Y.: Comstock. 555 pp.

Brooks, Maurice. 1965. *The Appalachians.* Cambridge: Houghton Mifflin, The Riverside Press. 346 pp.

Carr, Archie F. 1952. *Handbook of turtles: The turtles of the United States, Canada and Baja California.* Ithaca, N.Y.: Comstock. 542 pp.

Collins, Joseph T. 1974. *Amphibians and reptiles in Kansas.* Public Education Series 1. Lawrence: University of Kansas, Museum of Natural History. 283 pp.

_____, *et al.* 1982. Standard common and current scientific names for North American amphibians and reptiles. 2d ed. *Soc. Study Amphib. Rept. Herpet. Circ.* 12:1–28.

Conant, Roger. 1975. *A field guide to reptiles and amphibians of eastern and central North America.* Boston: Houghton Mifflin. 429 pp.

DeGraaf, Richard M., and Deborah D. Rudis. 1983. *Amphibians and reptiles of New England.* Amherst: University of Massachusetts Press. 85 pp.

Dickerson, M. C. [1906] 1969. *The frog book.* New York: Dover. 253 pp.

Duellman, William E., and Linda Trueb. 1986. *Biology of amphibians.* New York: McGraw Hill. 670 pp.

Dunn, E. R. 1926. *Salamanders of the family Plethodontidae.* Smith College 50th Ann. Publ. 7. 441 pp.

Ernst, Carl H., and P. W. Barbour. 1972. *Turtles of the United States.* Lexington: The University Press of Kentucky. 347 pp.

Goin, C. J., Olive B. Goin, and George R. Zug. 1978. *Introduction to herpetology.* San Francisco: W. H. Freeman. 378 pp.

Hudson, George E. 1972. Reprint. *The amphibians and reptiles of Nebraska.* Nebraska Conservation Bulletin 24. Lincoln: University of Nebraska. 146 pp.

Johnson, Tom R. 1977. *The amphibians of Missouri.* Public Education Series 6. Lawrence: University of Kansas, Museum of Natural History. 134 pp.

Kauffeld, C. 1957. *Snakes and snake hunting.* Garden City, N.Y.: Hanover House. 266 pp.

———. 1969. *Snakes: The keeper and the kept.* Garden City, N.Y.: Doubleday. 248 pp.

Klauber, L. M. 1972. *Rattlesnakes: Their habits, life histories, and influence on mankind.* 2d ed. 2 vols. Berkeley and Los Angeles: University of California Press.

Linzey, Donald W., and Michael J. Clifford. 1981. *Snakes of Virginia.* Charlottesville: The University Press of Virginia. 159 pp.

McCauley, Robert H. 1945. *The reptiles of Maryland and the District of Columbia.* Hagerstown, Md.: published by the author. 194 pp.

Martof, Bernard. 1956. *Amphibians and reptiles of Georgia.* Athens: University of Georgia Press. 260 pp.

———, W. M. Palmer, J. R. Bailey, and J. R. Harrison III. 1980. *Amphibians and reptiles of the Carolinas and Virginia.* Chapel Hill: University of North Carolina Press. 264 pp.

Minton, Sherman, Jr. 1972. *Amphibians and reptiles of Indiana.* Indiana Academy of Science Monograph 3. Indianapolis. 346 pp.

Mount, Robert H. 1975. *The reptiles and amphibians of Alabama.* Auburn University Agricultural Experiment Station. 347 pp.

Nickerson, Max Allen, and Charles E. Mays. 1973. *The hellbenders: North American "Giant Salamanders."* Publications in Biology and Geology 1. Milwaukee Public Museum. 106 pp.

Noble, G. K. 1931. *The biology of the amphibia.* New York: McGraw Hill. 577 pp.

Oliver, James A. 1955. *The natural history of North American amphibians and reptiles.* Princeton, N.J.: Van Nostrand. 359 pp.

Peters, James A. 1964. *Dictionary of herpetology.* New York: Hafner. 392 pp.

Pope, Clifford H. 1937. *Snakes alive and how they live.* New York: Viking Press. 238 pp.

———. 1939. *Turtles of the United States and Canada.* New York: Knopf. 343 pp.

Porter, K. R. 1972. *Herpetology.* Philadelphia: W. B. Saunders. 524 pp.

Pritchard, P. C. H. 1967. *Living turtles of the world.* Jersey City, N.J.: T.F.H. Publications. 288 pp.

Schmidt, K. P. 1953. *A check list of North American amphibians and reptiles.* 6th ed. Chicago: Amer. Soc. Ichthyol. and Herpetol. 280 pp.

_____, and D. Dwight Davis. 1941. *Field book of snakes of the United States and Canada.* New York: G. P. Putnam's Sons. 365 pp.

Simon, Hilda. 1979. *Easy identification guide to North American snakes.* New York: Dodd, Mead. 128 pp.

Smith, H. M. 1946. *Handbook of lizards: Lizards of the United States and Canada.* Ithaca, N.Y.: Comstock. 557 pp.

Smith, Hobart M. 1978. *Amphibians of North America: A guide to field identification.* New York: Golden Press. 160 pp.

_____, and Edmund D. Brodie, Jr. 1982. *Reptiles of North America.* New York: Golden Press. 240 pp.

Smith, Philip W. 1961. The amphibians and reptiles of Illinois. *Illinois Nat. Hist. Surv.* Bull. 28:1–298.

Stebbins, R. C. 1951. *Amphibians of western North America.* Berkeley and Los Angeles: University of California Press. 539 pp.

_____. 1966. *A field guide to western reptiles and amphibians.* Boston: Houghton Mifflin. 528 pp.

Wright. A. H., and A. A. Wright. 1949. *Handbook of frogs and toads.* Ithaca, N.Y.: Comstock. 640 pp.

_____. 1957. *Handbook of snakes of the United States and Canada.* 2 vols. Ithaca, N.Y.: Comstock. 1105 pp.

LITERATURE CITED

Agassiz, Louis. 1857. *Contributions to the natural history of the United States of America.* First monograph, vol. 1, pt. 2: North American Testudinata. Boston: Little, Brown and Co. Pp. 237–452.

Adler, Kraig. 1968. *Pseudemys scripta* in West Virginia: Archeological and modern records. *J. Herpetol.* 2:117–20.

Allen, William B. 1955. Some notes on reptiles. *Herpetologica* 11:228.

Anderson, James D., and P. J. Martino. 1967. Food habits of *Eurycea l. longicauda. Herpetologica* 23:105–08.

Angle, John. 1969. The reproductive cycle of the northern ravine salamander, *Plethodon richmondi richmondi,* in the Valley and Ridge Province of Pennsylvania and Maryland. *J. Washington Acad. Sci.* 59:192–202.

Ashton, Ray E., Jr., and Patricia A. Ashton. 1978. Movements and winter behavior of *Eurycea bislineata* (Amphibia, Urodela, Plethodontidae). *J. Herpetol.* 12:295–98.

Baldauf, R. J. 1952. Climatic factors influencing the breeding migration of the spotted salamander, *Ambystoma maculatum* (Shaw). *Copeia* 1952:178–81.

Banta, Arthur M., and Waldo L. McAtee. 1906. The life history of the cave salamander, *Spelerpes maculicaudus* (Cope). *Proc. U.S. Natl. Mus.* 30:67–83.

Barbour, Roger W. 1953. The amphibians of Big Black Mountain, Harlan County, Kentucky. *Copeia* 1953:84–89.

———. 1971. *Amphibians and reptiles of Kentucky.* Lexington: The University Press of Kentucky. 334 pp.

———. Michael J. Harvey, and James W. Hardin. 1969. Home range, movements, and activity of the eastern worm snake, *Carphophis amoenus amoenus. Ecology* 50:470–6.

Baumann, Walter L., and Michael Huels. 1982. Nests of the two-lined salamander, *Eurycea bislineata. J. Herpetol.* 16:81–83.

Bayless, Laurence D. 1972. A new turtle record, *Chrysemys floridana, for West Virginia. J. Herpetol.* 6:39–41.

Bechtel, Bernard H., and Elizabeth Bechtel. 1958. Reproduction in captive corn snakes, *Elaphe guttata guttata. Copeia* 1958:148–49.

Behler, John L., and F. Wayne King. 1979. *The Audubon Society field guide to North American reptiles and amphibians.* New York: Knopf. 719 pp.

Bell, Edwin L. 1956. Some aspects of the life history of the red salamander, *Pseudotriton r. ruber,* in Huntingdon County, Pa. *Mengel Naturalist* 3:10–13.

Bellis, Edward D. 1961. Growth of the wood frog, *Rana sylvatica. Copeia* 1961:74–77.

Besharse, J. C., and J. R. Holsinger. 1977. *Gyrinophilus subterraneus,* a new troglobitic salamander from southern West Virginia. *Copeia* 1977:624–34.

Bishop, Sherman C. 1920. Notes on the habits and development of the four-toed salamander, *Hemidactylium scutatum* (Schlegel). *N.Y. State Mus. Bull.* 219:251–82.

———. 1941. The salamanders of New York, *N.Y. State Mus. Bull.* 324:1–365.

Blair, Albert P. 1941. Variation, isolation mechanisms and hybridization in certain toads. *Genetics* 26:398–417.

Blanchard, Frank N. 1923. The life history of the four-toed salamander. *Amer. Nat.* 57:262–68.

———. 1926. Eggs and young of the eastern ringneck snake, *Diadophis punctatus edwardsii. Papers Michigan Acad. Sci. Arts, Letters* 7:279–92.

———. 1928. Topics from the life history and habits of the red-backed salamander in southern Michigan. *Amer. Nat.* 62:156–64.

———. 1930a. Further studies of the eggs and young of the eastern ringneck snake, *Diadophis punctatus edwardsii. Bull. Antivenin Inst. Amer.* 4:4–10.

———. 1930b. The stimulus to the breeding migration of the spotted salamander, *Ambystoma maculatum* Shaw. *Amer. Nat.* 64:154–67.

———. 1933. Late autumn collections and hibernating situations of the salamander *Hemidactylium scutatum* (Schlegel) in southern Michigan. *Copeia* 1933:216.

———. 1934a. The spring migration of the four-toed salamander *Hemidactylium scutatum* (Schlegel). *Copeia* 1934:50.

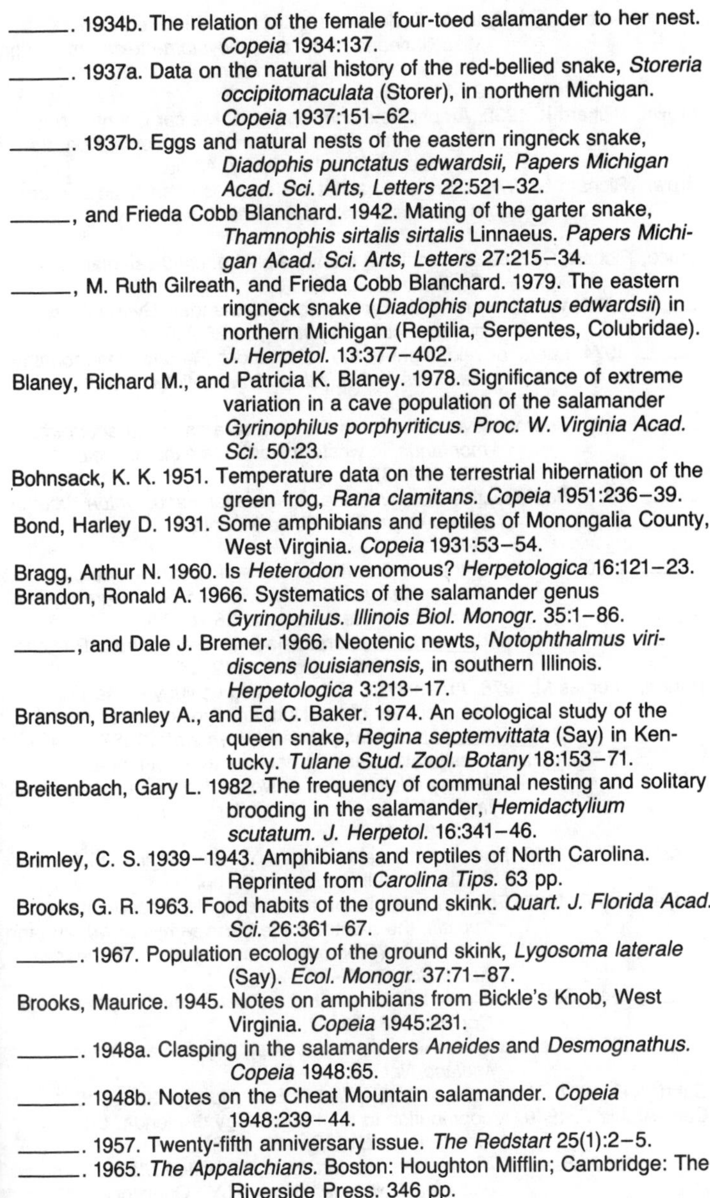

______. 1934b. The relation of the female four-toed salamander to her nest. *Copeia* 1934:137.

______. 1937a. Data on the natural history of the red-bellied snake, *Storeria occipitomaculata* (Storer), in northern Michigan. *Copeia* 1937:151–62.

______. 1937b. Eggs and natural nests of the eastern ringneck snake, *Diadophis punctatus edwardsii, Papers Michigan Acad. Sci. Arts, Letters* 22:521–32.

______, and Frieda Cobb Blanchard. 1942. Mating of the garter snake, *Thamnophis sirtalis sirtalis* Linnaeus. *Papers Michigan Acad. Sci. Arts, Letters* 27:215–34.

______, M. Ruth Gilreath, and Frieda Cobb Blanchard. 1979. The eastern ringneck snake (*Diadophis punctatus edwardsii*) in northern Michigan (Reptilia, Serpentes, Colubridae). *J. Herpetol.* 13:377–402.

Blaney, Richard M., and Patricia K. Blaney. 1978. Significance of extreme variation in a cave population of the salamander *Gyrinophilus porphyriticus. Proc. W. Virginia Acad. Sci.* 50:23.

Bohnsack, K. K. 1951. Temperature data on the terrestrial hibernation of the green frog, *Rana clamitans. Copeia* 1951:236–39.

Bond, Harley D. 1931. Some amphibians and reptiles of Monongalia County, West Virginia. *Copeia* 1931:53–54.

Bragg, Arthur N. 1960. Is *Heterodon* venomous? *Herpetologica* 16:121–23.

Brandon, Ronald A. 1966. Systematics of the salamander genus *Gyrinophilus. Illinois Biol. Monogr.* 35:1–86.

______, and Dale J. Bremer. 1966. Neotenic newts, *Notophthalmus viridiscens louisianensis,* in southern Illinois. *Herpetologica* 3:213–17.

Branson, Branley A., and Ed C. Baker. 1974. An ecological study of the queen snake, *Regina septemvittata* (Say) in Kentucky. *Tulane Stud. Zool. Botany* 18:153–71.

Breitenbach, Gary L. 1982. The frequency of communal nesting and solitary brooding in the salamander, *Hemidactylium scutatum. J. Herpetol.* 16:341–46.

Brimley, C. S. 1939–1943. Amphibians and reptiles of North Carolina. Reprinted from *Carolina Tips.* 63 pp.

Brooks, G. R. 1963. Food habits of the ground skink. *Quart. J. Florida Acad. Sci.* 26:361–67.

______. 1967. Population ecology of the ground skink, *Lygosoma laterale* (Say). *Ecol. Monogr.* 37:71–87.

Brooks, Maurice. 1945. Notes on amphibians from Bickle's Knob, West Virginia. *Copeia* 1945:231.

______. 1948a. Clasping in the salamanders *Aneides* and *Desmognathus. Copeia* 1948:65.

______. 1948b. Notes on the Cheat Mountain salamander. *Copeia* 1948:239–44.

______. 1957. Twenty-fifth anniversary issue. *The Redstart* 25(1):2–5.

______. 1965. *The Appalachians.* Boston: Houghton Mifflin; Cambridge: The Riverside Press. 346 pp.

Brown, Barbara A., Wynn W. Cudmore, and John O. Whitaker, Jr. 1982. Miscellaneous notes on *Ambystoma texanum* in Vigo County, Indiana. *Proc. Indiana Acad. Sci.* 92:473–78.

Brown, Richard K. 1932. Amphibians and reptiles of Mercer County, West Virginia, with notes on stomach contents. M.A. thesis, West Virginia University. 42 pp.

Brown, Richard L. 1974. Diets and habitat preferences of selected anurans in southeast Arkansas. *Amer. Midland Nat.* 91:468–73.

Bruce, Richard C. 1969. Fecundity in primitive plethodontid salamanders. *Evolution* 23:50–54.

———. 1972. Variation in the life cycle of the salamander, *Gyrinophilus prophyriticus. Herpetologica* 28:230–45.

———. 1974. Larval development of the salamander *Pseudotriton montanus diastictus* and *P. ruber. Amer. Midland Nat.* 92:173–90.

———. 1975. Reproductive biology and the mud salamander, *Pseudotriton montanus,* in western North Carolina. *Copeia* 1975:129–37.

———. 1978. Reproductive biology of the salamander *Pseudotriton ruber* in the southern Blue Ridge Mountains. *Copeia* 1978:417–23.

———. 1980. A model of the larval period of the spring salamander, *Gyrinophilus porphyriticus,* based on size-frequency distributions. *Herpetologica* 36:78–86.

———. 1985. Larval period and metamorphosis in the salamander *Eurycea bislineata. Herpetologica* 41:19–20.

Burton, Thomas M. 1976. An analysis of the feeding ecology of the salamanders of the Hubbard Brooks experimental forest, New Hampshire. *J. Herpetol.* 10:187–204.

———. 1977. Population estimates, feeding habitats and nutrient and energy relationships of *Notophthalmus v. viridescens,* in Mirror Lake, New Hampshire. *Copeia* 1977:139–43.

Cadbury, B. B. 1936. Notes on the salamanders of West Virginia. M.A. thesis, Cornell University. 92 pp.

Cagle, Fred B. 1937. Egg laying habits of the slider turtle *(Pseudemys troostii),* the painted turtle (*Chrysemys picta),* and the musk turtle *(Sternotherus odoratus). J. Tennessee Acad. Sci.* 12:87–95.

———. 1948. Sexual maturity in the male turtle, *Pseudemys scripta troostii. Copeia* 1948:108–11.

———. 1954. Observations on the life cycles of painted turtles. *Amer. Midland Nat.* 52:225–35.

Cahn, A.R. 1937. The turtles of Illinois. *Illinois Biol. Monogr.* 35:1–218.

Carr, Archie F. 1940. A contribution to the herpetology of Florida. *Univ. Florida Publ. Biol. Ser.* 3:1–118.

———. 1952. *Handbook of turtles: The turtles of the United States, Canada and Baja California.* Ithaca, N.Y.: Comstock. 542 pp.

Cervone, Thomas H. 1983. The natural history of *Virginia valeriae pulchra* (Serpentes; Colubridae). Ph. D. diss. St. Bonaventure University. 181 pp.

Clark, David B., and J. Whitfield Gibbons. 1969. Dietary shift in the turtle *Pseudemys scripta* (Schoepff) from youth to maturity. *Copeia* 1969:704–06.

Clausen, H. J. 1936. Observation on the brown snake *Storeria dekayi* (Holbrook), with especial reference to the habits and birth of young. *Copeia* 1936:98–102.

Clay, W. M., Roberta B. Case, and Robert Cunningham. 1955. On the taxonomic status of the slimy salamander, *Plethodon glutinosus* (Green), in southeastern Kentucky. *Trans. Kentucky Acad. Sci.* 16:57–65.

Cochran, Philip A., and David R. McConville. 1983. Feeding by *Trionyx spiniferus* in backwaters of the upper Mississippi River. *J. Herpetol.* 17:82–86.

_____, and David D. Lyons. 1985. *Necturus maculosus* (mudpuppy): Juvenile ecology. *Herp. Rev.* 16:53.

Collins, Joseph T. 1974. *Amphibians and reptiles in Kansas.* Public Education series 1. Lawrence: University of Kansas, Museum of Natural History. 283 pp.

_____, *et al.* 1982. Standard common and current scientific names for North American amphibians and reptiles. 2d ed. *Soc. Study Amphib. Rept. Herpet. Circ.* 12:1–28.

Conant, Roger. 1934. Observations on the eggs of the black kingsnake, *Lampropeltis getulus nigra* Yarrow. *Copeia* 1934:188–89.

_____. 1938. The reptiles of Ohio. *Amer. Midland Nat.* 20:1–200.

_____. 1951. *The reptiles of Ohio.* Notre Dame, Ind.: University of Notre Dame Press. 284 pp.

_____. 1975. *A field guide to reptiles and amphibians of eastern and central North America.* Boston: Houghton Mifflin. 429 pp.

_____, and Alexander Downs, Jr. 1940. Miscellaneous notes on the eggs and young of reptiles. *Zoologica* 25:33–48.

_____, Milton B. Trautman, and E. Bruce McClean. 1964. The false map turtle, *Graptemys pseudogeographica* (Gray) in Ohio. *Copeia* 1964:212–13.

Cope, E. D., and A. S. Packard, Jr. 1881. The fauna of Nikajack Cave. *Amer. Nat.* 15:877–82.

Cupp, Paul V., Jr. 1971. Fall courtship of the green salamander, *Aneides aeneus. Herpetologica* 27:308–10.

_____. 1980. Territoriality in the green salamander, *Aneides aeneus. Copeia.* 1980:463–68.

Danstedt, Rudolph Theodore, Jr. 1975. Local geographic variation and demographic parameters and body size of *Desmognathus fuscus* (Amphibia: Plethodontidae). *Ecology* 56:1054–67.

Davidson, John A. 1956. Notes on the food habits of the slimy salamander, *Plethodon glutinosus glutinosus. Herpetologica* 12:129–31.

Davis, D. Dwight. 1946. Observations on the burrowing behavior of the hog-nosed snake. *Copeia* 1946:75–78.

Devine, M. C. 1976. Species discrimination in mate selection by free living male garter snakes and experimental evidence for the role of pheromones. *Herp. Rev.* 7:79.

Duellman, William E. 1954. The salamander *Plethodon richmondi* in southwestern Ohio. *Copeia* 1954:40–45.

Edgren, Richard A. 1955. The natural history of the hog-nosed snakes, genus *Heterodon:* A review. *Herpetologica* 11:105–17.

Emlen, S. T. 1968. Territoriality in the bullfrog, *Rana catesbeiana. Copeia* 1968:240–43.

Ernst, Carl H. 1970. Reproduction in *Clemmys guttata. Herpetologica* 26:228–32.

———. 1971. Observations of the painted turtle, *Chrysemys picta. J. Herpetol.* 5:216–20.

———. 1974. Observations on the courtship of male *Graptemys pseudogeographica. J. Herpetol.* 8:377–78.

———. 1976. Ecology of the spotted turtle, *Clemmys guttata* (Reptilia, Testudines, Testudinidae) in southeastern Pennsylvania. *J. Herpetol.* 10:25–33.

———. 1982. Environmental temperatures and activities in wild spotted turtles, *Clemmys guttata. J. Herpetol.* 16:112–20.

———, and R. W. Barbour. 1972. *Turtles of the United States.* Lexington: The University Press of Kentucky. 347 pp.

Evans, Llewellyn T. 1953. The courtship pattern of the box turtle, *Terrepene c. carolina. Herpetologica* 9:189–92.

Ewing, H. E. 1943. Continued fertility in female box turtles following mating. *Copeia* 1943:112–14.

Finneran, Leo Charles. 1948. Reptiles in Branford, Connecticut. *Herpetologica* 4:123–26.

Fitch, Henry S. 1949. Study of snake populations in central California. *Amer. Midland Nat.* 41:513–79.

———. 1954. Life history and ecology of the five-lined skink, *Eumeces fasciatus. Univ. Kansas Publ., Mus. Nat. Hist.* 8:1–156.

———. 1960a. Autecology of the copperhead. *Univ. Kansas Publ., Mus. Nat. Hist.* 13:85–280.

———. 1960b. Criteria for determining sex and breeding maturity in snakes. *Herpetologica* 16:49–51.

———. 1963a. Natural history of the racer, *Coluber constrictor. Univ. Kansas Publ., Mus. Nat. Hist.* 15:351–468.

———. 1963b. Natural history of the black rat snake *(Elaphe o. obsoleta)* in Kansas. *Copeia* 1963:649–58.

———. 1965. An ecological study of the garter snake, *Thamnophis sirtalis. Univ. Kansas Publ., Mus. Nat. Hist.* 15:493–564.

———. 1970. *Reproductive cycles in lizards and snakes.* Misc. Publ 52. Kansas Univ. Mus. Nat. Hist. 247 pp.

———. 1975. A demographic study of the ringneck snake *(Diadophis punctatus)* in Kansas. *Univ. Kansas Publ., Mus. Nat. Hist.* 62:1–53.

———, and Michael V. Plummer. 1975. A preliminary ecological study of the soft-shelled turtle *Trionyx muticus* in the Kansas River. *Israel J. Zool.* 24:28–42.

Fitzpatrick, Lloyd. 1972. Energy allocation in the Allegheny Mountain salamander, *Desmognathus ochrophaeus. Ecol. Monogr.* 43:43–48.

Force, E. R. 1933. The age of attainment of sexual maturity of the leopard frog, *Rana pipiens* Schreber, in northern Michigan. *Copeia* 1933:128–31.

Ford, Neil B. 1978. Evidence for species specificity of pheromone trails in two sympatric garter snakes, *Thamnophis. Herp. Rev.* 9:10.

———. 1981. Seasonality of pheromone trailing behavior in two species of garter snake, *Thamnophis* (Colubridae). *Southwestern Nat.* 26:385–88.

———. 1982. Courtship behavior of the queen snake, *Regina septemvittata. Herp. Rev.* 13:72.

Forester, Dan C. 1977. Comments on the female reproductive cycle and philopatry by *Desmognathus ochrophaeus* (Amphibia, Urodela, Plethodontidae). *J. Herpetol.* 11:311–16.

———, and Daniel La Pasha. 1982. Failure of orientation to frog calls by migrating spotted salamanders. *Bull. Maryland Herp. Soc.* 18:143–51.

Fowler, James A. 1940. A note on the eggs of *Plethodon glutinosus. Copeia* 1940:133.

———. 1967. The upland chorus frog *(Pseudacris brachyphona)* in Maryland. *Bull. Maryland Herp. Soc.* 3:43–44.

Franz, Richard, and Herb Harris. 1965. Mass transformation and movement of the larval long-tailed salamander, *Eurycea longicauda longicauda* (Green). *J. Ohio Herp. Soc.* 5:32.

Fraser, Douglas F. 1974. Interactions between salamanders of the genus *Plethodon* in the central Appalachians. Ph.D. diss. University of Maryland. 153 pp.

———. 1976. Coexistence of salamanders in the genus *Phethodon:* A variation of the Santa Rosalia theme. *Ecology* 57:238–51.

Frum, W. Gene. 1947. *Graptemys geographica* in West Virginia. *Copeia* 1947:211.

Garton, John S. 1972. Courtship of the smallmouth salamander, *Ambystoma texanum,* in southern Illinois. *Herpetologica* 28:41–45.

Gates, J. Edward, and Edward L. Thompson. 1982. Small pool habitat selection by red-spotted newts in western Maryland. *J. Herpetol.* 16:7–15.

Gatz, A. J., Jr. 1971. Critical thermal maxima of *Ambystoma maculatum* (Shaw) and *Ambystoma jeffersonianum* (Green) in relation to time of breeding. *Herpetologica* 27:157–60.

Gibbons, Whitfield J. 1968. Reproduction potential, activity, and cycles in the painted turtle, *Chrysemys picta. Ecology* 49:399–409.

Goin, C. J., Olive B. Goin, and George R. Zug. 1978. *Introduction to herpetology.* San Francisco: W. H. Freeman. 378 pp.

Goldsmith, Steven K. 1984. Aspects of the natural history of the rough green snake, *Opheodrys aestivus* (Colubridae). *Southwestern Nat.* 29:445–52.

Gordon, R. E. 1952. A contribution to the life history and ecology of the plethodontid salamander, *Aneides aeneus* (Cope and Packard). *Amer. Midland Nat.* 47:666–701.

_____, and R. L. Smith. 1949. Notes on the life of the salamander, *Aneides aeneus. Copeia* 1949:173–75.

Grafton, C. R., and W. H. Dickerson. 1969. Influence of topography on rainfall in West Virginia. Water Research Institute Bull. 1. Morgantown: W. Virginia University. 45 pp.

Graham, Terry E. 1971. Eggs and hatchlings of the red-bellied turtle, *Chrysemys rubiventris,* from Plymouth, Massachusetts. *J. Herpetol.* 5:59–60.

Green, David M. 1984. Sympatric hybridization and allozyme variation in the toads *Bufo americanus* and *Bufo fowleri* in southern Ontario. *Copeia* 1984:18–26.

Green, N. Bayard. 1931. The amphibians and reptiles of Randolph County, West Virginia. M.S. thesis, West Virginia University. 95 pp.

_____. 1935. Further notes on the food habits of *Cryptobranchus alleganiensis. Proc. W. Virginia Acad. Sci.* 9:36.

_____. 1937. The amphibians and reptiles of Randolph County, West Virginia. *Herpetologica* 1:113–16.

_____. 1952. A study of the life history of *Pseudacris brachyphona* Cope in West Virginia with special reference to behavior and growth of marked individuals. Ph.D. diss. Ohio State University. 163 pp.

_____. 1961. Recent developments in herpetology in West Virginia. *Proc. W. Virginia Acad. Sci.* 33:21–27.

_____. 1963. The eastern spadefoot toad, *Scaphiopus holbrooki holbrooki* Harlan, in West Virginia. *Proc. W. Virginia Acad. Sci.* 35:15–19.

_____. 1967. Distribution, including a northernmost locality record, of *Desmognathus quadramaculatus* in West Virginia. *Proc. W. Virginia Acad. Sci.* 39:294–96.

_____. 1969. The ratio of crescent and cruciform patterns in populations of the mountain chorus frog, *Pseudacris brachyphona,* in West Virginia. *Proc. W. Virginia Acad. Sci.* 41:142–44.

_____, and Paul Brant. 1966. Salamanders found in West Virginia caves. *Proc. W. Virginia Acad. Sci.* 38:42–45.

_____, Paul Brant, Jr., and Bernard Dowler. 1967. *Eurycea lucifuga* in West Virginia: Its distribution, ecology, and life history. *Proc. W. Virginia Acad. Sci.* 39:297–304.

_____, and Neil D. Richmond. 1940. Two amphibians new to the herpetofauna of West Virginia *(Scaphiopus h. holbrooki* and *Ambystoma texanum).* Copeia 1940:27.

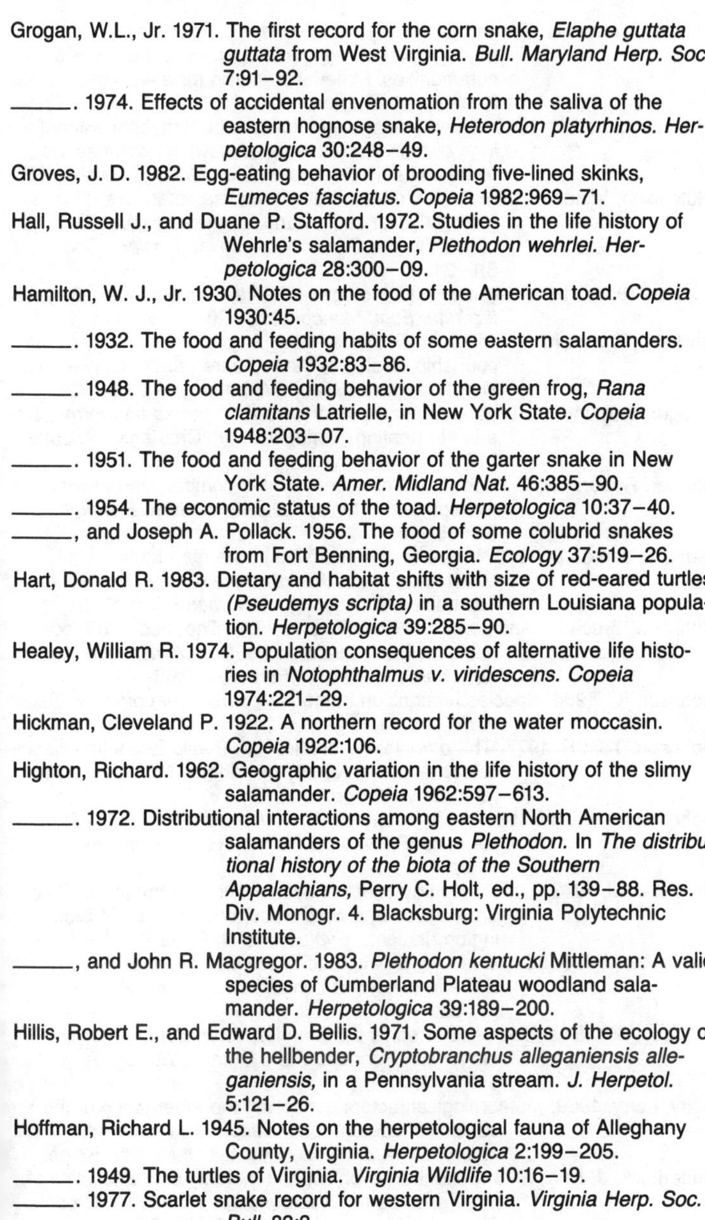

Grogan, W.L., Jr. 1971. The first record for the corn snake, *Elaphe guttata guttata* from West Virginia. *Bull. Maryland Herp. Soc.* 7:91–92.

______. 1974. Effects of accidental envenomation from the saliva of the eastern hognose snake, *Heterodon platyrhinos. Herpetologica* 30:248–49.

Groves, J. D. 1982. Egg-eating behavior of brooding five-lined skinks, *Eumeces fasciatus. Copeia* 1982:969–71.

Hall, Russell J., and Duane P. Stafford. 1972. Studies in the life history of Wehrle's salamander, *Plethodon wehrlei. Herpetologica* 28:300–09.

Hamilton, W. J., Jr. 1930. Notes on the food of the American toad. *Copeia* 1930:45.

______. 1932. The food and feeding habits of some eastern salamanders. *Copeia* 1932:83–86.

______. 1948. The food and feeding behavior of the green frog, *Rana clamitans* Latrielle, in New York State. *Copeia* 1948:203–07.

______. 1951. The food and feeding behavior of the garter snake in New York State. *Amer. Midland Nat.* 46:385–90.

______. 1954. The economic status of the toad. *Herpetologica* 10:37–40.

______, and Joseph A. Pollack. 1956. The food of some colubrid snakes from Fort Benning, Georgia. *Ecology* 37:519–26.

Hart, Donald R. 1983. Dietary and habitat shifts with size of red-eared turtles *(Pseudemys scripta)* in a southern Louisiana population. *Herpetologica* 39:285–90.

Healey, William R. 1974. Population consequences of alternative life histories in *Notophthalmus v. viridescens. Copeia* 1974:221–29.

Hickman, Cleveland P. 1922. A northern record for the water moccasin. *Copeia* 1922:106.

Highton, Richard. 1962. Geographic variation in the life history of the slimy salamander. *Copeia* 1962:597–613.

______. 1972. Distributional interactions among eastern North American salamanders of the genus *Plethodon.* In *The distributional history of the biota of the Southern Appalachians,* Perry C. Holt, ed., pp. 139–88. Res. Div. Monogr. 4. Blacksburg: Virginia Polytechnic Institute.

______, and John R. Macgregor. 1983. *Plethodon kentucki* Mittleman: A valid species of Cumberland Plateau woodland salamander. *Herpetologica* 39:189–200.

Hillis, Robert E., and Edward D. Bellis. 1971. Some aspects of the ecology of the hellbender, *Cryptobranchus alleganiensis alleganiensis,* in a Pennsylvania stream. *J. Herpetol.* 5:121–26.

Hoffman, Richard L. 1945. Notes on the herpetological fauna of Alleghany County, Virginia. *Herpetologica* 2:199–205.

______. 1949. The turtles of Virginia. *Virginia Wildlife* 10:16–19.

______. 1977. Scarlet snake record for western Virginia. *Virginia Herp. Soc. Bull.* 83:3.

Howard, James H., Richard L. Raesly, and Richard L. Thompson. 1984. Management of nongame species and ecological communities. Material prepared for a workshop, Univ. Kentucky, Lexington.

Hurlbert, Stuart H. 1969. The breeding migrations and interhabitat wanderings of the vermilion-spotted newt *Notophthalmus viridescens* (Rafinesque). *Ecol. Monogr.* 39:465–88.

Hutchison, Victor H. 1956. Notes on the plethodontid salamanders, *Eurycea lucifuga* (Rafinesque) and *Eurycea longicauda longicauda* Green. *Occas. Papers Nat. Speleol. Soc.* 3:1–24.

———. 1958. The distribution and ecology of the cave salamander, *Eurycea lucifuga. Ecol. Monogr.* 28:1–20.

Jackson, Crawford G., and John D. Davis. 1972. A quantitative study of the courtship display of the red-eared turtle, *Chrysemys scripta elegans* (Wied). *Herpetologica* 29:58–64.

Jaeger, Edmund C. 1966. *A source book of biological names and terms.* 3rd ed., 4th printing. Springfield, Ill.: Charles C. Thomas. 317 pp.

Jaeger, Robert. 1972. Food as a limited resource in competition between two species of terrestrial salamanders. *Ecology* 53:535–46.

Jenkins, James D. 1979. Notes on the courtship of the map turtle, *Graptemys pseudogeographica* (Gray) (Reptilia, Testudines, Emydidae). *J. Herpetol.* 13:129–31.

Johnson, Bruce K., and James L. Christiansen. 1976. The food and food habits of Blanchard's cricket frog, *Acris crepitans blanchardi,* in Iowa. *J. Herpetol.* 10:63–74.

Johnson, C. 1966. Species recognition in the *Hyla versicolor* complex. *Texas J. Sci.* 18:361–64.

Johnson, Tom R. 1977. The amphibians of Missouri. Public Education Series 6. Lawrence: University of Kansas, Museum of Natural History. 134 pp.

Johnson, Wilber W. 1961. A life history of *Plethodon wehrlei* in the high plateaus. Ph.D. diss. St. Bonaventure University. 91 pp.

Jones, J. M. 1973. Effects of thirty years of hybridization on the toads *Bufo americanus* and *Bufo woodhousei fowleri* at Bloomington, Indiana. *Evolution* 27:435–48.

Judd, W. W. 1954. Observations on the food of the little brownsnake, *Storeria dekayi,* at London, Ontario. *Copeia* 1954:62–64.

———. 1957. The food of Jefferson's salamander, *Ambystoma jeffersonianum,* in Rondeau Park, Ontario. *Ecology* 38:77–81.

Judy, Larry. 1969. Meteorological factors controlling the emergence of the eastern spadefoot toad, *Scaphiopus holbrookii holbrookii.* M.S. thesis, Marshall University. 53 pp.

Jutterbock, J. Eric. 1978. Sexual dimorphism and maturity characteristics of three species of *Desmognathus* (Amphibia, Urodela, Plethodontidae). *J. Herpetol.* 12:217–30.

———. 1984. Evidence for the recognition of specific status for *Desmognathus welteri. J. Herpetol.* 18:240–55.

Keen, Hubert. 1979. Feeding activity patterns in the salamander *Desmognathus ochrophaeus* (Amphibia, Urodela, Plethodontidae). *J. Herpetol.* 13:461–67.

———, and Lowell P. Orr. 1980. Reproductive cycle, growth, and maturation of northern female *Desmognathus ochrophaeus. J. Herpetol.* 14:7–10.

Keenlyne, K.D. 1972. Sexual differences in feeding habits of *Crotalus horridus horridus. J. Herpetol.* 6:234–37.

Knight, Allen W., and J. Whitfield Gibbons. 1968. Food of the painted turtle, *Chrysemys picta,* in a polluted river. *Amer. Midland Nat.* 80:558–62.

Korschgen, Leroy J., and Don L. Moyle. 1955. Food habits of the bullfrog in central Missouri farm ponds. *Amer. Midland Nat.* 54:332–41.

Krzysik, Anthony J. 1980. Microhabitat selection and brooding phenology of *Desmognathus fuscus fuscus* in western Pennsylvania. *J. Herpetol.* 14:291–92.

Labanick, George M. 1976. Prey availability, consumption, and selection of the cricket frog, *Acris crepitans* (Amphibia, Anura, Hylidae), *J. Herpetol.* 10:293–98.

Lagler, Karl F. 1943. Food habits and economic relations of the turtles of Michigan with special reference to fish management. *Amer. Midland Nat.* 2:257–312.

Lee, David S., and Arnold W. Norden. 1973. A food study of the green salamander, *Aneides aeneus. J. Herpetol.* 7:53–54.

Lee, R., Mingteh Chang, and Roger Calhoun. 1973. Elevation in West Virginia. *W. Virginia Agri. and Forestry* 5:5–9.

———, Stanislaw Tajehman, D. G. Boyer, and E. W. Repa. 1977. Normal precipitation in West Virginia. *W. Virginia Agri. Forestry* 7:12–18.

Linzey, Donald W. 1967. Food of the leopard frog, *Rana p. pipiens,* in central New York. *Herpetologica* 23:11–17.

List, J. C. 1950. Observations on the courtship behavior of *Thamnophis sirtalis sirtalis. Herpetologica* 6:71–74.

Little, Michael L. 1983. The zoogeography of the *Hyla versicolor* complex in the central Appalachians, including physiological and morphological analyses. Ph.D. diss. University of Louisville. 88 pp.

Llewellyn, Leonard M. 1943. The common pine snake in West Virginia. *Copeia* 1943:129.

Loncke, Daniel J., and Martyn E. Obbard. 1977. Tag success, dimensions, clutch size, and resting site fidelity for the snapping turtle, *Chelydra serpentina* (Reptilia, Testudines, Chelydridae) in Algonquin Park, Ontario, Canada. *J. Herpetol.* 11:243–44.

McCallister, Wayne H. 1963. Evidence of mild toxicity in the saliva of the hognose snake *(Heterodon). Herpetologica* 19:132–37.

McCauley, Robert H., Jr. 1945. *The reptiles of Maryland and the District of Columbia.* Hagerstown, Md.: published by the author. 194 pp.

McCoy, Clarence J., Jr. 1965. Mountain earth snake in West Virginia. *The Redstart,* Oct., 108.

McDowell, Samuel B. 1964. Partition of the genus *Clemmys* and related problems in the taxonomy of aquatic Testudinidae. *Proc. Zool. Soc. London* 142:239–79.

MacMahon, James A. 1957. Observations on mating in the corn snake, *Elaphe guttata guttata. Copeia* 1957:232.

MacNamara, Mark C. 1977. Food habits of terrestrial adult migrants and immature red efts of the red-spotted newt *Notophthalmus viridescens. Herpetologica* 33:127–32.

Maha, George C., Linda R. Maxson, and Richard Highton. 1983. Immunological evidence for the validity of *Plethodon kentucki. J. Herpetol.* 17:398–400.

Mahmoud, I. Y. 1968. Feeding behavior of kinosternid turtles. *Herpetologica* 24:300–05.

Marion, Ken R. 1970. Temperature as the reproductive cue for the female fence lizard, *Sceloporus undulatus. Copeia* 1970:562–64.

______. 1982. Reproductive cues for gondal development in temperature reptiles: Temperature and photoperiod effects on the testicular cycle of the lizard, *Sceloporus undulatus. Herpetologica* 38:26–30.

Martof, Bernard. 1952. Early transformation of the green frog, *Rana clamitans latreille. Copeia* 1952:115–16.

______. 1953. Territoriality in the green frog, *Rana clamitans. Ecology* 34:165–74.

______. 1956. Factors influencing size and composition of populations of *Rana clamitans. Amer. Midland Nat.* 56:224–45.

______, W. M. Palmer, J. R. Bailey, and J. R. Harrison III. 1980. *Amphibians and reptiles of the Carolinas and Virginia.* Chapel Hill: University of North Carolina Press. 257 pp.

Minton, Sherman A. 1944. Introduction to the study of the reptiles of Indiana. *Amer. Midland Nat.* 32:438–77.

______. 1972. *Amphibians and reptiles of Indiana.* Indiana Academy of Science Monograph 3. Indianapolis. 346 pp.

Mitchell, Joseph C. 1985. Female reproductive cycle and life history attributes in a Virginia population of painted turtles, *Chrysemys picta. J. Herpetol.* 19:218–26.

Mittleman, M. B. 1951. American Caudata VIII: Two new salamanders of the genus *Plethodon. Herpetologica* 7:105–12.

Moehn, Loren D. 1980. Microhabitat preference in the broadheaded skink. *Bull. Chicago Herp. Soc.* 15:49–53.

Mohr, C. E. 1931. Observations on the early breeding habits of *Ambystoma jeffersonianum* in central Pennsylvania. *Copeia* 1931:102–04.

______. 1943. The eggs of the long-tailed salamander, *Eurycea longicauda*

longicauda (Green). *Proc. Pennsylvania Acad. Sci.* 17:86.

Moore, J. E., and E. H. Strickland. 1955. Further notes on the food of Alberta Amphibians. *Amer. Midland Nat.* 54:253–56.

Mosaur, Walter. 1935. How fast can snakes travel? *Copeia* 1935:6–9.

Mount, Robert H. 1975. *The reptiles and amphibians of Alabama.* Auburn University Agriculture Experimental Station. 347 pp.

Mushinsky, Henry R. 1979. Mating behavior of the common water snake, *Nerodia sipedon sipedon* (Reptilia, Serpentes, Colubridae) in eastern Pennsylvania. *J. Herpetol.* 13:127–29.

Myers, Charles W. 1958. Notes on the eggs and larvae of *Eurycea lucifuga* Rafinesque. *Quart. J. Florida Acad. Sci.* 21:115–30.

Nagel, Jerry W. 1977. Life history of the redback salamander, *Plethodon cinereus,* in northeastern Tennessee. *Herpetologica* 33:13–18.

Nemuras, Kenneth T. 1967. Genus *Clemmys. Int. Turtle and Tortoise Soc. J.* 1:38–40.

Netting, M. G. 1931. A preliminary list of the amphibians and reptiles of West Virginia. Mimeographed list 1. Pittsburgh: Carnegie Museum of Natural History.

______. 1936a. Wehrle's salamander, *Plethodon wehrlei* Fowler and Dunn, in West Virginia. *Proc. W. Virginia Acad. Sci.* 10:89–93.

______. 1936b. The chain snake, *Lampropeltis getulus getulus* (L), in West Virginia and Pennsylvania. *Ann. Carnegie Mus.* 25:77–82.

______. 1938. The occurrence of the eastern tiger salamander, *Ambystoma t. tigrinum* (Green), in Pennsylvania and nearby states. *Ann. Carnegie Mus.* 27:159–66.

______. 1939. The ravine salamander, *Plethodon richmondi,* Netting and Mittleman, in Pennsylvania. *Proc. Pennsylvania Acad. Sci.* 13:50–51.

______. 1940. The spotted turtle, *Clemmys guttata:* An addition to the herpetofauna of West Virginia. *Proc. W. Virginia Acad. Sci.* 14:146–47.

______, and Neil Richmond. 1932. The green salamander, *Aneides aeneus,* in northern West Virginia. *Copeia* 1932:101–02.

______, N. Bayard Green, and Neil D. Richmond. 1946. The occurrence of Wehrle's salamander, *Plethodon wherlei* Fowler and Dunn, in Virginia. *Proc. Biol. Soc. Washington* 59:157–60.

New, John G. 1953. The young of the snake *Pituophis melanoleucus melanoleucus. Copeia* 1953:182–84.

Nichols, Thomas J. 1982. Courtship and copulatory behavior of captive eastern hognose snakes, *Heterodon platyrhinos. Herp. Rev.* 13:16–17.

Nickerson, M. A., and C. E. Mays. 1972. *The hellbenders.* Publ. Biol. Geol. 1. Milwaukee Public Museum. 106 pp.

Noble, G. K. 1926. The Long Island newt: A contribution to the life-history of *Triturus viridescens. Amer. Mus. Novitates* 228:1–11.

______. 1929. The relation of courtship to the secondary sexual characters

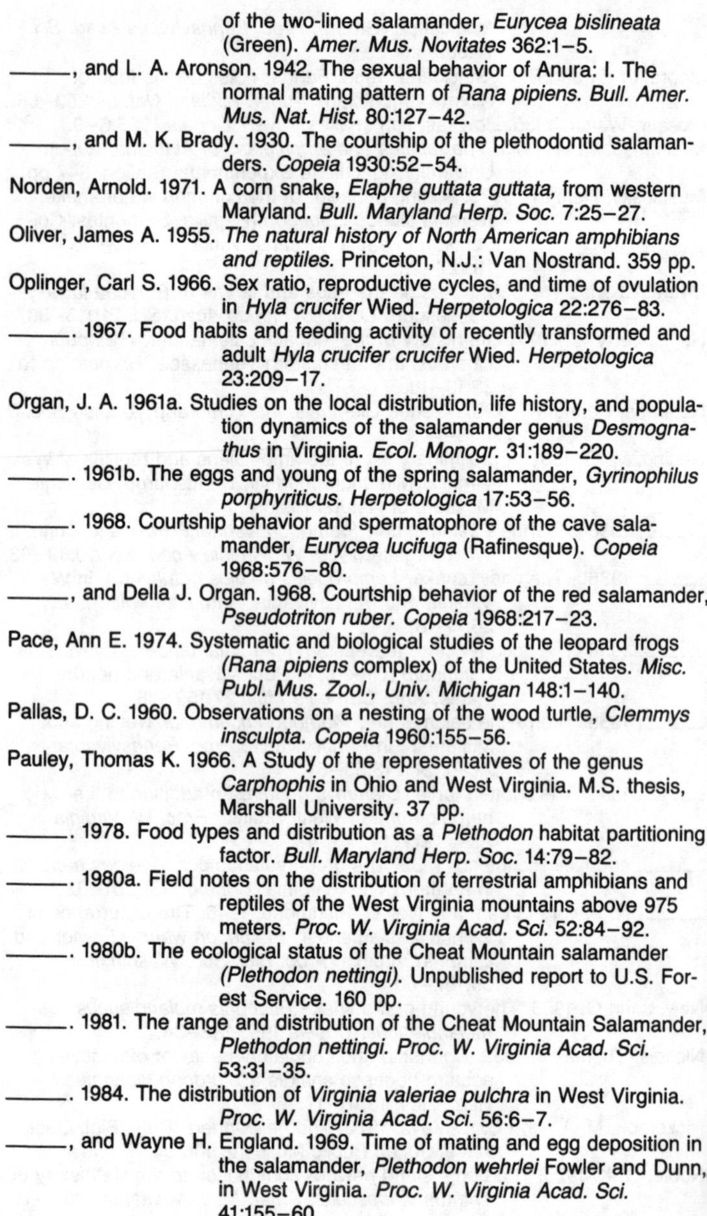

of the two-lined salamander, *Eurycea bislineata* (Green). *Amer. Mus. Novitates* 362:1–5.

———, and L. A. Aronson. 1942. The sexual behavior of Anura: I. The normal mating pattern of *Rana pipiens. Bull. Amer. Mus. Nat. Hist.* 80:127–42.

———, and M. K. Brady. 1930. The courtship of the plethodontid salamanders. *Copeia* 1930:52–54.

Norden, Arnold. 1971. A corn snake, *Elaphe guttata guttata,* from western Maryland. *Bull. Maryland Herp. Soc.* 7:25–27.

Oliver, James A. 1955. *The natural history of North American amphibians and reptiles.* Princeton, N.J.: Van Nostrand. 359 pp.

Oplinger, Carl S. 1966. Sex ratio, reproductive cycles, and time of ovulation in *Hyla crucifer* Wied. *Herpetologica* 22:276–83.

———. 1967. Food habits and feeding activity of recently transformed and adult *Hyla crucifer crucifer* Wied. *Herpetologica* 23:209–17.

Organ, J. A. 1961a. Studies on the local distribution, life history, and population dynamics of the salamander genus *Desmognathus* in Virginia. *Ecol. Monogr.* 31:189–220.

———. 1961b. The eggs and young of the spring salamander, *Gyrinophilus porphyriticus. Herpetologica* 17:53–56.

———. 1968. Courtship behavior and spermatophore of the cave salamander, *Eurycea lucifuga* (Rafinesque). *Copeia* 1968:576–80.

———, and Della J. Organ. 1968. Courtship behavior of the red salamander, *Pseudotriton ruber. Copeia* 1968:217–23.

Pace, Ann E. 1974. Systematic and biological studies of the leopard frogs *(Rana pipiens* complex) of the United States. *Misc. Publ. Mus. Zool., Univ. Michigan* 148:1–140.

Pallas, D. C. 1960. Observations on a nesting of the wood turtle, *Clemmys insculpta. Copeia* 1960:155–56.

Pauley, Thomas K. 1966. A Study of the representatives of the genus *Carphophis* in Ohio and West Virginia. M.S. thesis, Marshall University. 37 pp.

———. 1978. Food types and distribution as a *Plethodon* habitat partitioning factor. *Bull. Maryland Herp. Soc.* 14:79–82.

———. 1980a. Field notes on the distribution of terrestrial amphibians and reptiles of the West Virginia mountains above 975 meters. *Proc. W. Virginia Acad. Sci.* 52:84–92.

———. 1980b. The ecological status of the Cheat Mountain salamander *(Plethodon nettingi).* Unpublished report to U.S. Forest Service. 160 pp.

———. 1981. The range and distribution of the Cheat Mountain Salamander, *Plethodon nettingi. Proc. W. Virginia Acad. Sci.* 53:31–35.

———. 1984. The distribution of *Virginia valeriae pulchra* in West Virginia. *Proc. W. Virginia Acad. Sci.* 56:6–7.

———, and Wayne H. England. 1969. Time of mating and egg deposition in the salamander, *Plethodon wehrlei* Fowler and Dunn, in West Virginia. *Proc. W. Virginia Acad. Sci.* 41:155–60.

Pearson, Paul G. 1955. Population ecology of the spadefoot toad, *Scaphiopus h. holbrooki* (Harlan). *Ecol. Monogr.* 25:233–67.

Petokas, Peter J., and Maurice M. Alexander. 1980. The nesting of *Chelydra serpentina* in northern New York. *J. Herpetol.* 14:239–244.

Petranka, James W. 1982. Courtship behavior of the small-mouthed salamander (*Ambystoma texanum*) in central Kentucky. *Herpetologica* 38:333–36.

_____. 1984. Breeding migrations, breeding season, clutch size, and oviposition of stream-breeding *Ambystoma texanum. J. Herpetol.* 18:106–12.

_____, and John G. Petranka. 1981. On the evolution of nest site selection in the marbled salamander, *Ambystoma opacum. Copeia* 1981:387–91.

Pisani, George R. 1971. An unusually large litter of *Virginia valeriae pulchra. J. Herpetol.* 5:207–08.

Platt, D. R. 1969. Natural history of the hognose snakes *Heterodon platyrhinos* and *Heterodon nasicus. Univ. Kansas Publ., Mus. Nat. Hist.* 18:253–420.

Plummer, Michael V. 1977a. Activity, habitat, and population structure in the turtle, *Trionyx muticus. Copeia* 1977:431–40.

_____. 1977b. Reproduction and growth in the turtle, *Trionyx muticus. Copeia* 1977:440–47.

_____. 1981. Habitat utilization, diet, and movements of a temperate arboreal snake *(Opheodrys aestivus). J. Herpetol.* 15:425–32.

_____, and David B. Farrar. 1981. Sexual dietary differences in a population of *Trionyx muticus. J. Herpetol.* 15:175–79.

Pope, Clifford H. 1928. Some plethodontid salamanders from North Carolina and Kentucky with the description of a new race of *Leurognathus. Amer. Mus. Novitates* 306:1–19.

_____, and S. H. Pope. 1949. Notes on growth and reproduction of the slimy salamander *Plethodon glutinosus. Fieldiana: Zool.* 31:251–61.

Powers, Vernon N., and W. L. Tietjen. 1974. The comparative food habits of sympatric and allopatric salamanders, *Plethodon glutinosus* and *Plethodon jordani* in eastern Tennessee and adjacent area. *Herpetologica* 30:167–75.

Raleigh County Alligator. 1928. *West Virginia Wildlife* 6:19.

Ralin, Dennis B. 1968. Ecological and reproductive differentiation in the cryptic species of the *Hyla versicolor* complex Hylidae. *Southwestern Nat.* 13:283–300.

Raney, Edward C., and Ernest A. Lachner. 1942. Summer food of *Chrysemys picta marginata* in Chautauqua Lake, New York. *Copeia* 1942:83–85.

_____, and Robert M. Roecher. 1947. Food and growth of two species of watersnakes from western New York. *Copeia* 1947:171–74.

Reese, A. M. 1926. The venom of new-born copperheads. *Science* 53:357.

_____. 1929. Reptilia and Amphibia. *West Virginia Encyclopedia* 24:751.

Richmond, Neil D. 1947. Life history of *Scaphiopus holbrookii holbrookii* (Harlan), part I: Larval development and behavior. *Ecology* 28:53–67.

______. 1953. The false map turtle, a new addition to the fauna of West Virginia. *Proc. W. Virginia Acad. Sci.* 25:35.

______. 1954. The ground snake, *Haldea valeriae,* in Pennsylvania and West Virginia, with description of new subspecies. *Ann. Carnegie Mus.* 33:251–60.

______. 1964. The green frog (*Rana clamitans melanota*) developing in one season. *Herpetologica* 20:132.

______, and Grace Boggess. 1941. A key to the reptiles and amphibians of West Virginia. *W. Virginia Univ. Bull.* 42:1–9.

Ries, Kristen M., and Edward D. Bellis. 1966. Spring food habits of the red-spotted newt in Pennsylvania. *Herpetologica* 22:152–55.

Rossman, D. A., and Robert Powell. 1985. *Clonophis kirtlandii* (Kennicott). *Cat. Amer. Amphib. Rept.* 364.1–364.2.

Ryan, Michael J. 1980. The reproductive behavior of the bullfrog (*Rana catesbeiana*). *Copeia* 1980:108–14.

Savage, Thomas. 1967. The diet of rattlesnakes and copperheads in the Great Smoky Mountains National Park. *Copeia* 1967:226–27.

Sayler, Anne. 1966. The reproductive ecology of the redback salamander, *Plethodon cinereus,* in Maryland. *Copeia* 1966:183–93.

Schmidt, K. P., and D. Dwight Davis. 1941. *Field book of snakes of the United States and Canada.* New York: G. P. Putnam's Sons. 365 pp.

Seidel, Michael E. 1982. A taxonomic analysis of pseudemyd turtles (Testudines: Emydidae) from the New River, and phenetic relationships in the subgenus *Pseudemys. Brimleyana* 6:24–44.

______, and N. Bayard Green. 1981. Testudines: *Pseudemys scripta elegans* extension of range. *Herp. Rev.* 12:64.

______. 1982. On the occurrence of cooter turtles (subgenus *Pseudemys*) in the upper Ohio River Valley. *Herp. Rev.* 13:132–34.

______, and H. M. Smith. 1986. *Chrysemys, Pseudemys, Trachemys* (Testudines: Emydidae): Did Agassiz have it right? *Herpetologica* 42:238–44.

Semlitsch, Raymond D. 1980. Geographic and local variation in population parameters of the slimy salamander *Plethodon glutinosus. Herpetologica* 36:6–16.

Shaver, Clem L. 1931. Our poisonous snakes: Two rattlers and a moccasin. *W. Virginia Wildlife* 9:13.

Shoop, Robert C. 1965. Orientation of *Ambystoma maculatum:* Movements to and from breeding ponds. *Science* 149:558–59.

Sites, Jack W. 1978. The foraging strategy of the dusky salamander, *Desmognathus fuscus* (Amphibia, Urodela, Plethodontidae): An empirical approach to predation theory. *J. Herpetol.* 12:373–83.

Smith, Bertram G. 1907. The life history and habits of *Cryptobranchus alleganiensis. Biol. Bull.* 13:5–39.

Smith, H. M., and J. E. Huheey. 1960. The watersnake genus *Regina. Trans. Kansas Acad. Sci.* 63:156–64.

_____, and Fred N. White. 1955. Adrenal enlargement and its significance in the hognose snakes (*Heterodon*). *Herpetologica* 11:137–44.

Smith, Hobart M. 1946. *Handbook of lizards: Lizards of the United States and Canada.* Ithaca, N.Y.: Comstock. 557 pp.

Smith, Philip W. 1961. The amphibians and reptiles of Illinois. *Illinois Nat. Hist. Surv. Bull.* 28:1–298.

Stewart, Margaret M., and Peggy Sandison. 1972. Comparative food habits of sympatric mink frogs, bullfrogs, and green frogs. *J. Herpetol.* 6:241–44.

Stickel, Lucille F., William H. Stickel, and Frederick C. Schmid. 1980. Ecology of a Maryland population of black rat snakes (*Elaphe o. obsoleta*). *Amer. Midland Nat.* 103:1–14.

Strader, L. D. 1936. Herpetology of the eastern panhandle of West Virginia. *Proc. W. Virginia Acad. Sci.* 9:32–35.

Strang, Carl A. 1983. Spatial and temporal activity patterns in two terrestrial turtles. *J. Herpetol.* 17:43–47.

Surface, H. A. 1906. The serpents of Pennsylvania. *Monthly Bull. Div. Zool. Pennsylvania Dept. Agr.* 4:113–208.

_____. 1913. First report on the economic features of the amphibians of Pennsylvania. *Bi-monthly Zool. Bull. Div. Zool. Pennsylvania Dept. Agr.* 3:68–152.

Thompson, Edward L., J. Edward Gates, and Gary J. Taylor. 1980. Distribution and breeding habitat selection of the Jefferson salamander, *Ambystoma jeffersonianum* in Maryland. *J. Herpetol.* 14:113–20.

Tilley, Stephen G. 1973. Observations on the larval period and female reproductive ecology of *Desmognathus ochrophaeus* (Amphibia: Plethodontidae) in western North Carolina. *Amer. Midland Nat.* 89:394–407.

_____, and Donald W. Tinkle. 1968. A reinterpretation of the reproductive cycle and demography of the salamander *Desmognathus ochrophaeus. Copeia* 1968:299–303.

Ting, Han-Po. 1951. Duration of the tadpole stage of the green frog, *Rana clamitans. Copeia* 1951:82.

Tinkle, Donald W. 1961. Geographic variation in reproduction, size, sex ratio, and maturity of *Sternothaerus odoratus* (Testudinata: Chelydridae). *Ecology* 42:68–76.

_____, and R. E. Ballinger. 1972. *Sceloporus undulatus,* a study of intraspecific comparative demography of a lizard. *Ecology* 53:570–84.

Tobey, Franklin J. 1985. *Virginia's amphibians and reptiles: A distributional survey.* Virginia Herpetological Society. 114 pp.

Topping, Milton S., and Chris A. Ingersol. 1981. Fecundity in the hellbender, *Cryptobranchus alleganiensis. Copeia* 1981:873–76.

Trapido, Harold. 1944. The snakes of the genus *Storeria. Amer. Midland Nat.* 31:1–84.

Trautwein, Steven N. 1983. Hatching in captivity of a clutch of *Sceloporus undulatus hyacinthinus* eggs. *Herp. Rev.* 14:15–16.

Uhler, F. M., C. Cottam, and T. E. Clarke. 1939. Food of snakes of the George Washington National Forest, Virginia. *Trans. Fourth N. Amer. Wildlife Conf., Amer. Wildlife Inst.,* pp. 615–17.

U.S. Department of Commerce. 1973. *Monthly averages of temperature and precipitation for state climatic division, 1941–70.* Climatography of the United States 85. Asheville, N.C.: National Climatic Center.

Vogt, Richard C. 1981. Food partitioning in three sympatric species of map turtles, Genus *Graptemys* (Testudinata, Emydidae). *Amer. Midland Nat.* 105:102–11.

______, and C. J. McCoy. 1980. Status of the emydine turtle genera *Chrysemys* and *Pseudemys. Ann. Carnegie Mus.* 49:93–102.

Waldman, Bruce, and Michael J. Ryan. 1983. Thermal advantages of communal egg mass deposition in wood frogs (*Rana sylvatica*). *J. Herpetol.* 17:70–72.

Walker, C. F. 1932. *Pseudacris brachyphona,* a valid species. *Ohio J. Sci.* 32:379–84.

______. 1946. The amphibians of Ohio. Part I: The frogs and toads. *Ohio State Mus. Sci. Bull.* 1:1–102.

______, and Woodrow Goodpaster. 1941. The green salamander, *Aneides aeneus,* in Ohio. *Copeia* 1941:178.

Wallace, James T. 1969. A study on *Plethodon richmondi* from Mason County, Kentucky, with notes on its distribution within the state. *Trans. Kentucky Acad. Sci.* 29:38–44.

______, and Roger W. Barbour. 1957. Observations on the eggs and young of *Plethodon richmondi. Copeia* 1957:48.

Webb, Robert G. 1961. Observations on the life histories of turtles (genus *Pseudemys* and *Graptemys*) in Lake Texoma, Oklahoma. *Amer. Midland Nat.* 65:193–214.

______. 1962. North American recent soft-shelled turtles (Family Trionychidae). *Univ. Kansas Publ., Mus. Nat. Hist.* 10:429–611.

Wells, Kentwood D. 1977. Territoriality and male mating success in the green frog (*Rana clamitans*). *Ecology* 58:750–62.

Whitaker, John O., Jr. 1961. Habitat and food of mousetrapped young *Rana pipiens* and *Rana clamitans. Herpetologica* 17:173–179.

______, Wynn W. Cudmore, and Barbara A. Brown. 1982. Foods of larval, subadult, and adult smallmouth salamanders, *Ambystoma texanum,* from Vigo County, Indiana. *Indiana Acad. Sci.* 90:461–64.

Williams, Thomas A., and James L. Christiansen. 1981. The niches of two sympatric softshell turtles, *Trionyx muticus* and *Trionyx spiniferus,* in Iowa. *J. Herpetol.* 15:303–08.

Wilson, L. Wayne. 1941. An addition to the herpetofauna of West Virginia (*Leiolopisma unicolor*). *Copeia* 1941:268.

______. 1944. Amphibians of Droop Mountain State Park. *Proc. W. Virginia Acad. Sci.* 45:39–41.

______, and Saufley B. Friddle. 1946. Notes on the king snake in West Virginia. *Copeia* 1946: 47–48.

______. 1949. *Pseudemys rubriventris* in West Virginia. *Copeia* 1949:292.

______. 1950. The herpetology of Hardy County, West Virginia. *Amer. Midland Nat.* 43:165–67.

Wood, John T. 1953. Observations on the complements of ova and venting of the four-toed salamander in Virginia. *Amer. Nat.* 87:77–86.

______. 1955. The nesting of the four-toed salamander, *Hemidactylium scutatum* (Schlegel), in Virginia. *Amer. Midland Nat.* 53:381–89.

______, and O. K. Goodwin. 1954. Observations on the abundance, food, and feeding behavior of the newt, *Notophthalmus viridescens viridescens* (Rafinesque), in Virginia. *J. Elisha Mitchell Sci. Soc.* 70:27–30.

Woods, J. E. 1968. The ecology and natural history of a Mississippi population of *Aneides aeneus* and associated salamanders. Ph.D. diss. University of Southern Mississippi. 91 pp.

Woolverton, Ed. 1963. Winter survival of hatchling painted turtles in northern Minnesota. *Copeia* 1963:569–70.

Wright, A. H. 1914. Life histories of the Anura of Ithaca, N.Y. *Carnegie Inst. Publ.* 197:1–98.

______, and A. A. Allen. 1909. The early breeding habits of *Ambystoma punctatum. Amer. Midland Nat.* 43:687–92.

______, and A. A. Wright. 1952. List of the snakes of the United States and Canada by states and provinces. *Amer. Midland Nat.* 48:574–603.

______, and A. A. Wright. 1957. *Handbook of snakes of the United States and Canada.* 2 vols. Ithaca, N.Y.: Comstock. 1105 pp.

Wyman, Richard Lee. 1971. The courtship behavior of the small-mouthed salamander, *Ambystoma texanum. Herpetologica* 27:491–98.

Zehr, David R. 1962. Stages in the normal development of the common garter snake, *Thamnophis sirtalis sirtalis. Copeia* 1962:322–29.

Zenisek, Cyril James. 1963. A study of the natural history and ecology of the leopard frog, *Rana pipiens* Schraber. Ph.D. diss. Ohio State University. 153 pp.

Zucchero, Peter J. 1933. Amphibians and reptiles of Lewis County, West Virginia. M.S. thesis, West Virginia University. 63 pp.

WORKS CONSULTED

Adler, Kraig. 1963. An ecological study of the snake, *Natrix erythrogaster,* with remarks on its postglacial dispersal. *J. Ohio Herp. Soc.* 4:61–62.

Albert, James G., and Laurence E. Bayless. 1971. Daytime spring microhabitats of some common amphibians in southern West Virginia. *Proc. W. Virginia Acad. Sci.* 43:117–22.

Alexander, W. P. 1927. The Allegheny hellbender and its habitat. *Hobbies Buffalo Soc. Nat. Sci.* 7:13–18.

Allard, H. A. 1935. The natural history of the box turtle. *Scientific Monthly* 41:325–38.

Allen, Tom. 1983. The lowly lizard. *Wonderful West Virginia* 46:14–15.

Altig, R. 1970. A key to the tadpoles of the continental United States and Canada. *Herpetologica* 26:180–207.

Anderson, James D. 1967. *Ambystoma maculatum* (Shaw). *Cat. Amer. Amphib. Rept.* 51.1–51.4.

———. 1967. *Ambystoma opacum* (Gravenhorst). *Cat. Amer. Amphib. Rept.* 46.1–46.2.

———. 1967. *Ambystoma texanum* (Matthes). *Cat. Amer. Amphib. Rept.* 37.1–37.2.

———, and P. J. Martino. 1966. The life history of *Eurycea l. longicauda* associated with ponds. *Amer. Midland Nat.* 75:257–79.

Answer to question concerning *Sistrurus.* 1930. *W. Virginia Wildlife* 8:15.

Ashton, Ray E., Jr. 1975. A study of movement, home range, and winter behavior of *Desmognathus fuscus* (Rafinesque). *J. Herpetol.* 9:85–91.

———, Stephen R. Edwards, and George R. Pisani. 1976. Endangered and threatened amphibians and reptiles of the United States. *Soc. Study Amphib. Rept. Misc. Publ. Circ.* 5:1–65.

Atkinson, D. A., and M. G. Netting. 1927. The distribution and habits of the massasauga. *Bull. Antivenin Inst. America* 1:40–44.

Auffenberg, Walter. 1955. A reconsideration of the racer, *Coluber constrictor,* in eastern United States. *Tulane Stud. Zool.* 2:89–155.

Babcock, Harold L. 1919. The turtles of New England. *Mem. Boston Soc. Nat. Hist.* 8:323–431.

Bailey, J. R. 1937. Notes on plethodont salamanders of the southeastern United States. *Occas. Papers Mus. Zool., Univ. Michigan* 364:1–10.

Baird, Spencer F. 1850. Revision of the North American Tailed-Batrachia, with descriptions of new genera and species. *J. Acad. Nat. Sci.* (Philadelphia) 1:281–92.

Baldauf, R. J. 1947. *Desmognathus f. fuscus* eating of its own species. *Copeia* 1947:66.

Barbour, Roger W. 1946. Food habits of *Desmognathus fuscus* in Kentucky. *Copeia* 1946:48–49.

———. 1950. A new subspecies of the salamander *Desmognathus fuscus. Copeia* 1950: 277–78.

———. 1960. A study of the worm snake, *Carphophis amoenus* Say, in Kentucky. *Trans. Kentucky Acad. Sci.* 21:10–16.

———, and Rodney M. Hays. 1957. The genus *Desmognathus* in Kentucky. *Amer. Midland Nat.* 58:352–59.

_____, and Elmon P. Walters. 1941. Notes on the breeding habits of *Pseudacris brachyphona. Copeia* 1941:116.

Barthalmus, G. T., and E. D. Bellis. 1972. Home range, homing, and homing mechanism of the salamander, *Desmognathus fuscus. Copeia* 1972:632–42.

Barton, B. S. 1812. *A memoir concerning an animal of the class Reptilia or Amphibia which is known in the United States by the names of alligator or hell-bender.* Philadelphia: Griggs and Dickinson. 26 pp.

Bayless, Laurence D. 1971. New records of amphibians and reptiles for southern West Virginia. *Proc. W. Virginia Acad. Sci.* 43:123–25.

_____. 1979. New herpetological records for southern West Virginia. *Proc. W. Virginia Acad. Sci.* 51:65–67.

Beightol, Don. 1973. Tasty "jug-o-rums." *Wonderful West Virginia* 37:6.

Bishop, Sherman C. 1925. The life of the red salamander. *Natural History* 25:385–89.

_____. 1926. Notes on the habits and development of the mudpuppy, *Necturus maculosus* (Rafinesque). *N.Y. State Mus. Bull.* 268:1–60.

_____. 1927. The amphibians and reptiles of Allegany State Park. *N.Y. State Mus. Handbook* 3:1–141.

_____. 1941. Notes on salamanders with descriptions of several new forms (*Pseudotriton montanus diastictus*). *Occas. Papers Mus. Zool., Univ. Michigan* 451:1–27.

_____, and H. P. Chrisp. 1933. The nests and young of the Allegheny salamander, *Desmognathus fuscus ochrophaeus. Copeia* 1933:194–98.

Blair, Albert P. 1941. Variation of two characters in *Bufo fowleri* and *Bufo americanus. Amer. Mus. Novitates* 1343:1–5.

_____. 1943. Geographical variation of ventral markings in toads. *Amer. Midland Nat.* 29:615–20.

Blanchard, Frank N. 1921. A revision of the king snakes, genus *Lampropeltis. Bull. U.S. Natl. Mus.* 114:1–260.

_____. 1923. The snakes of the genus *Virginia. Papers Michigan Acad. Sci. Arts Letters* 3:343–65.

_____. 1924. The forms of *Carphophis. Papers Michigan Acad. Sci. Arts Letters* 4:527–30.

_____. 1942. The ring-neck snakes, genus *Diadophis. Bull. Chicago Acad. Sci.* 7:1–144.

Blaney, Richard M. 1973. *Lampropeltis. Cat. Amer. Amphib. Rept.* 150.1–150.2.

Bleakney, Sherman. 1957. The egg-laying habits of the salamander, *Ambystoma jeffersonianum. Copeia* 1957:141.

Blem, Charles R. 1981. *Heterodon platirhinos. Cat. Amer. Amphib. Rept.* 282.1–282.2.

Blymyser, Michael J., and Burd S. McGinnes. 1977. Observations on possible detrimental effects of clearcutting on terrestrial amphibians. *Bull. Maryland Herp. Soc.* 13:79–83.

Bolden, G. C. 1929. The "low down" on the rattler. *W. Virginia Wildlife* 7:32.

Bothner, Richard C., and Terry R. Moore. 1964. A collection of *Haldea valeriae pulchra* from western Pennsylvania with notes on some litters of their young. *Copeia* 1964:709–10.

Boulenger, G. A. 1920. A monograph of the American frogs of the genus *Rana*. *Proc. Amer. Acad. Arts Sci.* 55:413–80.

Bowers, Robert R. 1956. Demons of the Deep (Turtles). *W. Virginia Conservation* 20:2–5.

Bradshaw, W. N. 1966. An albino eastern ringneck snake, *Diadophis punctatus* (Linnaeus), from West Virginia. *Proc. W. Virginia Acad. Sci.* 38:13–14.

Brady, Maurice K. 1924. Eggs of *Desmognathus phoca* (Matthes). *Copeia* 127:29.

Brandon, Ronald A. 1964. An annotated and illustrated key to multi-stage larvae of Ohio salamanders. *Ohio J. Sci.* 64:252–58.

______. 1967. *Gyrinophilus porphyriticus* Green. *Cat. Amer. Amphib. Rept.* 33.1–33.3.

______, and J. M. Rutherford. 1967. Albinos in a cavernicolous population of the salamander, *Gyrinophilus porphyriticus*, in West Virginia. *Amer. Midland Nat.* 78:517–40.

Branin, M. L. 1935. Courtship activities and extra-seasonal ovulation of the four-toed salamander, *Hemidactylium scutatum* (Schlegel). *Copeia* 1935:172–75.

Breiding, George, 1973. Reptiles, snakes, and birds. *Wonderful West Virginia* 37:30.

Brooks, F. E. 1932. I don't like snakes. *W. Virginia Review* 9:186.

Brooks, G. R. 1963. Population ecology of the ground skink. *Ecol. Monogr.* 37:71–87.

______. 1975. *Scincella lateralis* Say. *Cat. Amer. Amphib. Rept.* 169.1–169.4.

Brown, Charles E., and Bernard S. Martof. 1966. The function of the nasolabial groove of plethodontid salamanders. *Physiol. Zool.* 39:357–67.

Brown, J. Slidell. 1929. Slidell Brown's pet rattlesnake. *W. Virginia Wildlife* 7:10–11.

______. 1929. Snake stories. *W. Virginia Wildlife,* June 14–15.

Brown, P. S., S. A. Hastings, and B. E. Frye, 1977. A comparison of the water balance in five species of plethodontid salamanders. *Physiol. Zool.* 50:203–14.

Bruce, Richard C. 1968. Life history studies of the salamanders of the genus *Pseudotriton* (Caudata: *Plethodontidae*). Ph.D. diss., Duke University, 222 pp.

______. 1968. The role of the Blue Ridge Embayment in the zoogeography of the green salamander, *Aneides aeneus*. *Herpetologica* 24:185–94.

______. 1978. Life-history patterns of the salamander *Gyrinophilus porphyriticus* in the Cowee Mountains, North Carolina. *Herpetologica* 34:53–64.

______. 1982. Egg-laying, larval periods, and metamorphosis of *Eurycea bislineata* and *Eurycea junaluska* at Santeelah Creek, North Carolina. *Copeia* 1982:755–62.

______. 1982. Larval periods and metamorphosis in two species of salamanders in the genus *Eurycea*. *Copeia* 1982:117–27.

Buck, Ed. 1956. Blacksnake immune to rattlesnake poison. *W. Virginia Conservation* 19:23–25.

Bury, R. Bruce, and Carl H. Ernst. 1977. *Clemmys* Ritgen. *Cat. Amer. Amphib. Rept.* 203.1–203.2.

Butler, Jim. 1965. A friend has been slandered. *W. Virginia Conservation* 19:29–31.

______. 1966. A misunderstood fella named copperhead. *W. Virginia Conservation* 30:20–22.

Cagle, Fred B. 1953. An outline for the study of a reptile life history. *Tulane Stud. in Zool.* 1:31–52.

______. 1956. An outline for the study of an amphibian life history. *Tulane Stud. in Zool.* 4:79–110.

Cantner, Dan. 1959. The snake. *W. Virginia Conservation* 23:25–27.

Channell, L. S., and B. D. Valentine. 1972. A yellow albino *Desmognathus fuscus* from West Virginia. *J. Herpetol.* 6:144–46.

Christman, Steven P. 1982. *Storeria dekayi* (Holbrook). *Cat. Amer. Amphib. Rept.* 306:1–306.4.

Clanton, Wesley. 1934. An unusual situation in the salamander *Ambystoma jeffersonianum* (Green). *Occas. Papers Mus. Zool., Univ. Michigan* 290:1–14.

Clark, Hugh. 1952. Notes on the egg-laying habits of *Heterodon platyrhinos* (L). *Herpetologica* 8:28.

______. 1952. A preliminary ovimetric study on *Heterodon platyrhinos* (L). *Herpetologica* 8:29–32.

Collins, H. H. 1931. Sex ratio in adult populations of *Triturus viridescens*. *Proc. Pennsylvania Acad. Sci.* 5:101.

Collins, Joseph T., and James L. Knight. 1980. *Crotalus horridus* Linnaeus. *Cat. Amer. Amphib. Rept.* 253.1–253.2.

Conant, Roger. 1955. Notes on *Natrix erythrogaster* from the eastern and western extremes of its range. *Nat. Hist. Miscellanea, Chicago Acad. Sci.* 147:1–3.

______. 1956. Common names for North American amphibians and reptiles. *Amer. Soc. Ich. Herp.* 3:172–85.

______. 1978. Distributional patterns of North American snakes: Some examples of the effects of Pleistocene glaciation and subsequent climatic changes. *Bull. Maryland Herp. Soc.* 14:241–59.

Conn, J. Stephen. 1974. Snake watching for fun. *Wonderful West Virginia* 37:19–21.

Cook, Francis R. 1964. Communal egg-laying in the smooth green snake. *Herpetologica* 20:206.

Cooper, John E. 1958. The snake *Haldea valeriae pulchra* in Maryland. *Herpetologica* 14:121–22.

______. 1962. Cave records for salamander, *Plethodon r. richmondi*. *Herpetologica* 17:250–55.

______. 1965. Cave associated herpetozoa I: An annotated dichotomous key to the adult cave associated salamanders of Maryland, Pennsylvania, Virginia, and West Virginia. *Baltimore Grotto News* 8:150–63.

Cope, Edward D. 1889. The Batrachia of North America. *Bull. U.S. Natl. Mus.* 34:1–525.

______. 1900. Crocodilians, lizards, and snakes of North America. *Rept. U.S. Natl. Mus. for 1898,* 153–1294.

Crenshaw, J. W., Jr. 1955. Life history of *Sceloporus u. undulatus. Amer. Midland Nat.* 54:257–98.

Cupp, Paul V., and Donald T. Towles. 1983. A new variant of *Plethodon wehrlei* in Kentucky and West Virginia. *Trans. Kentucky Acad. Sci.* 44:157–58.

Czarnowski, R. 1976. A note on the feeding behavior of a *Clemmys insculpa. Bull. Maryland Herp. Soc.* 12:103.

Darlington, Philip J., Jr. 1957. *Zoogeography: The geographical distribution of animals.* New York: John Wiley, 675 pp.

Dennis, David M. 1962. Notes on the nesting habits of *Desmognathus fuscus fuscus* (Raf.) in Licking County, Ohio. *J. Ohio Herp. Soc.* 3:28–35.

Ditmars, Raymond L. 1930. The poisonous snakes of the New World. *Bull. N.Y. Zool. Soc.* 33:79–132.

Dodd, C. Kenneth, Jr. 1981. *A bibliography of endangered and threatened amphibians and reptiles in the United States and its territories.* Smithsonian Herpetological Information Service 49. Office of Endangered Species, U.S. Fish and Wildlife Service.

Doty, David L., and Kerry L. Cartier. 1972. The great snake fake. *Wonderful West Virginia* 36:9–11.

Dundee, Harold A. 1971. *Crytpobranchus a. alleganiensis* (Daudin). *Cat. Amer. Amphib. Rept.* 101.1–101.4.

Dunn, E. R. 1916. Two new salamanders of the genus *Desmognathus. Proc. Biol. Soc. Washington* 29:73–76.

______. 1917. The salamanders of the genera *Desmognathus* and *Leurognathus. Proc. U.S. Natl. Mus.* 53:393–433.

Dury, Ralph. 1932. Recent acquisitions to the Department of Herpetology. *Proc. Junior Soc. Nat. Sci.* 3:26–28.

______, and R. S. Williams. 1933. Notes on some Kentucky amphibians and reptiles. *Bull. Baker-Hunt Mus.* 1:1–22.

Eaton, Theodore H., Jr. 1956. Larvae of some Appalachian plethodontid salamanders. *Herpetologica* 12:303–11.

Edgren, Richard A. 1957. Melanism in hog-nosed snakes. *Herpetologica* 13:131–35.

Ernst, Carl H. 1967. A mating aggregation of the turtle *Clemmys guttata. Copeia* 1967:463–74.

______. 1968. Homing ability in the spotted turtle, *Clemmys guttata* (Schneider). *Herpetologica* 24:77–78.

______. 1970. Home range of the spotted turtle, *Clemmys guttata. Copeia* 1970:391–93.

______. 1971. *Chrysemys picta* (Schneider) *Cat. Amer. Amphib. Rept.* 106.1–106.4.

______. 1972. *Clemmys guttata* (Schneider). *Cat. Amer. Amphib. Rept.* 124.1–124.2.

______. 1972. *Clemmys insculpta* (LeConte). *Cat. Amer. Amphib. Rept.* 125.1–125.2.

_____. 1975. Growth of the spotted turtle, *Clemmys guttata. J. Herpetol.* 9:313–18.

Evans, Llewellyn T. 1961. Aquatic courtship of the wood turtle, *Clemmys insculpa. Amer. Zool.* 1:353.

Ewing, H. E. 1935. Further notes on the reproduction of the eastern box turtle, *Terrapene carolina* (Linnaeus). *Copeia* 1935:102.

Farley, G. M. 1978. Don't tread on me. *Wonderful West Virginia* 42:5, 7–9, 31.

Fitch, Henry S. 1980. *Thamnophis sirtalis* (Linnaeus). *Cat. Amer. Amphib. Rept.* 270.1–270.4.

_____, and Harry W. Greene. 1965. Breeding cycle of the ground skink, *Lygosoma laterale. Univ. Kansas Publ., Mus. Nat. Hist.* 15:565–75.

_____, and R. R. Fleet. 1970. Natural history of the milk snake (*Lampropeltis triangulum*) in northeastern Kansas. *Herpetologica* 26:387–96.

Foil, John A., Jr. 1981. Territorial behavioral and population structure of the common snapping turtle, *Chelydra serpentina serpentia.* Paper presented at SSAR meeting in Memphis, Tenn., August 9–14, 1981.

Fowler, Henry W. 1914. Note on the swamp tree toad (*Pseudacris triseriatus*). *Copeia* 1914:4.

_____. 1915. Number of young produced by common snakes. *Copeia* 1915:15–16.

_____, and Emmett R. Dunn. 1917. Notes on salamanders: Brief key to *Desmognathus fuscus, Eurycea, Pseudotriton, Gyrinophilus* larvae, and comments about color pattern development. *Proc. Acad. Nat. Sci.* (Philadelphia) 69:7–28.

Fowler, James A. 1951. Preliminary observations on an aggregation of *Plethodon dixi. Herpetologica* 7:147–48.

_____. 1952. The eggs of *Plethodon dixi. The American Caver* 52:61.

Franz, Richard. 1964. The eggs of the long-tailed salamander from a Maryland cave. *Herpetologica* 20:216.

Fraser, Douglas F. 1976. Empirical evaluation of the hypotheses of food competition in salamanders of the genus *Plethodon. Ecology* 57:459–71.

Friend, F. E. 1929. More about snakes. *W. Virginia Wildlife* 7:37–38.

Frost, Darrel R. 1985. *Amphibian species of the world.* Lawrence, Kans.: Allen Press and the Association of Systematic Collections. 732 pp.

Frost, S. W. 1935. The food of *Rana catesbeiana* Shaw. *Copeia* 1935:15–18.

Gatz, A. J., Jr. 1973. Algal entry into the eggs of *Ambystoma maculatum. J. Herpetol.* 7:137–38.

Gilbert, Frank A., N. Bayard Green, and Edward Seeber. 1941. The ecology of McCullough's Pond. *Proc. W. Virginia Acad. Sci.* 107–10.

Gillingham, James C. 1979. Reproductive behavior of the rat snake of eastern North America, genus *Elaphe. Copeia* 1979:319–31.

Gloyd, H. K. 1940. The rattlesnakes, genera *Sistrurus* and *Crotalus:* A study in zoogeography and evolution. *Chicago Acad. Sci. Spec. Publ.* 4:1–266.

_____, and R. Conant. 1943. A synopsis of the American forms of *Agkistrodon* (copperheads and moccasins). *Bull. Chicago Acad. Sci.* 7:147–70.

Gordon, David M., and Ross D. MacCulloch. 1980. An investigation of the ecology of the map turtle, *Graptemys geographica* (Le Sueur), in the northern part of its range. *Can. J. Zool.* 58:2210–19.

Gordon, R. E. 1967. *Aneides aeneus* (Cope and Packard). *Cat. Amer. Amphib. Rept.* 30.1–30.2.

Gosner, K. L. 1942. Lip curling of the red-bellied snake. *Copeia* 1942:181–82.

_____, and Irving H. Black. 1954. Larval development in *Bufo woodhousei fowleri* and *Scaphiopus holbrooki holbrooki. Copeia* 1954:251–55.

_____, and Irving H. Black. 1957. Larval development in New Jersey Hylidae. *Copeia* 1957:31–36.

Gray, Robert H. 1971. Fall activity and overwintering of the cricket frog (*Acris crepitans*) in central Illinois. *Copeia* 1971:748–50.

Green, N. Bayard. 1934. *Cryptobranchus alleganiensis* in West Virginia. *Proc. W. Virginia Acad. Sci.* 17:28–30.

_____. 1936. The amphibians of Tucker County, W. Va. *Proc. W. Virginia Acad. Sci.* 10:80–83.

_____. 1938. The breeding habits of *Pseudacris brachyphona* (Cope) with a description of the eggs and tadpole. *Copeia* 1938:79–82.

_____. 1938. A new salamander, *Plethodon nettingi,* from West Virginia. *Ann. Carnegie Mus.* 27:295–99.

_____. 1941. Representatives of the genus *Gyrinophilus* in West Virginia. *Proc. W. Virginia Acad. Sci.* 15:179–83.

_____. 1943. The salamanders of West Virginia. *W. Virginia Conservation* 6:16–18.

_____. 1943. The snakes of West Virginia. *W. Virginia Conservation* 6:16–18.

_____. 1948. *Annotated check list of amphibians and reptiles known from West Virginia.* West Virginia Conservation Commission.

_____. 1948. The spade foot toad, *Scaphiopus h. holbrooki,* breeding in southern Ohio. *Copeia* 1948:65.

_____. 1953. A key to the eggs of W. Va. Salientia. *Proc. W. Virginia Acad. Sci.* 24:36–38.

_____. 1953. Snakes. *W. Virginia Conservation* 10:11–12.

_____. 1955. The ambystomid salamanders in West Virginia. *Proc. W. Virginia Acad. Sci.* 27:16–18.

_____. 1964. Post metamorphic growth in the mountain chorus frog, *Pseudacris brachyphona* Cope. *Proc. W. Virginia Acad. Sci.* 36:34–38.

_____. 1969. The occurrence and distribution of turtles in West Virginia. *Proc. W. Virginia Acad. Sci.* 41:1–14.

———. 1976. The amphibians of West Virginia. *W. Virginia Encyclopedia* 1:73–85.

———. 1976. The reptiles of West Virginia. *W. Virginia Encyclopedia* 18:4015–29.

———, and Bernard Dowler. 1967. Amphibians and reptiles of the Little Kanawha River Basin. *Proc. W. Virginia Acad. Sci.* 38:50–57.

———, and Duane Pursley. 1975. West Virginia snakes. *Wonderful West Virginia* 39:2–3, 6–7, 27.

Grobman, Arnold B. 1941. A contribution to the knowledge of variation in *Opheodrys vernalis* (Harlan) with the description of a new subspecies. *Univ. Michigan Mus. Zool. Misc. Publ.* 50:1–38.

———. 1944. The distribution of the salamanders of the genus *Plethodon* in eastern United States and Canada. *Ann. N.Y. Acad. Sci.* 45:261–316.

———. 1945. The identity of *Desmognathus phoca* (Matthes) and of *Desmognathus monticola* Dunn. *Proc. Biol. Soc. Washington.* 58:39–44.

Groves, J. D. 1972. A note on climbing in the stinkpot, *Sternotherus odoratus. Bull. Maryland Herp. Soc.* 8:87.

Guilday, John E., and Donald P. Tanner. 1965. Vertebrate remains from the Mount Carbon Site, (46-Fa-7), Fayette County, West Virginia. *The W. Virginia Archeologist* 18:1–14.

Hall, Russell J. 1976. Summer foods of the salamander, *Plethodon wehrlei. J. Herpetol.* 10:129–31.

Handlan, John. 1938. West Virginia's "vermin-killing contests" of 1937. *The Redstart* 5.27–29.

Hansen, K. L. 1958. Breeding pattern of the eastern spadefoot toad. *Herpetologica* 14:56–67.

Hardy, Jerry D., Jr. 1952. A concentration of juvenile spotted salamanders, *Ambystoma maculatum* (Shaw). *Copeia* 1952:181.

———, and John H. Gillespie. 1976. Hybridization between *Rana pipiens* and *Rana palustris* in a modified natural environment. *Bull. Maryland Herp. Soc.* 12:41–53.

Harper, F. 1935. Eggs and young of the pilot blacksnake and the fox snake. *Amer. Midland Nat.* 16:932–35.

———. 1947. A new cricket frog (*Acris*) from the middle western states. *Proc. Biol. Soc. Washington* 60:39–40.

Harris, Herbert S., Jr., and Daniel J. Lyons. 1968. The green salamander, *Aneides aeneus* Cope and Packard, in Maryland. *Bull. Maryland Herp. Soc.* 4:1–6.

Harwig, S. H. 1966. Rattlesnakes are where and when you find them (abstract). *J. Ohio Herp. Soc.* 5:163.

Hecht, M. K. 1958. A synopsis of the mud puppies of eastern North America. *Proc. Staten Island Inst. Arts Sci.* 21:4–38.

Hensley, M. 1959. Albinism in North American amphibians and reptiles. *Publ. Mus. Michigan State Univ. Biol. Ser.* 1:135–59.

Highton, Richard. 1956. The life history of the slimy salamander, *Plethodon glutinosus,* in Florida. *Copeia* 1956:75–93.

_____. 1959. The inheritance of the color phases of *Plethodon cinereus*. *Copeia* 1959:33–37.

_____. 1962. Revision of North American salamanders of the genus *Plethodon*. *Bull. Florida State Mus.* 6:1–367.

_____. 1968. Geographic variation in the red-backed salamander in the Middle Atlantic states (abstract). *J. Herpetol.* 2:175.

_____. 1986a. *Plethodon kentucki* Mittleman. *Cat. Amer. Amphib. Rept.* 382.1–382.2.

_____. 1986b. *Plethodon nettingi* Green. *Cat. Amer. Amphib. Rept.* 383.1–383.2.

_____, and A. Larson. 1979. The genetic relationships of the salamanders of the genus *Plethodon*. *Syst. Zool.* 28:579–99.

Hoffman, Richard L. 1980. *Pseudacris brachyphona* (Cope). *Cat. Amer. Amphib. Rept.* 234.1–234.2.

Hossinger, Dawn D. 1970. Notes on the thermal properties of frog eggs. *Herpetologica* 26:49–51.

_____, James D. Anderson, and George H. Dalrymple. 1970. The early life history and ecology of *Ambystoma tigrinum* and *Ambystoma opacum* in New Jersey. *Amer. Midland Nat.* 84:474–95.

Hudson, R. G. 1955. Observations on the larvae of the salamander *Eurycea bislineata bislineata*. *Herpetologica* 11:202–04.

Hutchison, Victor H. 1966. *Eurycea lucifuga* Rafinesque. *Cat. Amer. Amphib. Rept.* 24.1–24.2.

Inger, R. F., and P. J. Clark. 1943. Partition of the genus *Coluber*. *Copeia* 1943:141–45.

Ireland, Patrick H. 1979. *Eurycea longicauda* (Green). *Cat. Amer. Amphib. Rept.* 221.1–221.4.

Johnson, Ed. 1979. The bullfrog. *Wonderful West Virginia* 42:24.

Johnson, Richard M. 1953. A contribution to the life history of the lizard *Lygosoma laterale* (Say). *Tulane Stud. Zool.* 1:11–27.

Jones, Mary Holmes. 1975. Turtle centenarian of the reptile family. *Wonderful West Virginia* 39:18–19.

Keely, Josiah. 1928. Some snakes. *W. Virginia Wildlife* 1928:18–19, 35.

Keen, Hubert W. 1975. Breeding and larval development of three species of *Ambystoma* in central Kentucky (Amphibia: Urodela). *Herpetologica* 31:18–19.

King, Willis, 1935. Ecological observations on *Ambystoma opacum*. *Ohio J. Sci.* 35:4–15.

Knight, E. Leslie, and David S. Lee. 1968. The use of salamanders as fishing bait. *Bull. Maryland Herp. Soc.* 4:86–88.

Krajnovick, Ron. 1973. Snake. *Wonderful West Virginia.* 37:21.

Kumpf, K. F., and S. C. Yeaton. 1932. Observations on the courtship behavior of *Ambystoma jeffersonianum*. *Amer. Mus. Novitates* 546:1–7.

Lachner, E. A. 1942. An aggregation of snakes and salamanders during hibernation. *Copeia* 1942:262–63.

Landreth, Hobart F., and Denzel E. Ferguson. 1966. Evidence of sun-compass orientation in the chorus frog, *Pseudacris triseriata*. *Herpetologica* 22:106–12.

Lewis, Thomas Howard. 1951. The biology of *Scincella laterale*. *Amer. Midland Nat.* 45:232–40.

Lightburn, Robert G. 1975. Herptiles of Ritchie County, W. Va. *The Redstart* 42:101–03.

Lively, Ronald C., and Laurence E. Bayless. 1972. Herpetology of two farm ponds in southern West Virginia, with new records for Monroe County. *Proc. W. Virginia Acad. Sci.* 44:89–92.

Livezey, R. L., and A. H. Wright. 1947. A synoptic key to the salientian eggs of the United States. *Amer. Midland Nat.* 37:178–222.

Llewellyn, Leonard M. 1940. The amphibians and reptiles of Mineral County, West Virginia. *Proc. W. Virginia Acad. Sci.* 41:148–50.

McAlister, W. H. 1962. Variation in *Rana pipiens* Schreiber in Texas. *Amer. Midland Nat.* 67:334–63.

McCauley, Robert H., Jr. 1939. Differences in the young of *Eumeces fasciatus* and *Eumeces laticeps*. *Copeia* 1939:93–95.

MacGregor, H., C. H. Horner, C. A. Owen, and I. Parker. 1973. Observations on centromeric heterochromatin and satellite DNA in salamanders of the genus *Plethodon*. *Chromosoma* 43:329–48.

Martof, Bernard. 1970. *Rana sylvatica* LeConte. *Cat. Amer. Amphib. Rept.* 86.1–86.4.

______. 1975. *Pseudotriton montanus* Baird. *Cat. Amer. Amphib. Rept.* 166.1–166.2.

______. 1975. *Pseudotriton ruber* (Latreille). *Cat. Amer. Amphib. Rept.* 167.1–167.3.

Maxwell, Jack H. 1961. Don't shake a stick at snakes. *W. Virginia Conservation* 25:9–12.

Mayo, N. 1952. Bullfrog farming and frogging in Florida. *Florida Dept. Agri. Bull.* 56.

Meads, James Henry, II. 1972. Ecological distribution of amphibians in Jackson County, West Virginia. M.S. thesis, Marshall University. 80 pp.

Mecham, John S. 1967. *Notophthalmus viridescens viridescens* (Rafinesque). *Cat. Amer. Amphib. Rept.* 53.1–53.4.

______. 1971. Vocalizations of the leopard frog, *Rana pipiens,* and three related Mexican species. *Copeia* 1971:505–16.

Medden, R. V. 1929–31. Tales of the rattlesnake: From the works of early travellers in America. *Bull. Antivenin Inst. Amer.* 3–5.

Miller, Glenn M. 1964. A record length long-tailed salamander, *Eurycea longicauda longicauda* (Green). *J. Ohio Herp. Soc.* 4:106.

Minton, Sherman A., Jr. 1969. The feeding strike of the timber rattlesnake. *J. Herpetol.* 3:121–24.

Mitchell, Joseph C. 1977. Salamanders in Virginia. *Virginia Wildlife* 38:16–19.

______. 1981. *A bibliography of Virginia amphibians and reptiles.* Smithsonian Herp. Inf. Serv. 50. 51 pp.

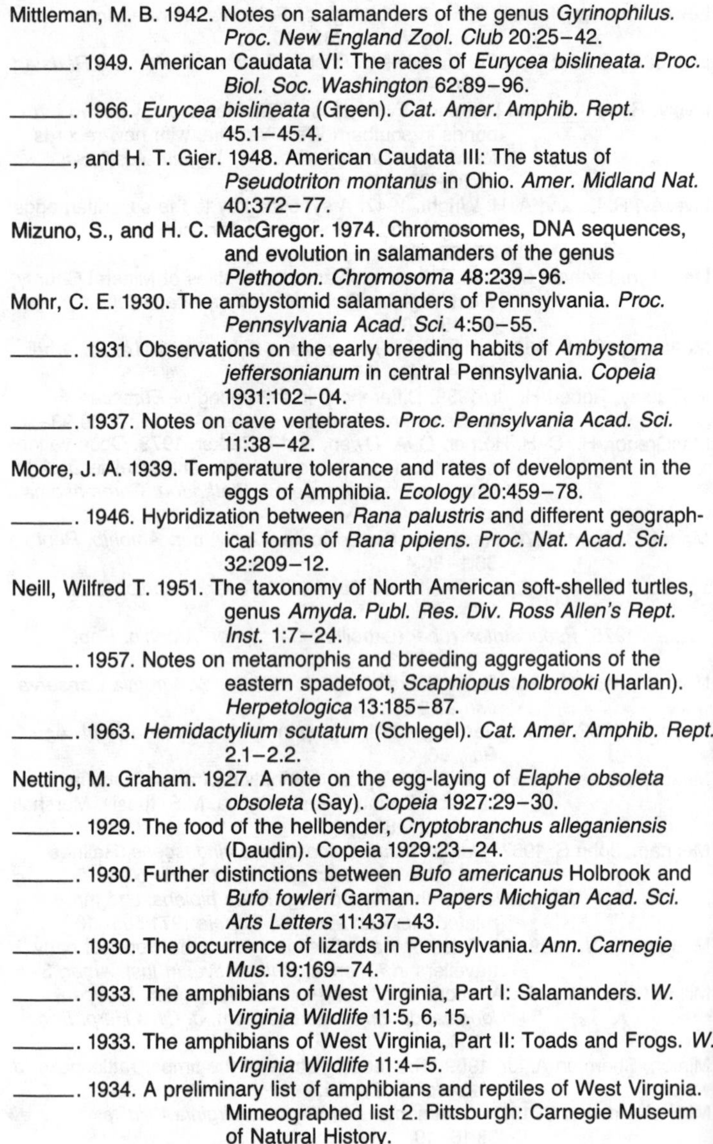

Mittleman, M. B. 1942. Notes on salamanders of the genus *Gyrinophilus*. *Proc. New England Zool. Club* 20:25–42.

______. 1949. American Caudata VI: The races of *Eurycea bislineata. Proc. Biol. Soc. Washington* 62:89–96.

______. 1966. *Eurycea bislineata* (Green). *Cat. Amer. Amphib. Rept.* 45.1–45.4.

______, and H. T. Gier. 1948. American Caudata III: The status of *Pseudotriton montanus* in Ohio. *Amer. Midland Nat.* 40:372–77.

Mizuno, S., and H. C. MacGregor. 1974. Chromosomes, DNA sequences, and evolution in salamanders of the genus *Plethodon. Chromosoma* 48:239–96.

Mohr, C. E. 1930. The ambystomid salamanders of Pennsylvania. *Proc. Pennsylvania Acad. Sci.* 4:50–55.

______. 1931. Observations on the early breeding habits of *Ambystoma jeffersonianum* in central Pennsylvania. *Copeia* 1931:102–04.

______. 1937. Notes on cave vertebrates. *Proc. Pennsylvania Acad. Sci.* 11:38–42.

Moore, J. A. 1939. Temperature tolerance and rates of development in the eggs of Amphibia. *Ecology* 20:459–78.

______. 1946. Hybridization between *Rana palustris* and different geographical forms of *Rana pipiens. Proc. Nat. Acad. Sci.* 32:209–12.

Neill, Wilfred T. 1951. The taxonomy of North American soft-shelled turtles, genus *Amyda. Publ. Res. Div. Ross Allen's Rept. Inst.* 1:7–24.

______. 1957. Notes on metamorphis and breeding aggregations of the eastern spadefoot, *Scaphiopus holbrooki* (Harlan). *Herpetologica* 13:185–87.

______. 1963. *Hemidactylium scutatum* (Schlegel). *Cat. Amer. Amphib. Rept.* 2.1–2.2.

Netting, M. Graham. 1927. A note on the egg-laying of *Elaphe obsoleta obsoleta* (Say). *Copeia* 1927:29–30.

______. 1929. The food of the hellbender, *Cryptobranchus alleganiensis* (Daudin). Copeia 1929:23–24.

______. 1930. Further distinctions between *Bufo americanus* Holbrook and *Bufo fowleri* Garman. *Papers Michigan Acad. Sci. Arts Letters* 11:437–43.

______. 1930. The occurrence of lizards in Pennsylvania. *Ann. Carnegie Mus.* 19:169–74.

______. 1933. The amphibians of West Virginia, Part I: Salamanders. *W. Virginia Wildlife* 11:5, 6, 15.

______. 1933. The amphibians of West Virginia, Part II: Toads and Frogs. *W. Virginia Wildlife* 11:4–5.

______. 1934. A preliminary list of amphibians and reptiles of West Virginia. Mimeographed list 2. Pittsburgh: Carnegie Museum of Natural History.

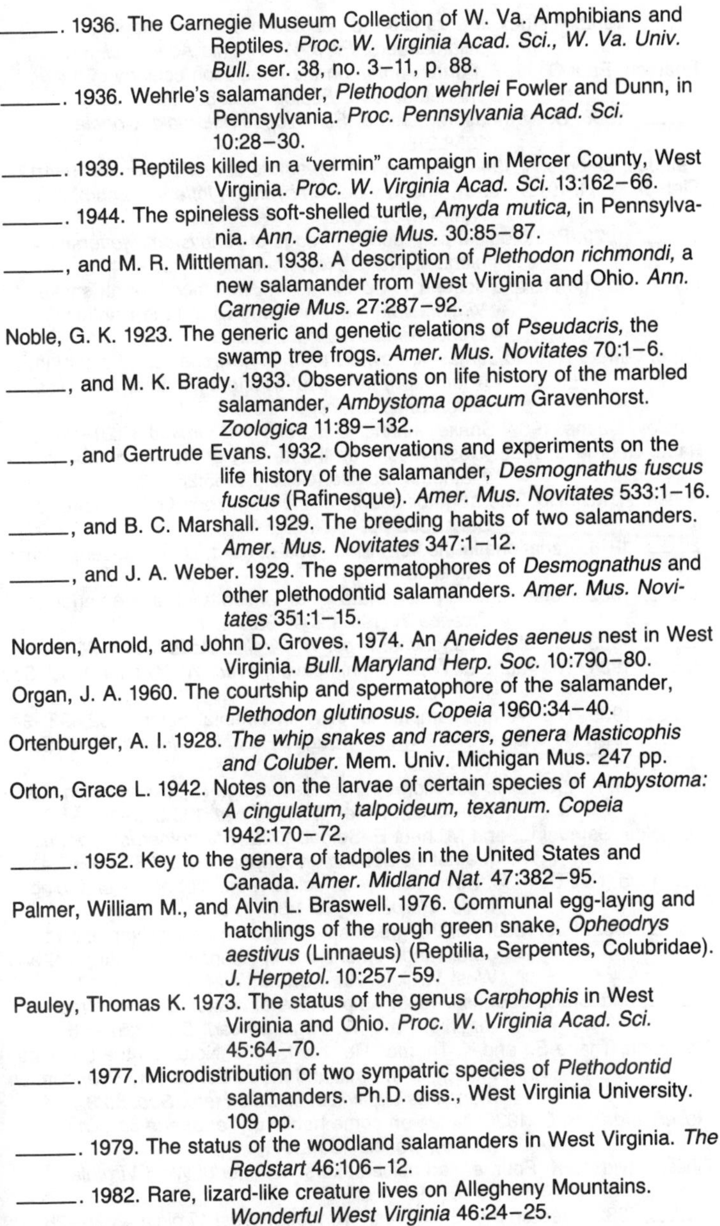

_____. 1936. The Carnegie Museum Collection of W. Va. Amphibians and Reptiles. *Proc. W. Virginia Acad. Sci., W. Va. Univ. Bull.* ser. 38, no. 3–11, p. 88.

_____. 1936. Wehrle's salamander, *Plethodon wehrlei* Fowler and Dunn, in Pennsylvania. *Proc. Pennsylvania Acad. Sci.* 10:28–30.

_____. 1939. Reptiles killed in a "vermin" campaign in Mercer County, West Virginia. *Proc. W. Virginia Acad. Sci.* 13:162–66.

_____. 1944. The spineless soft-shelled turtle, *Amyda mutica,* in Pennsylvania. *Ann. Carnegie Mus.* 30:85–87.

_____, and M. R. Mittleman. 1938. A description of *Plethodon richmondi,* a new salamander from West Virginia and Ohio. *Ann. Carnegie Mus.* 27:287–92.

Noble, G. K. 1923. The generic and genetic relations of *Pseudacris,* the swamp tree frogs. *Amer. Mus. Novitates* 70:1–6.

_____, and M. K. Brady. 1933. Observations on life history of the marbled salamander, *Ambystoma opacum* Gravenhorst. *Zoologica* 11:89–132.

_____, and Gertrude Evans. 1932. Observations and experiments on the life history of the salamander, *Desmognathus fuscus fuscus* (Rafinesque). *Amer. Mus. Novitates* 533:1–16.

_____, and B. C. Marshall. 1929. The breeding habits of two salamanders. *Amer. Mus. Novitates* 347:1–12.

_____, and J. A. Weber. 1929. The spermatophores of *Desmognathus* and other plethodontid salamanders. *Amer. Mus. Novitates* 351:1–15.

Norden, Arnold, and John D. Groves. 1974. An *Aneides aeneus* nest in West Virginia. *Bull. Maryland Herp. Soc.* 10:790–80.

Organ, J. A. 1960. The courtship and spermatophore of the salamander, *Plethodon glutinosus. Copeia* 1960:34–40.

Ortenburger, A. I. 1928. *The whip snakes and racers, genera Masticophis and Coluber.* Mem. Univ. Michigan Mus. 247 pp.

Orton, Grace L. 1942. Notes on the larvae of certain species of *Ambystoma: A cingulatum, talpoideum, texanum. Copeia* 1942:170–72.

_____. 1952. Key to the genera of tadpoles in the United States and Canada. *Amer. Midland Nat.* 47:382–95.

Palmer, William M., and Alvin L. Braswell. 1976. Communal egg-laying and hatchlings of the rough green snake, *Opheodrys aestivus* (Linnaeus) (Reptilia, Serpentes, Colubridae). *J. Herpetol.* 10:257–59.

Pauley, Thomas K. 1973. The status of the genus *Carphophis* in West Virginia and Ohio. *Proc. W. Virginia Acad. Sci.* 45:64–70.

_____. 1977. Microdistribution of two sympatric species of *Plethodontid* salamanders. Ph.D. diss., West Virginia University. 109 pp.

_____. 1979. The status of the woodland salamanders in West Virginia. *The Redstart* 46:106–12.

_____. 1982. Rare, lizard-like creature lives on Allegheny Mountains. *Wonderful West Virginia* 46:24–25.

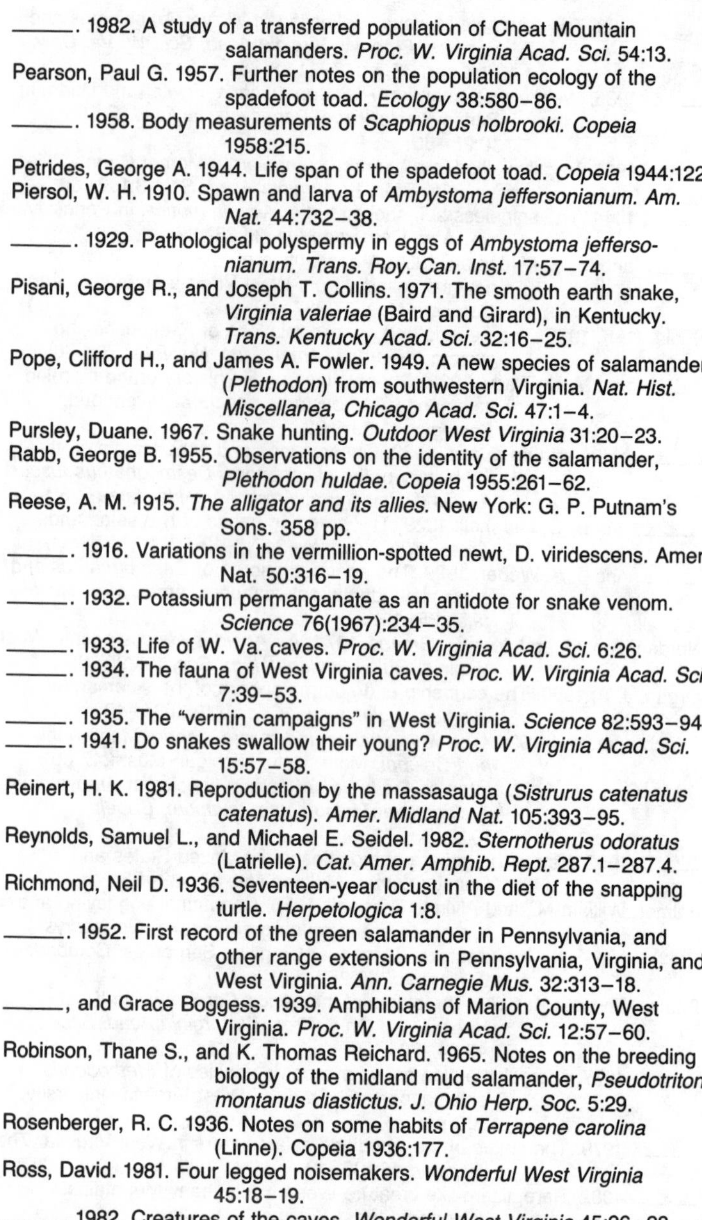

———. 1982. A study of a transferred population of Cheat Mountain salamanders. *Proc. W. Virginia Acad. Sci.* 54:13.

Pearson, Paul G. 1957. Further notes on the population ecology of the spadefoot toad. *Ecology* 38:580–86.

———. 1958. Body measurements of *Scaphiopus holbrooki. Copeia* 1958:215.

Petrides, George A. 1944. Life span of the spadefoot toad. *Copeia* 1944:122.

Piersol, W. H. 1910. Spawn and larva of *Ambystoma jeffersonianum. Am. Nat.* 44:732–38.

———. 1929. Pathological polyspermy in eggs of *Ambystoma jeffersonianum. Trans. Roy. Can. Inst.* 17:57–74.

Pisani, George R., and Joseph T. Collins. 1971. The smooth earth snake, *Virginia valeriae* (Baird and Girard), in Kentucky. *Trans. Kentucky Acad. Sci.* 32:16–25.

Pope, Clifford H., and James A. Fowler. 1949. A new species of salamander (*Plethodon*) from southwestern Virginia. *Nat. Hist. Miscellanea, Chicago Acad. Sci.* 47:1–4.

Pursley, Duane. 1967. Snake hunting. *Outdoor West Virginia* 31:20–23.

Rabb, George B. 1955. Observations on the identity of the salamander, *Plethodon huldae. Copeia* 1955:261–62.

Reese, A. M. 1915. *The alligator and its allies.* New York: G. P. Putnam's Sons. 358 pp.

———. 1916. Variations in the vermillion-spotted newt, D. viridescens. Amer. Nat. 50:316–19.

———. 1932. Potassium permanganate as an antidote for snake venom. *Science* 76(1967):234–35.

———. 1933. Life of W. Va. caves. *Proc. W. Virginia Acad. Sci.* 6:26.

———. 1934. The fauna of West Virginia caves. *Proc. W. Virginia Acad. Sci.* 7:39–53.

———. 1935. The "vermin campaigns" in West Virginia. *Science* 82:593–94.

———. 1941. Do snakes swallow their young? *Proc. W. Virginia Acad. Sci.* 15:57–58.

Reinert, H. K. 1981. Reproduction by the massasauga (*Sistrurus catenatus catenatus*). *Amer. Midland Nat.* 105:393–95.

Reynolds, Samuel L., and Michael E. Seidel. 1982. *Sternotherus odoratus* (Latrielle). *Cat. Amer. Amphib. Rept.* 287.1–287.4.

Richmond, Neil D. 1936. Seventeen-year locust in the diet of the snapping turtle. *Herpetologica* 1:8.

———. 1952. First record of the green salamander in Pennsylvania, and other range extensions in Pennsylvania, Virginia, and West Virginia. *Ann. Carnegie Mus.* 32:313–18.

———, and Grace Boggess. 1939. Amphibians of Marion County, West Virginia. *Proc. W. Virginia Acad. Sci.* 12:57–60.

Robinson, Thane S., and K. Thomas Reichard. 1965. Notes on the breeding biology of the midland mud salamander, *Pseudotriton montanus diastictus. J. Ohio Herp. Soc.* 5:29.

Rosenberger, R. C. 1936. Notes on some habits of *Terrapene carolina* (Linne). Copeia 1936:177.

Ross, David. 1981. Four legged noisemakers. *Wonderful West Virginia* 45:18–19.

———. 1982. Creatures of the caves. *Wonderful West Virginia* 45:26–28.

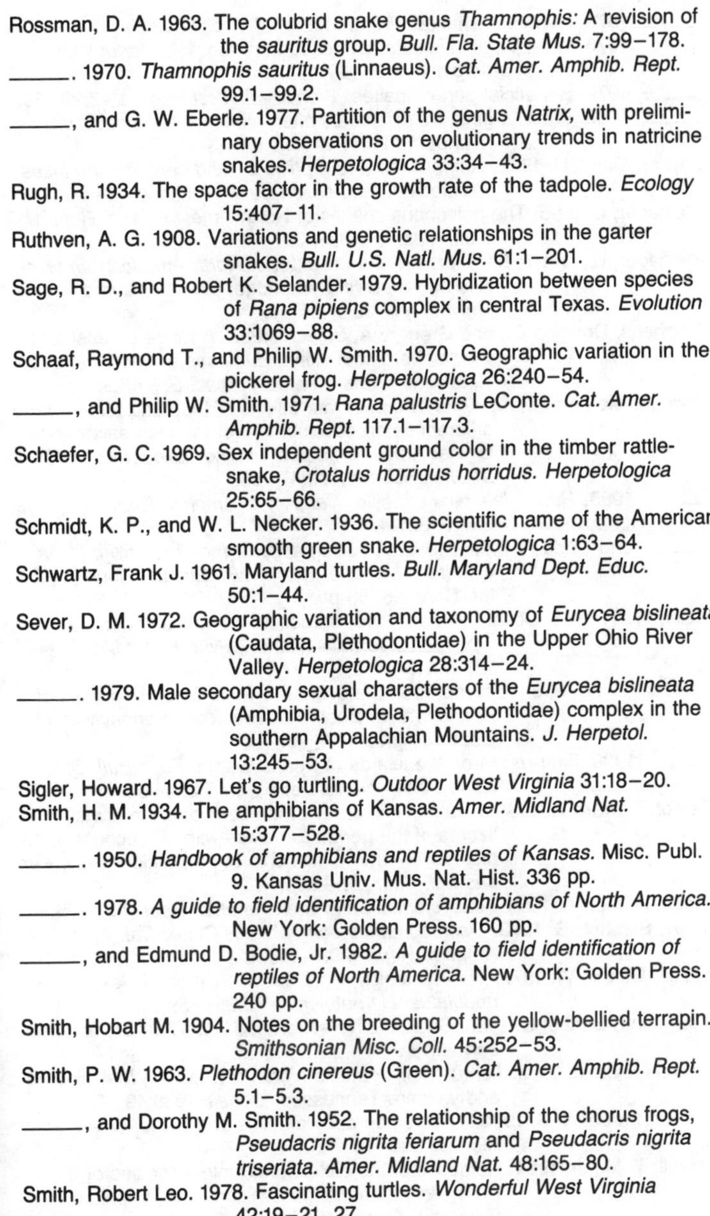

Rossman, D. A. 1963. The colubrid snake genus *Thamnophis:* A revision of the *sauritus* group. *Bull. Fla. State Mus.* 7:99–178.

______. 1970. *Thamnophis sauritus* (Linnaeus). *Cat. Amer. Amphib. Rept.* 99.1–99.2.

______, and G. W. Eberle. 1977. Partition of the genus *Natrix,* with preliminary observations on evolutionary trends in natricine snakes. *Herpetologica* 33:34–43.

Rugh, R. 1934. The space factor in the growth rate of the tadpole. *Ecology* 15:407–11.

Ruthven, A. G. 1908. Variations and genetic relationships in the garter snakes. *Bull. U.S. Natl. Mus.* 61:1–201.

Sage, R. D., and Robert K. Selander. 1979. Hybridization between species of *Rana pipiens* complex in central Texas. *Evolution* 33:1069–88.

Schaaf, Raymond T., and Philip W. Smith. 1970. Geographic variation in the pickerel frog. *Herpetologica* 26:240–54.

______, and Philip W. Smith. 1971. *Rana palustris* LeConte. *Cat. Amer. Amphib. Rept.* 117.1–117.3.

Schaefer, G. C. 1969. Sex independent ground color in the timber rattlesnake, *Crotalus horridus horridus. Herpetologica* 25:65–66.

Schmidt, K. P., and W. L. Necker. 1936. The scientific name of the American smooth green snake. *Herpetologica* 1:63–64.

Schwartz, Frank J. 1961. Maryland turtles. *Bull. Maryland Dept. Educ.* 50:1–44.

Sever, D. M. 1972. Geographic variation and taxonomy of *Eurycea bislineata* (Caudata, Plethodontidae) in the Upper Ohio River Valley. *Herpetologica* 28:314–24.

______. 1979. Male secondary sexual characters of the *Eurycea bislineata* (Amphibia, Urodela, Plethodontidae) complex in the southern Appalachian Mountains. *J. Herpetol.* 13:245–53.

Sigler, Howard. 1967. Let's go turtling. *Outdoor West Virginia* 31:18–20.

Smith, H. M. 1934. The amphibians of Kansas. *Amer. Midland Nat.* 15:377–528.

______. 1950. *Handbook of amphibians and reptiles of Kansas.* Misc. Publ. 9. Kansas Univ. Mus. Nat. Hist. 336 pp.

______. 1978. *A guide to field identification of amphibians of North America.* New York: Golden Press. 160 pp.

______, and Edmund D. Bodie, Jr. 1982. *A guide to field identification of reptiles of North America.* New York: Golden Press. 240 pp.

Smith, Hobart M. 1904. Notes on the breeding of the yellow-bellied terrapin. *Smithsonian Misc. Coll.* 45:252–53.

Smith, P. W. 1963. *Plethodon cinereus* (Green). *Cat. Amer. Amphib. Rept.* 5.1–5.3.

______, and Dorothy M. Smith. 1952. The relationship of the chorus frogs, *Pseudacris nigrita feriarum* and *Pseudacris nigrita triseriata. Amer. Midland Nat.* 48:165–80.

Smith, Robert Leo. 1978. Fascinating turtles. *Wonderful West Virginia* 42:19–21, 27.

———. 1978. Harmless snakes. *Wonderful West Virginia* 42:18–19, 31.

———. 1978. West Virginia is salamander country too. *Wonderful West Virginia* 42:26–27.

———. 1979. Beneficial garter snakes. *Wonderful West Virginia* 43:28–29.

———. 1980. West Virginia water snakes often mistaken for moccasin. *Wonderful West Virginia* 44:10–11.

Snyder, David H. 1972. *Amphibians and reptiles of land between the lakes (Kentucky).* Tennessee Valley Authority. 84 pp.

Steineger, L. 1895. The poisonous snakes of North America. *Ann. Rept. U.S. Natl. Mus. for 1893,* 337–487.

Steineger, L., and T. Barbour. 1917. *A checklist of North American amphibians and reptiles.* Cambridge, Mass.: Harvard University Press. 125 pp.

Stephens, Douglas E., and Gregory A. Sievert. 1982. A range extension for the northern coal skink, *Eumeces a. anthracinus,* in Kentucky. *Trans. Kentucky Acad. Sci.* 43:80.

Stewart, Margaret McB. 1956. The separate effects of food and temperature differences on development of marbled salamander larvae: *Ambystoma opacum,* not taxonomic. *J. Elisha Mitchell Sci. Soc.* 72:47–56.

———. 1983. *Rana clamitans* Latreille. *Cat. Amer. Amphib. Rept.* 337.1–337.4.

———, and Linda F. Biuso. 1982. *A bibliography of the green frog, Rana clamitans Latreille, 1801–1981.* Smithsonian Herp. Inf. Serv. 56. 53 pp.

Stille, W. T. 1954. Observations on the reproduction and distribution, *Opheodrys vernalis* (Harlan). *Nat. Hist. Misc.* 127:1–11.

Surface, H. A. 1908. First report on the economic features of the turtles of Pennsylvania. *Zool. Bull. Div. Zool. Pennsylvania Dept. of Agr.* 6:107–95.

———. 1908. First report on the lizards of Pennsylvania. *Zool. Bull. Div. Zool. Pennsylvania Dept. Agr.* 5:234–58.

Taylor, Edward H. 1935. A taxonomic study of the cosmopolitan scincid lizards of the genus *Eumeces* with an account of the distribution and relationship of its species. *Univ. Kansas Sci. Bull.* 23:1–643.

Tihen, Joseph A. 1969. *Ambystoma. Cat. Amer. Amphib. Rept.* 75.1–75.4.

Tilley, Stephen G. 1973. *Desmognathus ochrophaeus* Cope. *Cat. Amer. Amphib. Rept.* 129.1–129.4.

Tinkle, Donald W. 1972. The dynamics of a Utah population of *Sceloporus undulatus. Herpetologica* 28:351–59.

Townsend, Barthel C. 1956. Snakes alive–and dead. *W. Virginia Conservation* 20:18-20.

Trapido, Harold. 1938. *Lampropeltis getulus nigra* (Yarrow) in West Virginia and western Tennessee. *Copeia* 1938:49.

Turner, Frederick B. 1962. The demography of frogs and toads. *Quart. Rev. Biol.* 37:303–14.

Uzzell, T. M., Jr. 1964. Relations of the diploid and triploid species of the *Ambystoma jeffersonianum* complex (Amphibia, Caudata). *Copeia* 1964:257–300.

______. 1967. *Ambystoma jeffersonianum* (Green). *Cat. Amer. Amphib. Rept.* 47.1–47.2.

Valentine, Barry D. 1974. *Desmognathus quadramaculatus* (Holbrook). *Cat. Amer. Amphib. Rept.* 153.1–153.4.

Viosca, Percy, Jr. 1924. Observations on the life history of *Ambystoma opacum. Copeia* 1924:86–88.

______. 1931. Principles of bullfrog (*Rana catesbeiana*) culture. *Trans. Amer. Fish. Soc.* 61:162–69.

Viparina, Sally, and John J. Just. 1975. The life period, growth, and differentiation of *Rana catesbeiana* larvae occurring in nature. *Copeia* 1975:103–09.

Vogt, Richard C. 1980. Natural history of the map turtles *Graptemys pseudogeographica* and *G. ouchitensis* in Wisconsin. *Tulane Stud. Zool. and Botany* 22:17–48.

Volpe, E. Peter. 1952. Physiological evidence for natural hybridization of *Bufo americanus* and *Bufo fowleri. Evolution* 6:393–406.

Wake, David B. 1966. Comparative osteology and evolution of the lungless salamanders, Family Plethodontidae. *Mem. Southern California Acad. Sci.* 4:1–111.

Ward, Joseph P. 1984. *Relationships of chrysemyd turtles of North America (Testudines: Emydidae).* Special Publ. 21. The Museum of Texas Tech University. 50 pp.

Wasserman, Aaron O. 1968. *Scaphiopus holbrookii* (Harlan). *Cat. Amer. Amphib. Rept.* 70.1–70.4.

Webb, Robert G. 1973. *Trionyx muticus* LeSueur. *Cat. Amer. Amphib. Rept.* 139.1–139.2.

______. 1973. *Trionyx spiniferus* LeSueur. *Cat. Amer. Amphib. Rept.* 140.1–140.4.

Welcker, Peter S. 1973. The reptiles and amphibians of Gilmer County. *Proc. W. Virginia Acad. Sci.* 45:1–7.

Weller, W. H. 1930. Notes on amphibians collected in Carter County, Kentucky. *Proc. Cincinnati Junior Soc. of Nat. Sci.* 1:6–9.

Welter, Wilfred A., and Katherine Carr. 1939. Amphibians and reptiles of Northeastern Kentucky. *Copeia* 1939:128–30.

Wemple, Peter. 1971. The eastern spiny soft-shelled turtle, *Trionyx spinifer spinifer,* LeSueur, in Maryland. *Bull. Maryland Herp. Soc.* 7:35.

West, Roy. 1932. The black snake. *W. Virginia Wildlife* 7:13.

West Virginia Biological Survey. 1936. A preliminary bibliography of West Virginia Biology (vol. 1). *W. Va. Univ. Bull.,* ser. 37, nos. 5–11:1–20.

Whitford, Walter G., and Allen Vinegar. 1966. Homing, survivorship, and overwintering of larvae in spotted salamanders, *Ambystoma maculatum. Copeia* 1966:515–19.

Whitt, S. K. 1979. The salamanders of Virginia. Part I, Family Plethodontidae. *Cent. Virginia Herp. Soc. Bull.* 2:3–10.

Wilson, Larry David. 1978. *Coluber constrictor* Linnaeus. *Cat. Amer. Amphib. Rept.* 218.1–218.4.

Wood, John T. 1944. Fall aggregation of the queen snake. *Copeia* 1944:253.

———. 1945. Ovarian eggs of *Plethodon richmondi. Herpetologica* 2:206–07.

———. 1949. Observations on *Natrix septemvittata* in southwestern Ohio. *Amer. Midland Nat.* 42:744–50.

Wright, A. H. 1920. *Frogs: Their natural history and utilization.* U.S. Bureau of Fisheries, Document 888. 44 pp.

———. 1924. A key to the eggs of the Salientia east of the Mississippi River. *Amer. Nat.* 58:375–81.

———. 1929. Synopsis and description of North American tadpoles. *Proc. U.S. Nat. Mus.* 74:1–70.

———, and Harold Trapido. 1940. *Pseudotriton montanus montanus* in West Virginia. *Copeia* 1940:133.

Wylie, William L. 1966. Encounter with a green salamander. *W. Virginia Conservation* 30:24–26.

———. 1971. Green salamanders. *Wonderful West Virginia* 35:12.

Zahl, Paul A. 1972. The shadowy world of salamanders. *National Geographic* 142:104–17.

Index

Note: Species accounts are given in **boldface** numbers.